Austin/Rover Diesel Engine Owners Workshop Manual

A K Legg LAE MIMI

Models covered

This manual covers the Austin/Rover MDi (Perkins "Prima") 1994 cc (2.0 litre) Diesel engine used in the Austin/Rover Maestro and Montego

Covers both normally-aspirated and Turbo versions

ABCDE
FGHIJ
KLMNO

THE
BOOK

Haynes Publishing
Sparkford Nr Yeovil
Somerset BA22 7JJ England

Haynes Publications, Inc
861 Lawrence Drive
Newbury Park
California 91320 USA

Acknowledgements

Thanks are due to Duckhams Oils, who provided lubrication data, and to Creech Motors Ltd., Evercreech, Shepton Mallet, Somerset, for their technical assistance. Thanks are also due to Sykes-Pickavant Limited, who provided some of the workshop tools, and to all those people at Sparkford and Newbury Park who helped in the production of this manual.

© **Haynes Publishing 1993**

A book in the **Haynes Owners Workshop Manual Series**

Printed by J. H. Haynes & Co. Ltd., Sparkford, Nr Yeovil, Somerset BA22 7JJ, England

ISBN 1 85010 857 9

British Library Cataloguing in Publication Data

A catalogue record for this book is available from the British Library.

We take great pride in the accuracy of information given in this manual, but vehicle manufacturers make alterations and design changes during the production run of a particular vehicle of which they do not inform us. No liability can be accepted by the authors or publishers for loss, damage or injury caused by any errors in, or omissions from, the information given.

Restoring and Preserving our Motoring Heritage

Few people can have had the luck to realise their dreams to quite the same extent and in such a remarkable fashion as John Haynes, Founder and Chairman of the Haynes Publishing Group.

Since 1965 his unique approach to workshop manual publishing has proved so successful that millions of Haynes Manuals are now sold every year throughout the world, covering literally thousands of different makes and models of cars, vans and motorcycles.

A continuing passion for cars and motoring led to the founding in 1985 of a Charitable Trust dedicated to the restoration and preservation of our motoring heritage. To inaugurate the new Museum, John Haynes donated virtually his entire private collection of 52 cars.

Now with an unrivalled international collection of over 210 veteran, vintage and classic cars and motorcycles, the Haynes Motor Museum in Somerset is well on the way to becoming one of the most interesting Motor Museums in the world.

A 70 seat video cinema, a cafe and an extensive motoring bookshop, together with a specially constructed one kilometre motor circuit, make a visit to the Haynes Motor Museum a truly unforgettable experience.

Every vehicle in the museum is preserved in as near as possible mint condition and each car is run every six months on the motor circuit.

Enjoy the picnic area set amongst the rolling Somerset hills. Peer through the William Morris workshop windows at cars being restored, and browse through the extensive displays of fascinating motoring memorabilia.

From the 1903 Oldsmobile through such classics as an MG Midget to the mighty 'E' type Jaguar, Lamborghini, Ferrari Berlinetta Boxer, and Graham Hill's Lola Cosworth, there is something for everyone, young and old alike, at this Somerset Museum.

Haynes Motor Museum

Situated mid-way between London and Penzance, the Haynes Motor Museum is located just off the A303 at Sparkford, Somerset (home of the Haynes Manual) and is open to the public 7 days a week all year round, except Christmas Day and Boxing Day.

Telephone 01963 440804.

Contents

About this manual

Its aim

The aim of this manual is to help you get the best value from your vehicle. It can do so in several ways. It can help you decide what work must be done (even should you choose to get it done by a garage), provide information on routine maintenance and servicing, and give a logical course of action and diagnosis when random faults occur. However, it is hoped that you will use the manual by tackling the work yourself. On simpler jobs it may even be quicker than booking the car into a garage and going there twice, to leave and collect it. Perhaps most important, a lot of money can be saved by avoiding the costs a garage must charge to cover its labour and overheads.

The manual has drawings and descriptions to show the function of the various components so that their layout can be understood. Then the tasks are described and photographed in a clear step-by-step sequence so that even a novice can do the work.

Unlike most Haynes manuals, which cover a particular vehicle in different trim levels and engine sizes, this book covers one engine and its associated equipment as fitted to a range of vehicles. Items which are common to Diesel and petrol models - eg bodywork and running gear - are not covered in this book. For such items, the reader is advised to refer to the model-specific manual appropriate to his/her car - refer to the rear cover of this manual.

Its arrangement

The manual is divided into Chapters, each covering a logical subdivision of the vehicle. The Chapters are each divided into Sections, numbered with single figures, eg 5; and the Sections into paragraphs, or sub-sections and paragraphs.

It is freely illustrated, especially in those parts where there is a detailed sequence of operations to be carried out. There are two forms of illustration: figures and photographs. The figures are numbered in sequence with decimal numbers, according to their position in the Chapter - eg Fig. 6.4 is the fourth drawing/illustration in Chapter 6. Photographs carry the same number (either individually or in related groups) as the Section and paragraph to which they relate.

There is an alphabetical index at the back of the manual, as well as a contents list at the front. Each Chapter is also preceded by its own individual contents list.

References to the "left" or "right" of the vehicle are in the sense of a person in the driver's seat facing forward.

Unless otherwise stated, nuts and bolts are removed by turning anti-clockwise, and tightened by turning clockwise.

Vehicle manufacturers continually make changes to specifications and recommendations, and these, when notified, are incorporated into our manuals at the earliest opportunity.

We take great pride in the accuracy of information given in this manual, but vehicle manufacturers make alterations and design changes during the production run of a particular vehicle of which they do not inform us. No liability can be accepted by the authors or publishers for loss, damage or injury caused by any errors in, or omissions from, the information given.

Project vehicles

The main project vehicle used in the preparation of this manual, and appearing in many of the photographic sequences, was a 1992 Austin Maestro Turbo Clubman D.

Introduction to the Austin/Rover MDi (Perkins "Prima") Diesel engine

The Austin/Rover MDi (Perkins "Prima") Diesel engine covered in this manual is of 1994 cc (2.0 litre) capacity, and was first fitted to Maestro 500 and 700 Van models in September 1986. The Turbo version of the engine was fitted to Montego Saloon and Estate models in October 1988, and the naturally-aspirated (non-Turbo) engine was fitted to Maestro Hatchback models in March 1990. Turbo versions were available in the Maestro Hatchback models in 1992.

The engine is of four-cylinder, overhead camshaft, in-line design, being mounted transversely in the engine compartment, with the gearbox on the left-hand side. The cylinders are machined directly in the cast-iron cylinder block, and aluminium alloy pistons are fitted. Fuel injection is direct into combustion chambers formed in the piston crowns. The injectors are of single-stage type on early models, and two-stage type on later models.

Advantages of the Diesel engine are increased fuel economy and longer engine life when compared to the petrol equivalent.

Routine maintenance tasks are few and are easily carried out, although some jobs, such as valve clearance adjustment, will require the purchase or construction of special tools.

Outside the engine compartment, the vehicles to which the engine is fitted are much the same in both Diesel and petrol versions. For complete coverage of a particular vehicle, the appropriate manual for the petrol engine model concerned will be required as well.

General dimensions, weights and capacities

Dimensions

Overall length:
Maestro Hatchback	4050 mm (159.5 in)
Maestro Van	4351 mm (171.3 in)
Montego Saloon and Estate	4466 mm (175.8 in)

Overall width:
All models	1940 mm (76.0 in)

Overall height:
Maestro Hatchback	1424 mm (56.1 in)
Maestro Van with 13 inch wheels	1623 mm (63.9 in)
Maestro Van with 14 inch wheels	1653 mm (65.1 in)
Montego Saloon	1420 mm (55.9 in)
Montego Estate (without roof rack)	1445 mm (56.9 in)

Wheelbase:
Maestro Hatchback	2514 mm (99.0 in)
Maestro Van	2553 mm (100.5 in)
Montego Saloon and Estate	2571 mm (101.2 in)

Turning circle:
Maestro Hatchback	10.2 m (33.5 ft)
Maestro Van	10.5 m (34.5 ft)
Montego Saloon and Estate	10.5 m (34.5 ft)

Ground clearance:
Maestro Hatchback	160 mm (6.3 in)
Maestro Van with 13 inch wheels	160 mm (6.3 in)
Maestro Van with 14 inch wheels	190 mm (7.5 in)
Montego Saloon	154 mm (6.1 in)
Montego Estate	163 mm (6.4 in)

Weights:

Kerb weight:
Maestro Hatchback	1095 kg (2414 lb)
Maestro 500 and 700 Van	1070 kg (2359 lb)
Montego Saloon	1100 to 1155 kg (2425 to 2546 lb)
Montego Estate	1160 to 1240 kg (2557 to 2734 lb)

Maximum gross vehicle weight:
Maestro Hatchback	1510 kg (3330 lb)
Maestro 500 Van	1650 kg (3638 lb)
Maestro 700 Van	1840 kg (4057 lb)
Montego Saloon	1600 kg (3528 lb)
Montego Estate	1770 kg (3903 lb)

Maximum roof rack load:
Maestro Hatchback and Van	75 kg (165 lb)
Montego with removable type rack	70 kg (154 lb)
Montego with integral roof rack	100 kg (220 lb)

Maximum towing weight:
Maestro Hatchback	1125 kg (2481 lb)
Maestro Van with unbraked trailer	425 kg (937 lb)
Maestro Van with braked trailer	1000 kg (2205 lb)
Montego Saloon and Estate	1070 kg (2359 lb)

Capacities (approx)

Engine oil (including filter)	5.25 litres (9.0 pints)
Cooling system (including heater)	7.5 litres (13.2 pints)

Fuel tank:
Except Van	50 litres (11 gallons)
Van	54 litres (12 gallons)
Gearbox	2.0 litres (3.52 pints)

Conversion factors

Length (distance)

Inches (in)	X 25.4	= Millimetres (mm)	X 0.0394	= Inches (in)
Feet (ft)	X 0.305	= Metres (m)	X 3.281	= Feet (ft)
Miles	X 1.609	= Kilometres (km)	X 0.621	= Miles

Volume (capacity)

Cubic inches (cu in; in³)	X 16.387	= Cubic centimetres (cc; cm³)	X 0.061	= Cubic inches (cu in; in³)
Imperial pints (Imp pt)	X 0.568	= Litres (l)	X 1.76	= Imperial pints (Imp pt)
Imperial quarts (Imp qt)	X 1.137	= Litres (l)	X 0.88	= Imperial quarts (Imp qt)
Imperial quarts (Imp qt)	X 1.201	= US quarts (US qt)	X 0.833	= Imperial quarts (Imp qt)
US quarts (US qt)	X 0.946	= Litres (l)	X 1.057	= US quarts (US qt)
Imperial gallons (Imp gal)	X 4.546	= Litres (l)	X 0.22	= Imperial gallons (Imp gal)
Imperial gallons (Imp gal)	X 1.201	= US gallons (US gal)	X 0.833	= Imperial gallons (Imp gal)
US gallons (US gal)	X 3.785	= Litres (l)	X 0.264	= US gallons (US gal)

Mass (weight)

Ounces (oz)	X 28.35	= Grams (g)	X 0.035	= Ounces (oz)
Pounds (lb)	X 0.454	= Kilograms (kg)	X 2.205	= Pounds (lb)

Force

Ounces-force (ozf; oz)	X 0.278	= Newtons (N)	X 3.6	= Ounces-force (ozf; oz)
Pounds-force (lbf; lb)	X 4.448	= Newtons (N)	X 0.225	= Pounds-force (lbf; lb)
Newtons (N)	X 0.1	= Kilograms-force (kgf; kg)	X 9.81	= Newtons (N)

Pressure

Pounds-force per square inch (psi; lbf/in²; lb/in²)	X 0.070	= Kilograms-force per square centimetre (kgf/cm²; kg/cm²)	X 14.223	= Pounds-force per square inch (psi; lbf/in²; lb/in²)
Pounds-force per square inch (psi; lbf/in²; lb/in²)	X 0.068	= Atmospheres (atm)	X 14.696	= Pounds-force per square inch (psi; lbf/in²; lb/in²)
Pounds-force per square inch (psi; lbf/in²; lb/in²)	X 0.069	= Bars	X 14.5	= Pounds-force per square inch (psi; lbf/in²; lb/in²)
Pounds-force per square inch (psi; lbf/in²; lb/in²)	X 6.895	= Kilopascals (kPa)	X 0.145	= Pounds-force per square inch (psi; lbf/in²; lb/in²)
Kilopascals (kPa)	X 0.01	= Kilograms-force per square centimetre (kgf/cm²; kg/cm²)	X 98.1	= Kilopascals (kPa)
Millibar (mbar)	X 100	= Pascals (Pa)	X 0.01	= Millibar (mbar)
Millibar (mbar)	X 0.0145	= Pounds-force per square inch (psi; lbf/in²; lb/in²)	X 68.947	= Millibar (mbar)
Millibar (mbar)	X 0.75	= Millimetres of mercury (mmHg)	X 1.333	= Millibar (mbar)
Millibar (mbar)	X 0.401	= Inches of water (inH₂O)	X 2.491	= Millibar (mbar)
Millimetres of mercury (mmHg)	X 0.535	= Inches of water (inH₂O)	X 1.868	= Millimetres of mercury (mmHg)
Inches of water (inH₂O)	X 0.036	= Pounds-force per square inch (psi; lbf/in²; lb/in²)	X 27.68	= Inches of water (inH₂O)

Torque (moment of force)

Pounds-force inches (lbf in; lb in)	X 1.152	= Kilograms-force centimetre (kgf cm; kg cm)	X 0.868	= Pounds-force inches (lbf in; lb in)
Pounds-force inches (lbf in; lb in)	X 0.113	= Newton metres (Nm)	X 8.85	= Pounds-force inches (lbf in; lb in)
Pounds-force inches (lbf in; lb in)	X 0.083	= Pounds-force feet (lbf ft; lb ft)	X 12	= Pounds-force inches (lbf in; lb in)
Pounds-force feet (lbf ft; lb ft)	X 0.138	= Kilograms-force metres (kgf m; kg m)	X 7.233	= Pounds-force feet (lbf ft; lb ft)
Pounds-force feet (lbf ft; lb ft)	X 1.356	= Newton metres (Nm)	X 0.738	= Pounds-force feet (lbf ft; lb ft)
Newton metres (Nm)	X 0.102	= Kilograms-force metres (kgf m; kg m)	X 9.804	= Newton metres (Nm)

Power

Horsepower (hp)	X 745.7	= Watts (W)	X 0.0013	= Horsepower (hp)

Velocity (speed)

Miles per hour (miles/hr; mph)	X 1.609	= Kilometres per hour (km/hr; kph)	X 0.621	= Miles per hour (miles/hr; mph)

Fuel consumption*

Miles per gallon, Imperial (mpg)	X 0.354	= Kilometres per litre (km/l)	X 2.825	= Miles per gallon, Imperial (mpg)
Miles per gallon, US (mpg)	X 0.425	= Kilometres per litre (km/l)	X 2.352	= Miles per gallon, US (mpg)

Temperature

Degrees Fahrenheit = (°C x 1.8) + 32   Degrees Celsius (Degrees Centigrade; °C) = (°F - 32) x 0.56

It is common practice to convert from miles per gallon (mpg) to litres/100 kilometres (l/100km), where mpg (Imperial) x l/100 km = 282 and mpg (US) x l/100 km = 235

Conversion factors

Safety first!

However enthusiastic you may be about getting on with the job in hand, do take the time to ensure that your safety is not put at risk. A moment's lack of attention can result in an accident, as can failure to observe certain elementary precautions. There will always be new ways of having accidents, and the following points do not pretend to be a comprehensive list of all dangers; they are intended rather to make you aware of the risks, and to encourage a safety-conscious approach to all work you carry out on your vehicle.

Essential DOs and DON'Ts

DON'T rely on a single jack when working underneath the vehicle. Always use reliable additional means of support, such as axle stands, securely placed under a structural part of the vehicle that you know will not give way.

DON'T attempt to loosen or tighten high-torque nuts (eg wheel hub nuts) while the vehicle is on a jack; it may be pulled off.

DON'T start the engine without first ascertaining that the transmission is in neutral (or "Park" where applicable) and the handbrake applied.

DON'T suddenly remove the filler cap from a hot cooling system - cover it with a cloth, and release the pressure gradually first, or you may get scalded by escaping coolant.

DON'T attempt to drain oil, automatic transmission fluid, or coolant until you are sure it has cooled sufficiently to avoid scalding you.

DON'T grasp any part of the engine, exhaust or catalytic converter without first ascertaining that it is sufficiently cool to avoid burning you.

DON'T allow brake fluid or antifreeze to contact vehicle paintwork.

DON'T syphon toxic liquids such as fuel, brake fluid or antifreeze by mouth, or allow them to remain on your skin.

DON'T inhale dust - it may be injurious to health (see *Asbestos* below).

DON'T allow any spilt oil or grease to remain on the floor - wipe it up straight away, before someone slips on it.

DON'T use ill-fitting spanners or other tools which may slip and cause injury.

DON'T attempt to lift a heavy component which may be beyond your capability - get assistance.

DON'T rush to finish a job, or take unverified short cuts.

DON'T allow children or animals in or around an unattended vehicle.

DON'T park vehicles with catalytic converters over combustible materials such as dry grass, oily rags, etc if the engine has recently been run. As catalytic converters reach extremely high temperatures, any such materials in close proximity may ignite.

DON'T run vehicles equipped with catalytic converters without the exhaust system heat shields fitted.

DO wear eye protection when using power tools such as an electric drill, sander, bench grinder etc, and when working under the vehicle.

DO use a barrier cream on your hands prior to undertaking dirty jobs - it will protect your skin from infection, as well as making the dirt easier to remove afterwards; but make sure your hands aren't left slippery. Note that long term contact with used engine oil can be a health hazard.

DO keep loose clothing (cuffs, tie etc) and long hair well out of the way of moving mechanical parts.

DO remove rings, wristwatch etc, before working on the vehicle - especially the electrical system.

DO ensure that any lifting tackle or jacking equipment used has a safe working load rating adequate for the job, and is used precisely as recommended by the equipment manufacturer.

DO keep your work area tidy - it is only too easy to fall over articles left lying around.

DO get someone to check periodically that all is well when working alone on the vehicle.

DO carry out work in a logical sequence, and check that everything is correctly assembled and tightened afterwards.

DO remember that your vehicle's safety affects that of yourself and others. If in doubt on any point, get specialist advice.

IF, in spite of following these precautions, you are unfortunate enough to injure yourself, seek medical attention as soon as possible.

Asbestos

Certain friction, insulating, sealing, and other products - such as brake linings, brake bands, clutch linings, gaskets, etc - contain asbestos. *Extreme care must be taken to avoid inhalation of dust from such products, since it is hazardous to health.* If in doubt, assume that they *do* contain asbestos.

Fire

Remember at all times that fuel is highly flammable. Never smoke, or have any kind of naked flame around, when working on the vehicle. But the risk does not end there - a spark caused by an electrical short-circuit, by two metal surfaces contacting each other, by careless use of tools, or even by static electricity built up in your body under certain conditions, can ignite fuel vapour, which in a confined space is highly explosive. The vapour produced by spilling oil or hydraulic fluid onto hot metal, such as an exhaust manifold, can also be flammable or explosive.

Whenever possible, disconnect the battery earth terminal before working on any part of the fuel or electrical system, and never risk spilling fuel on to a hot engine or exhaust. Catalytic converters run at extremely high temperatures, and consequently can be an additional fire hazard. Observe the precautions outlined elsewhere in this section.

It is recommended that a fire extinguisher of a type suitable for fuel and electrical fires is kept handy in the garage or workplace at all times. Ideally, a suitable extinguisher should also be carried in the vehicle. Never try to extinguish a fuel or electrical fire with water. If a vehicle fire does occur, take note of the remarks below about hydrofluoric acid.

Note: *Any reference to a "torch" appearing in this manual should always be taken to mean a hand-held battery-operated electric lamp or flashlight. It does NOT mean a welding/gas torch or blowlamp.*

Hydrofluoric acid

Hydrofluoric acid is extremely corrosive. It is formed when certain types of synthetic rubber, which may be found in O-rings, oil seals, brake hydraulic system seals, fuel hoses etc, are exposed to temperatures above 400°C. The obvious circumstance in which this could happen on a vehicle is in the case of a fire. The rubber does not burn, but changes into a charred or sticky substance which contains the acid. *Once formed, the acid remains dangerous for years. If it gets onto the skin it may be necessary to amputate the limb concerned.*

When dealing with a vehicle which has suffered a fire, or with components salvaged from such a vehicle, always wear protective gloves and discard them carefully after use. Bear this in mind if obtaining components from a car breaker.

Fumes

Certain fumes are highly toxic, and can quickly cause unconsciousness and even death if inhaled to any extent, especially if inhalation takes place through a lighted cigarette or pipe. Fuel vapour comes into this category, as do the vapours from certain solvents such as trichloroethylene. Any draining or pouring of such volatile fluids should be done in a well-ventilated area.

When using cleaning fluids and solvents, read the instructions carefully. Never use materials from unmarked containers - they may give off poisonous vapours.

Never run the engine of a motor vehicle in an enclosed space such as a garage. Exhaust fumes contain carbon monoxide, which is extremely poisonous; if you need to run the engine, always do so in the open air, or at least have the rear of the vehicle outside the workplace. Although Diesel engines have greatly-reduced carbon monoxide emissions, the above precautions should still be observed.

If you are fortunate enough to have the use of an inspection pit, never drain or pour fuel, and never run the engine, while the vehicle is standing over it; the fumes, being heavier than air, will concentrate in the pit, with possibly lethal results.

Diesel fuel

Diesel injection pumps supply fuel at very high pressure. Extreme care must be taken when working on the fuel injectors and fuel pipes. It is advisable to place an absorbent cloth around the union before slackening a fuel pipe. *Never expose the hands, face or any other part of the body to injector spray: the high working pressure can penetrate the skin, with potentially-fatal results.* Injector test rigs produce similarly high pressures, and must be treated with the same respect.

Diesel fuel is more irritating to the skin than petrol. It is also harmful to the eyes. Besides the use of a barrier cream to protect the hands, consider using lightweight disposable gloves when fuel spillage is inevitable. Change out of fuel-soaked clothing as soon as possible.

Spilt diesel fuel does not evaporate like petrol. Clear up spillages promptly, to avoid accidents caused by slippery patches on the workshop floor. Note also that diesel attacks tarmac surfaces: if working at the roadside or in a drive, put down newspaper or a plastic sheet if fuel spillage is expected.

The battery

Batteries which are sealed for life require special precautions, which are normally outlined on a label attached to the battery. Such precautions are primarily related to situations involving battery charging and jump starting from another vehicle.

With a conventional battery, never cause a spark, or allow a naked light, in close proximity to it. It will normally be giving off a certain amount of hydrogen gas, which is highly explosive.

Whenever possible, disconnect the battery earth terminal before working on the fuel or electrical systems.

If possible, loosen the filler plugs or cover when charging the battery from an external source. Do not charge at an excessive rate, or the battery may burst. Special care should be taken with the use of high charge-rate boost chargers to prevent the battery from overheating.

Take care when topping-up and when carrying the battery. The acid electrolyte, even when diluted, is very corrosive, and should not be allowed to contact clothing, eyes or skin.

Always wear eye protection when cleaning the battery, to prevent the caustic deposits from entering your eyes.

The vehicle electrical system

Take care when making alterations or repairs to the vehicle wiring. Electrical faults are the commonest cause of vehicle fires. Make sure that any accessories are wired correctly, using an appropriately-rated fuse and wire of adequate current-carrying capacity. When possible, avoid the use of "piggy-back" or self-splicing connectors to power additional electrical equipment from existing feeds; make up a new feed with its own fuse instead.

When considering the current which a new circuit will have to handle, do not overlook the switch, especially when planning to use an existing switch to control additional components - for instance, if spotlights are to be fed via the main lighting switch. For preference, a relay should be used to switch heavy currents. If in doubt, consult an auto electrical specialist.

Any wire which passes through a body panel or bulkhead must be protected from chafing with a grommet or similar device. A wire which is allowed to chafe bare against the bodywork will cause a short-circuit, and possibly a fire.

Mains electricity and electrical equipment

When using an electric power tool, inspection light, diagnostic equipment etc, which works from the mains, always ensure that the appliance is correctly connected to its plug and that, where necessary, it is properly earthed. Do not use such appliances in damp conditions and, again, beware of creating a spark or applying excessive heat in the vicinity of fuel or fuel vapour. Also ensure that the appliances meet the relevant national safety standards.

If mains-powered equipment has to be used out of doors, connection via a residual current circuit breaker (RCB) socket is strongly recommended. Such sockets are readily available from electrical and DIY shops.

Jacking and vehicle support

The jack provided with the vehicle is designed primarily for emergency wheel changing, and its use for servicing and overhaul work on the vehicle is best avoided. Instead, a more substantial workshop jack (trolley jack or similar) should be used. Whichever type is employed, it is essential that additional safety support is provided by means of axle stands designed for this purpose. Never use makeshift means such as wooden blocks or piles of house bricks, as these can easily topple or, in the case of bricks, disintegrate under the weight of the vehicle. Further information on the correct positioning of the jack and axle stands is provided in the "Jacking, towing and wheel changing" section.

If removal of the wheels is not required, the use of drive-on ramps is recommended. Caution should be exercised to ensure that they are correctly aligned with the wheels, and that the vehicle is not driven too far along them so that it promptly falls off the other ends, or tips the ramps.

Jacking, towing and wheel changing

To change a wheel, remove the spare wheel and the emergency jack supplied with the vehicle, apply the handbrake and chock the wheel diagonally opposite the one to be changed. Make sure that the vehicle is located on firm level ground, and then slightly loosen the wheel nuts with the brace provided (where applicable, remove the wheel trim first, using the special tool in the kit). Locate the jack head in

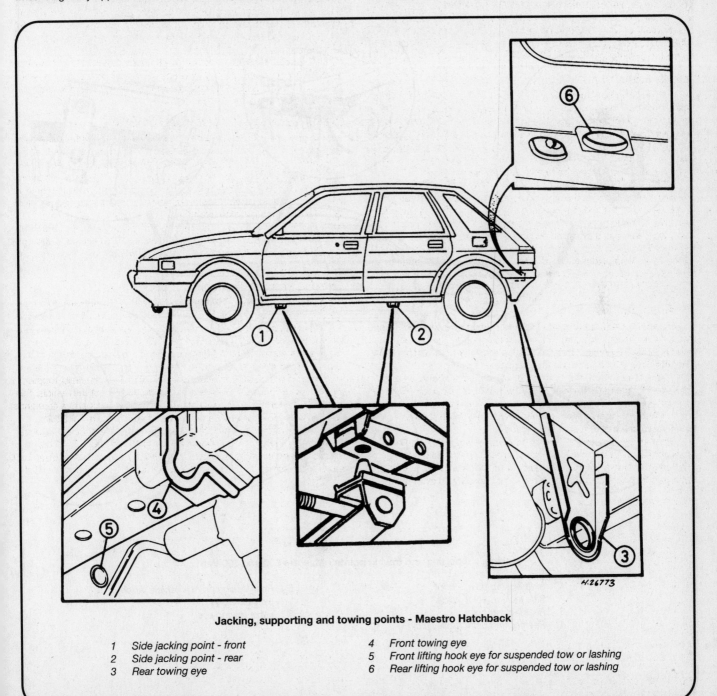

Jacking, supporting and towing points - Maestro Hatchback

1   Side jacking point - front
2   Side jacking point - rear
3   Rear towing eye
4   Front towing eye
5   Front lifting hook eye for suspended tow or lashing
6   Rear lifting hook eye for suspended tow or lashing

the jacking point nearest to the wheel to be changed, and raise the jack using the handle provided. When the wheel is clear of the ground, remove the nuts and lift off the wheel. Fit the spare wheel and moderately tighten the nuts. Lower the vehicle, and then tighten the nuts securely. Refit the wheel trim (where applicable). With the punctured wheel in position, remove the chock, and stow the jack and tools.

When jacking up the car to carry out repair or maintenance tasks, a pillar or trolley type jack of suitable lifting capacity must be used, supplemented with axle stands positioned only beneath the appropriate points under the vehicle. The accompanying illustrations of the vehicle indicate the jacking and support points (according to type). On Saloon and Estate models, note that the vehicle must never be jacked up at the rear under the axle beam.

Never work under, around or near a raised vehicle unless it is adequately supported in at least two places with axle stands.

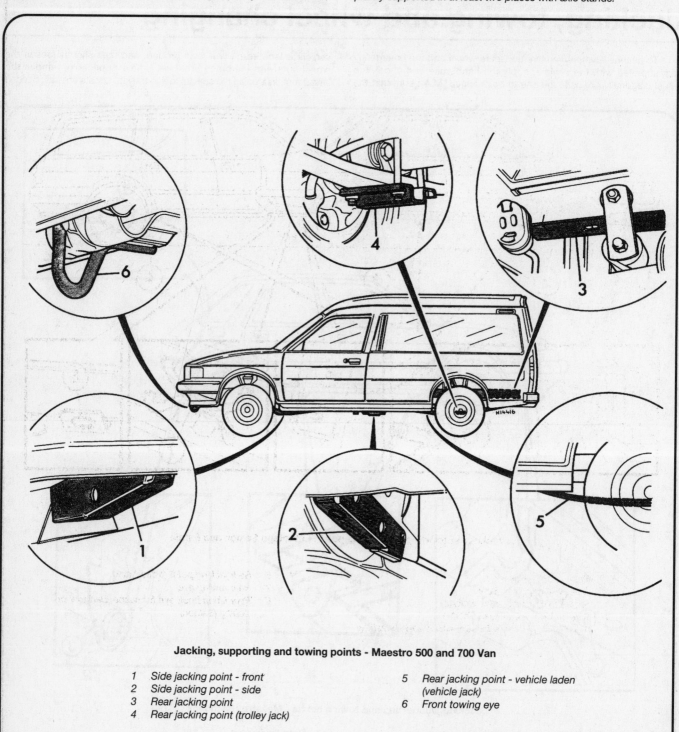

Jacking, supporting and towing points - Maestro 500 and 700 Van

1	Side jacking point - front	5	Rear jacking point - vehicle laden (vehicle jack)
2	Side jacking point - side	6	Front towing eye
3	Rear jacking point		
4	Rear jacking point (trolley jack)		

The car may be towed (for breakdown recovery purposes only) using the towing eyes positioned at the front and rear of the vehicle.

These eyes are intended for towing loads only, and must not be used for lifting the car either directly or indirectly.

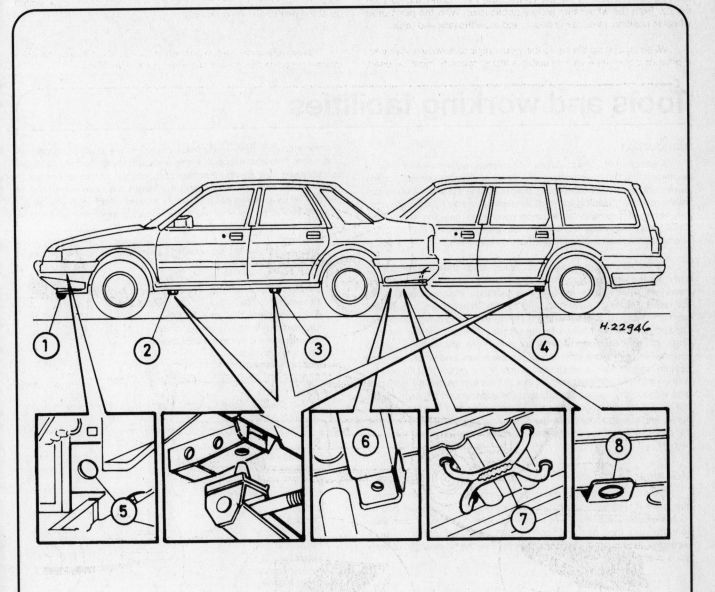

Jacking, supporting and towing points - Montego Saloon and Estate

1   Front towing eye
2   Side jacking point - front
3   Side jacking point - rear (Saloon)
4   Side jacking point - rear (Estate)
5   Front lifting hook eye for suspended tow or lashing

6   Rear jacking point (trolley jack)
7   Rear towing eye
8   Rear lifting hook eye for suspended tow or lashing (Saloon)

Tools and working facilities

Introduction

A selection of good tools is a fundamental requirement for anyone contemplating the maintenance and repair of a motor vehicle. For the owner who does not possess any, their purchase will prove a considerable expense, offsetting some of the savings made by doing-it-yourself. However, provided that the tools purchased meet the relevant national safety standards and are of good quality, they will last for many years and prove an extremely worthwhile investment.

To help the average owner to decide which tools are needed to carry out the various tasks detailed in this manual, we have compiled three lists of tools under the following headings: *Maintenance and minor repair, Repair and overhaul,* and *Special.* Newcomers to practical mechanics should start off with the *Maintenance and minor repair* tool kit, and confine themselves to the simpler jobs around the vehicle. Then, as confidence and experience grow, more difficult tasks can be undertaken, with extra tools being purchased as, and when, they are needed. In this way, a *Maintenance and minor repair* tool kit can be built up into a *Repair and overhaul* tool kit over a considerable period of time without any major cash outlays. The experienced do-it-yourselfer will have a tool kit good enough for most repair and overhaul procedures, and will add tools from the *Special* category when it is felt that the expense is justified by the amount of use to which these tools will be put.

Maintenance and minor repair tool kit

The tools given in this list should be considered as a minimum requirement if routine maintenance, servicing and minor repair operations are to be undertaken. We recommend the purchase of combination spanners (ring one end, open-ended the other); although more expensive than open-ended ones, they do give the advantages of both types of spanner.

Combination spanners:
    Metric - 8, 9, 10, 11, 12, 13, 14, 15, 17 & 19 mm
Adjustable spanner - 35 mm jaw (approx)
Gearbox drain plug key
Set of feeler gauges
Brake bleed nipple spanner
Screwdrivers:
    Flat-bladed - approx 100 mm long x 6 mm dia
    Cross-bladed - approx 100 mm long x 6 mm dia
Combination pliers
Hacksaw (junior)
Tyre pump
Tyre pressure gauge
Oil can
Oil filter removal tool
Fine emery cloth
Wire brush (small)
Funnel (medium size)

Repair and overhaul tool kit

These tools are virtually essential for anyone undertaking any major repairs to a motor vehicle, and are additional to those given in the *Maintenance and minor repair* list. Included in this list is a comprehensive set of sockets. Although these are expensive, they will be found invaluable as they are so versatile - particularly if various drives are included in the set. We recommend the half-inch square-drive type, as this can be used with most proprietary torque wrenches. If you cannot afford a socket set, even bought piecemeal, then inexpensive tubular box spanners are a useful alternative.

The tools in this list will occasionally need to be supplemented by tools from the Special list.

Sockets (or box spanners) to cover range in previous list
Reversible ratchet drive (for use with sockets)
Extension piece, 250 mm (for use with sockets)
Universal joint (for use with sockets)
Torque wrench (for use with sockets)
Self-locking grips
Ball pein hammer
Soft-faced mallet (plastic/aluminium or rubber)
Screwdrivers:
    Flat-bladed - long & sturdy, short (chubby), and narrow
    (electrician's) types
    Cross-bladed - Long & sturdy, and short (chubby) types
Pliers:
    Long-nosed
    Side cutters (electrician's)
    Circlip (internal and external)
Cold chisel - 25 mm
Scriber
Scraper
Centre-punch
Pin punch
Hacksaw
Brake hose clamp
Brake bleeding kit
Selection of twist drills
Steel rule/straight-edge
Allen keys (inc. splined/Torx type)
Selection of files
Wire brush
Axle stands
Jack (strong trolley or hydraulic type)
Light with extension lead

Special tools

The tools in this list are those which are not used regularly, are expensive to buy, or which need to be used in accordance with their manufacturers' instructions. Unless relatively difficult mechanical jobs are undertaken frequently, it will not be economic to buy many of these tools. Where this is the case, you could consider clubbing together with friends (or joining a motorists' club) to make a joint purchase, or borrowing the tools against a deposit from a local garage or tool hire specialist. It is worth noting that many of the larger DIY superstores now carry a large range of special tools for hire at modest rates.

The following list contains only those tools and instruments freely available to the public, and not those special tools produced by the vehicle manufacturer specifically for its dealer network. You will find occasional references to these manufacturers' special tools in the text of this manual. Generally, an alternative method of doing the job without the vehicle manufacturers' special tool is given. However, sometimes there is no alternative to using them. Where this is the case and the relevant tool cannot be bought or borrowed, you will have to entrust the work to a franchised garage.

Valve spring compressor
Valve grinding tool
Piston ring compressor
Piston ring removal/installation tool
Cylinder bore hone
Injector puller for removing injectors
Balljoint separator
Coil spring compressors (where applicable)
Two/three-legged hub and bearing puller
Impact screwdriver
Micrometer and/or vernier calipers
Dial test indicator
Optical or pulse-sensitive tachometer
Universal electrical multi-meter
Glow plug tester
Cylinder compression gauge
Hand-operated vacuum pump and gauge
Brake shoe steady spring cup removal tool (where applicable)
Bush and bearing removal/installation set
Stud extractors
Tap and die set
Lifting tackle
Trolley jack

Buying tools

For practically all tools, a tool factor is the best source, since he will have a very comprehensive range compared with the average garage or accessory shop. Having said that, accessory shops often offer excellent quality tools at discount prices, so it pays to shop around.

Remember, you don't have to buy the most expensive items on the shelf, but it is always advisable to steer clear of the very cheap tools. There are plenty of good tools around at reasonable prices, but always aim to purchase items which meet the relevant national safety standards. If in doubt, ask the proprietor or manager of the shop for advice before making a purchase.

Care and maintenance of tools

Having purchased a reasonable tool kit, it is necessary to keep the tools in a clean and serviceable condition. After use, always wipe off any dirt, grease and metal particles using a clean, dry cloth, before putting the tools away. Never leave them lying around after they have been used. A simple tool rack on the garage or workshop wall, for items such as screwdrivers and pliers, is a good idea. Store all normal spanners and sockets in a metal box. Any measuring instruments, gauges, meters, etc, must be carefully stored where they cannot be damaged or become rusty.

Take a little care when tools are used. Hammer heads inevitably become marked, and screwdrivers lose the keen edge on their blades from time to time. A little timely attention with emery cloth or a file will soon restore items like this to a good serviceable finish.

Working facilities

Not to be forgotten when discussing tools is the workshop itself. If anything more than routine maintenance is to be carried out, some form of suitable working area becomes essential.

It is appreciated that many an owner-mechanic is forced by circumstances to remove an engine or similar item without the benefit of a garage or workshop. Having done this, however, any repairs should always be done under the cover of a roof.

Wherever possible, any dismantling should be done on a clean, flat workbench or table at a suitable working height.

Any workbench needs a vice; one with a jaw opening of 100 mm is suitable for most jobs. As mentioned previously, some clean dry storage space is also required for tools, as well as for any lubricants, cleaning fluids, touch-up paints and so on, which become necessary.

Another item which may be required, and which has a much more general usage, is an electric drill with a chuck capacity of at least 8 mm. This, together with a good range of twist drills, is virtually essential for fitting accessories.

Last, but not least, always keep a supply of old newspapers and clean, lint-free rags available, and try to keep any working area as clean as possible.

Spanner jaw gap and bolt size comparison table

Jaw gap - in (mm)	Spanner size	Bolt size
0.197 (5.00)	5 mm	M 2.5
0.216 (5.50)	5.5 mm	M 3
0.218 (5.53)	7/32 in AF	
0.236 (6.00)	6 mm	M 3.5
0.250 (6.35)	1/4 in AF	
0.275 (7.00)	7 mm	M 4
0.281 (7.14)	9/32 in AF	
0.312 (7.92)	5/16 in AF	
0.315 (8.00)	8 mm	M 5
0.343 (8.71)	11/32 in AF	
0.375 (9.52)	3/8 in AF	
0.394 (10.00)	10 mm	M 6
0.406 (10.32)	13/32 in AF	
0.433 (11.00)	11 mm	M 7
0.437 (11.09)	7/16 in AF	1/4 in SAE
0.468 (11.88)	15/32 in AF	
0.500 (12.70)	1/2 in AF	5/16 in SAE
0.512 (13.00)	13 mm	M8
0.562 (14.27)	9/16 in AF	3/8 in SAE
0.593 (15.06)	19/32 in AF	
0.625 (15.87)	5/8 in AF	7/16 in SAE
0.669 (17.00)	17 mm	M 10
0.687 (17.44)	11/16 in AF	
0.709 (19.00)	19 mm	M 12
0.750 (19.05)	3/4 in AF	1/2 in SAE
0.781 (19.83)	25/32 in AF	
0.812 (20.62)	13/16 in AF	
0.866 (22.00)	22 mm	M 14
0.875 (22.25)	7/8 in AF	9/16 in SAE
0.937 (23.79)	15/16 in AF	5/8 in SAE
0.945 (24.00)	24 mm	M 16
0.968 (24.58)	31/32 in AF	
1.000 (25.40)	1 in AF	11/16 in SAE
1.062 (26.97)	1 1/16 in AF	3/4 in SAE
1.063 (27.00)	27 mm	M 18
1.125 (28.57)	1 1/8 in AF	
1.182 (30.00)	30 mm	M 20
1.187 (30.14)	1 3/16 in AF	
1.250 (31.75)	1 1/4 in AF	7/8 in SAE
1.260 (32.00)	32 mm	M 22
1.312 (33.32)	1 5/16 in AF	
1.375 (34.92)	1 3/8 in AF	
1.418 (36.00)	36 mm	M 24
1.437 (36.49)	1 7/16 in AF	1 in SAE
1.500 (38.10)	1 1/2 in AF	
1.615 (41.00)	41 mm	M 27

General repair procedures

Whenever servicing, repair or overhaul work is carried out on the vehicle or its components, it is necessary to observe the following procedures and instructions. This will assist in carrying out the operation efficiently and to a professional standard of workmanship.

Cleanliness

It is vitally important that no dirt whatsoever is allowed to enter the fuel injection system. Even the smallest particles can cause damage to the fuel injection pump and the injectors. The entry of water into the fuel system is also highly undesirable, especially if components are to be left standing idle for any length of time. With this in mind, observe the following precautions.

(a) Always clean fuel pipe unions, and any nearby components, before disconnection or removal.

(b) Place removed or dismantled components on a clean working area. Cover or plug open unions and orifices to keep dirt out, using clean material which will not shed dust or debris - for instance, cling film or aluminium foil.

(c) When cleaning components, do not use fluffy rags.

Note also that diesel fuel attacks rubber components more vigorously than petrol. Avoid contamination of hoses and drivebelts in the engine bay. A camshaft drivebelt or injection pump drivebelt which has been contaminated with fuel should be renewed.

Joint mating faces and gaskets

When separating components at their mating faces, never insert screwdrivers or similar implements into the joint between the faces in order to prise them apart. This can cause severe damage, resulting in oil leaks, coolant leaks, etc upon reassembly. Separation is usually achieved by tapping along the joint with a soft-faced hammer in order to break the seal. However, note that this method may not be suitable where dowels are used for component location.

Where a gasket is used between the mating faces of two components, ensure that it is renewed on reassembly, and fit it dry unless otherwise stated in the repair procedure. Make sure that the mating faces are clean and dry, with all traces of old gasket removed. When cleaning a joint face, use a tool which is not likely to score or damage the face, and remove any burrs or nicks with an oilstone or fine file.

Make sure that tapped holes are cleaned with a pipe cleaner, and keep them free of jointing compound, if this is being used, unless specifically instructed otherwise.

Ensure that all orifices, channels or pipes are clear, and blow through them, preferably using compressed air.

Oil seals

Oil seals can be removed by levering them out with a wide flat-bladed screwdriver or similar implement. Alternatively, a number of self-tapping screws may be screwed into the seal, and these used as a purchase for pliers or some similar device in order to pull the seal free.

Whenever an oil seal is removed from its working location, either individually or as part of an assembly, it should be renewed.

The very fine sealing lip of the seal is easily damaged, and will not seal if the surface it contacts is not completely clean and free from scratches, nicks or grooves. If the original sealing surface of the component cannot be restored, and the manufacturer has not made provision for slight relocation of the seal relative to the sealing surface, the component should be renewed.

Protect the lips of the seal from any surface which may damage them in the course of fitting. Use tape or a conical sleeve where possible. Lubricate the seal lips with oil before fitting and, on dual-lipped seals, fill the space between the lips with grease.

Unless otherwise stated, oil seals must be fitted with their sealing lips toward the lubricant to be sealed.

Use a tubular drift or block of wood of the appropriate size to install the seal and, if the seal housing is shouldered, drive the seal down to the shoulder. If the seal housing is unshouldered, the seal should be fitted with its face flush with the housing top face (unless otherwise instructed).

Screw threads and fastenings

Seized nuts, bolts and screws are quite a common occurrence where corrosion has set in, and the use of penetrating oil or releasing fluid will often overcome this problem if the offending item is soaked for a while before attempting to release it. The use of an impact driver may also provide a means of releasing such stubborn fastening devices when used in conjunction with the appropriate screwdriver bit or socket. If none of these methods works, it may be necessary to resort to the careful application of heat, or the use of a hacksaw or nut splitter device.

Studs are usually removed by locking two nuts together on the threaded part, and then using a spanner on the lower nut to unscrew the stud. Studs or bolts which have broken off below the surface of the component in which they are mounted can sometimes be removed using a proprietary stud extractor. Always ensure that a blind tapped hole is completely free from oil, grease, water or other fluid before installing the bolt or stud. Failure to do this could cause the housing to crack, due to the hydraulic action of the bolt or stud as it is screwed in.

When tightening a castellated nut to accept a split pin, tighten the nut to the specified torque, where applicable, and then tighten further to the next split pin hole (unless otherwise stated). Never slacken the nut to align the split pin hole, unless stated in the repair procedure.

When checking or retightening a nut or bolt to a specified torque setting, slacken the nut or bolt by a quarter of a turn, and then retighten to the specified setting. However, this should not be attempted where angular tightening has been used.

For some screw fastenings, notably cylinder head bolts or nuts, torque wrench settings are no longer specified for the latter stages of tightening, "angle-tightening" being called up instead. Typically, a fairly low torque wrench setting will be applied to the bolts/nuts in the correct sequence, followed by one or more stages of tightening through specified angles.

Locknuts, locktabs and washers

Any fastening which will rotate against a component or housing in the course of tightening should always have a washer between it and the relevant component or housing.

Spring or split washers should always be renewed when they are used to lock a critical component such as a big-end bearing retaining bolt or nut. Locktabs which are folded over to retain a nut or bolt should always be renewed. If this is not possible, they should at least be folded in an unused area of the tab, rather than refolded along the same crease.

Self-locking nuts can be reused in non-critical areas, providing resistance can be felt when the locking portion passes over the bolt or stud thread. However, it should be noted that self-locking nuts tend to lose their effectiveness after long periods of use, and in such cases should be renewed as a matter of course.

Split pins must always be replaced with new ones of the correct size for the hole.

When thread-locking compound is found on the threads of a fastener which is to be re-used, it should be cleaned off with a wire brush and solvent, and fresh compound applied on reassembly.

Special tools

Some repair procedures in this manual entail the use of special tools such as a press, two or three-legged pullers, spring compressors etc. Wherever possible, suitable readily-available alternatives to the manufacturer's special tools are described, and are shown in use. In some instances, where no alternative is possible, it has been necessary to resort to the use of a manufacturer's tool, and this has been done for reasons of safety as well as the efficient completion of the repair operation. Unless you are highly skilled and have a thorough understanding of the procedures described, never attempt to bypass the use of any special tool when the procedure described specifies its use. Not only is there a very great risk of personal injury, but expensive damage could be caused to the components involved.

Environmental considerations

Some adjustment screws or access plugs on the fuel injection pump will be found to be "tamperproofed" with paint, plastic caps, lead seals or locking wire. The main purpose of tamperproofing is to discourage, and to detect, emission-related adjustments by unqualified operators. In some parts of Europe (though not yet in the UK), it is an offence to use a vehicle with missing or broken tamperproof seals. Before removing or breaking a tamperproof seal, check that no anti-pollution laws are being broken by so doing. Fit a new seal on completion of the work, where this is required by law. Do not break seals on a vehicle which is still under warranty, or the warranty may be invalidated. Note also that a manufacturer may refuse to accept an old injection pump in part exchange if tamperproof seals are broken.

When disposing of used engine oil, brake fluid, antifreeze etc, give due consideration to any detrimental environmental effects. Do not, for instance, pour any of the above liquids down drains into the general sewage system or onto the ground to soak away. Many local council refuse tips provide a facility for waste oil disposal, as do some garages. If none of these facilities are available, consult your local Environmental Health Department for further advice.

Fuel injection system

Cleanliness is vital for reliable operation and long life of the fuel injection system components. Always clean around fuel system unions before disconnecting them, and plug or cap open unions to keep dirt and moisture out. ("Fingers" cut from discarded rubber or plastic gloves, secured with rubber bands or cable ties, are ideal for this.) Avoid using compressed air for cleaning in the vicinity of open fuel system unions, as there is a risk of dirt being blown into them.

Booster battery (jump) starting

When jump starting a car using a booster battery, observe the following precautions.

(a) *Before connecting the booster battery, make sure that the ignition is switched off.*

(b) *Ensure that all electrical equipment (lights, heater, wipers etc) is switched off.*

(c) *Make sure that the booster battery is the same voltage as the discharged one in the vehicle.*

(d) *If the battery is being jump started from the battery in another vehicle, the two vehicles MUST NOT TOUCH each other.*

(e) *Make sure that the transmission is in neutral (manual gearbox) or Park (automatic transmission).*

Connect one jump lead between the positive (+) terminals of the two batteries. Connect the other jump lead first to the negative (-) terminal of the booster battery, and then to a good earthing point on the vehicle to be started, such as a bolt or bracket on the engine block, at least 45 cm from the battery if possible. Make sure that the jump leads will not come into contact with the fan, drivebelts or other moving parts of the engine.

Start the engine using the booster battery, then with the engine running at idle speed, disconnect the jump leads in the reverse order of connection.

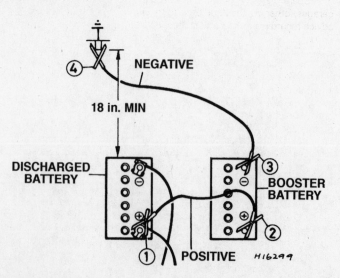

Jump start lead connections for negative earth - connect leads in order shown

Buying spare parts
and vehicle identification numbers

Buying spare parts

Spare parts are available from many sources; for example, Rover garages, other garages and accessory shops, and motor factors. Our advice regarding spare part sources is as follows.

Officially-appointed Rover garages - This is the best source for parts which are peculiar to your vehicle, and are not generally available (eg complete cylinder heads, internal gearbox components, badges, interior trim etc). It is also the only place at which you should buy parts if the vehicle is still under warranty. To be sure of obtaining the correct parts, it will be necessary to give the storeman the vehicle identification number, and if possible, take the old parts along for positive identification. Many parts are available under a factory exchange scheme - any parts returned should always be clean. It obviously makes good sense to go straight to the specialists on your vehicle for this type of part, as they are best equipped to supply you.

Other garages and accessory shops - These are often very good places to buy materials and components needed for the maintenance of your vehicle (eg oil filters, bulbs, drivebelts, oils and greases, touch-up paint, filler paste, etc). They also sell general accessories, usually have convenient opening hours, charge lower prices, and can often be found not far from home.

Motor factors - Good factors will stock all the more important components which wear out comparatively quickly (eg exhaust systems, brake pads, seals and hydraulic parts, clutch components, bearing shells, pistons, valves etc). Motor factors will often provide new or reconditioned components on a part exchange basis - this can save a considerable amount of money.

Vehicle identification numbers

Modifications are a continuing and unpublicised process in vehicle manufacture, quite apart from major model changes. Spare parts manuals and lists are compiled upon a numerical basis, the individual vehicle identification numbers being essential to correct identification of the component concerned.

When ordering spare parts, always give as much information as possible. Quote the vehicle model, year of manufacture, body and engine numbers as appropriate.

The *vehicle identification number (VIN)* is stamped on a plate attached to the left-hand door pillar, below the door lock striker pin. Some models also have the VIN etched on the front and rear screens.

The *body colour and trim codes* are also stamped on the VIN plate.

The *engine number* is stamped on the front face of the cylinder block, below the injectors.

The *gearbox number* is stamped on the front face of the gearbox bellhousing.

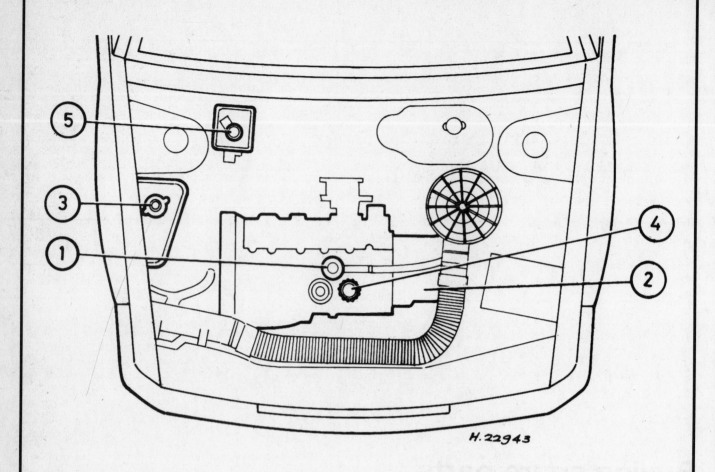

H. 22943

Recommended lubricants and fluids

Component or system	Lubricant type/recommendation	Duckhams specification
1 **Engine**	Multigrade engine oil, viscosity 10W/40 to 15W/50, to API SG/CD	Duckhams Diesel, QXR, Hypergrade Plus or Hypergrade
2 **Gearbox**	Multigrade engine oil, viscosity 10W/40 (15W/40 oil may be used for topping-up)	Duckhams QXR or 10W/40 Motor Oil (Duckhams Diesel may be used for topping-up)
3 **Cooling system**	Ethylene glycol-based antifreeze	Duckhams Universal Antifreeze and Summer Coolant
4 **Power steering**	Dexron IID type ATF	Duckhams Uni-Matic
5 **Brake hydraulic system**	Hydraulic fluid to FMVSS 116 DOT 4 or SAE J1703C	Duckhams Universal Brake and Clutch Fluid

Routine maintenance

Maintenance is essential for ensuring safety, and desirable for the purpose of getting the best in terms of performance and economy from your vehicle. Over the years, the need for periodic lubrication has been greatly reduced, if not totally eliminated. This has unfortunately tended to lead some owners to think that because no such action is required, the items either no longer exist, or will last forever. This is certainly not the case; it is essential to carry out regular visual examination as comprehensively as possible, in order to spot any potential defects at an early stage before they develop into major expensive repairs.

The following service schedules are a list of the maintenance requirements, and the intervals at which they should be carried out, as recommended by the manufacturers. Where applicable, these procedures are covered in greater detail throughout this manual, near the beginning of each Chapter.

Every 250 miles (400 km) or weekly - whichever occurs first

Engine, cooling system, and brakes (Chapters 1, 2 and the relevant Chapter in petrol-engine manual)

    Check engine oil level, and top-up if necessary
    Check coolant level, and top-up if necessary
    Check brake fluid level in the reservoir, and top-up if necessary

Lights and wipers

    Check operation of all lights, wipers and washers
    Check and if necessary top-up the washer reservoir

Tyres

    Check tyre pressures (including the spare)
    Visually examine tyres for wear or damage

Every 12 000 miles (20 000 km) or 12 months - whichever occurs first

---

Engine (Chapter 1)

    Renew engine oil and oil filter

Cooling system (Chapter 2)

    Check antifreeze concentration, and top-up with neat antifreeze if necessary
    Check water pump/alternator drivebelt for condition and tension

Fuel and exhaust systems (Chapter 3)

    Check all fuel hoses and pipes for security and condition. Also check exhaust system and heat shields
    Check all pressure-sensing hoses and vacuum pipes
    Check EGR system components
    Renew fuel filter
    Check smoke emissions (commencing at 36 000 miles, then every 12 000 miles thereafter)
    Drain water from fuel filter

Clutch (Chapter 4)

    Check cable self-adjusting mechanism

Manual gearbox (Chapter 5)

Check gearbox oil level, and top-up if necessary

Driveshafts (Chapter 6)

Check driveshaft joints and rubber boots

Braking system (see relevant Chapter in petrol-engine manual)

Check brake linings, drums, discs, calipers, hoses and pipes
Adjust handbrake (first 12 000 miles only)

Suspension and steering (Chapter 8)

Check all suspension and steering joints
Check power steering fluid level
Check condition and tension of power steering pump drivebelt
Check condition of power steering hydraulic hoses and connections

Bodywork (see relevant Chapter in petrol-engine manual)

Corrosion inspection
Check windscreen for cracks
Lubricate locks, strikers, latches and door hinges

Electrical system (see relevant Chapter in petrol-engine manual)

Check lamps, horns, system warning indicators, headlamp wipers and washers
Check battery connections

Road test

Carry out road test, and check for correct function of all vehicle systems and controls

---

Every 24 000 miles (40 000 km) or 2 years - whichever occurs first

In addition to all the items in the 12-monthly service, carry out the following:

Engine (Chapter 1)

Check crankcase vent hoses
Check/renew engine breather PCV valve

Cooling system (Chapter 2)

Renew coolant (at first 36 000 miles, then every 24 000 miles thereafter)
Check all cooling system hoses and connections

Fuel and exhaust system (Chapter 3)

Renew air cleaner element

Gearbox (Chapter 5)

Renew the gearbox oil

Braking system (Chapter 7 and relevant Chapter in petrol-engine manual)

Check handbrake
Renew brake fluid (every 2 years, regardless of mileage)

Every 36 000 miles (60 000 km) or 3 years - whichever occurs first

In addition to all the items in the previous services, carry out the following:

Engine (Chapter 1)

Check and adjust valve clearances

Every 48 000 miles (80 000 km) or 4 years - whichever occurs first

In addition to all the items in the previous services, carry out the following:

Fuel and exhaust system (Chapter 3)

Clean fuel lift pump strainer

Every 72 000 miles (120 000 km) or 6 years - whichever occurs first

In addition to all the items in the previous services, carry out the following:

Engine (Chapter 1)

Renew the timing belt

Engine and underbonnet component locations (1992 Maestro Turbo)

1	Speedometer cable	10	EGR modulator valve	19	Throttle potentiometer
2	Brake fluid reservoir	11	Air cleaner and housing	20	Fast idle solenoid
3	Thermostat housing	12	Battery	21	Radiator top hose
4	Fuel lift pump	13	Air inlet hose	22	Timing belt cover
5	Self-adjusting clutch cable	14	Accelerator cable	23	Cooling system expansion tank
6	EGR valve	15	Engine oil filler cap	24	Right-hand engine mounting
7	Brake vacuum pump	16	Crankcase ventilation PCV valve	25	Front suspension top mounting
8	Fuel filter and housing	17	Engine oil level dipstick		
9	Windscreen washer fluid reservoir	18	Fuel injection pump		

Front underbody view (1992 Maestro Turbo)

1   Water pump/alternator drivebelt
2   Engine oil drain plug on sump
3   Right-hand driveshaft
4   Rear engine mounting
5   Engine oil cooler
6   Gearbox
7   Radiator bottom hose
8   Left-hand driveshaft
9   Brake hydraulic and fuel pipes
10 Gearbox support rod
11 Gearchange rod
12 Exhaust pipe
13 Driveshaft damper
14 Front brake caliper
15 Oil filter

Fault diagnosis

Introduction

The vehicle owner who does his or her own maintenance according to the recommended service schedules should not have to use this section of the manual very often. Modern component reliability is such that, provided those items subject to wear or deterioration are inspected or renewed at the specified intervals, sudden failure is comparatively rare. Faults do not usually just happen as a result of sudden failure, but develop over a period of time. Major mechanical failures in particular are usually preceded by characteristic symptoms over hundreds or even thousands of miles. Those components which do occasionally fail without warning are often small and easily carried in the vehicle.

With any fault finding, the first step is to decide where to begin investigations. Sometimes this is obvious, but on other occasions, a little detective work will be necessary. The owner who makes half-a-dozen haphazard adjustments or replacements may be successful in curing a fault (or its symptoms), but will be none the wiser if the fault recurs, and ultimately may have spent more time and money than was necessary. A calm and logical approach will be found to be more satisfactory in the long run. Always take into account any warning signs or abnormalities that may have been noticed in the period preceding the fault - power loss, high or low gauge readings, unusual smells, etc - and remember that failure of components such as fuses or spark plugs may only be pointers to some underlying fault.

The pages which follow here are intended to help in cases of failure to start or breakdown on the road. There is also a fault diagnosis Section at the end of each Chapter, which should be consulted if the preliminary checks prove unfruitful. Whatever the fault, certain basic principles apply, and these are as follows.

Verify the fault. This is simply a matter of being sure that you know what the symptoms are before starting work. This is particularly important if you are investigating a fault for someone else, who may not have described it very accurately.

Don't overlook the obvious. For example, if the vehicle won't start, is there fuel in the tank? (Don't take anyone else's word on this particular point, and don't trust the fuel gauge either!) If an electrical fault is indicated, look for loose or broken wires before digging out the test gear.

Cure the disease, not the symptom. Substituting a flat battery with a fully-charged one will get you off the hard shoulder, but if the underlying cause is not attended to, the new battery will go the same way.

Don't take anything for granted. Particularly, don't forget that a "new" component may itself be defective (especially if it's been rattling around in the boot for months), and don't leave components out of a fault diagnosis sequence just because they are new or recently fitted. When you do finally diagnose a difficult fault, you'll probably realise that all the evidence was there from the start.

Electrical faults

Electrical faults can be more puzzling than straightforward mechanical failures, but they are no less susceptible to logical analysis if the basic principles of operation are understood. Vehicle electrical wiring exists in extremely-unfavourable conditions - heat, vibration and chemical attack - and the first things to look for are loose or corroded connections and broken or chafed wires, especially where the wires pass through holes in the bodywork, or are subject to vibration.

All metal-bodied vehicles in current production have one pole of the battery "earthed", ie connected to the vehicle bodywork, and in nearly all modern vehicles it is the negative (-) terminal. The various

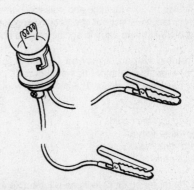

A simple test lamp is useful for checking electrical faults

electrical components - motors, bulbholders etc - are also connected to earth, either by means of a lead or directly by their mountings. Electric current flows through the component and then back to the battery via the bodywork. If the component mounting is loose or corroded, or if a good path back to the battery is not available, the circuit will be incomplete, and malfunction will result. The engine and/or gearbox are also earthed by means of flexible metal straps to the body or subframe; if these straps are loose or missing, starter motor and alternator trouble may result.

Assuming the earth return to be satisfactory, electrical faults will be due either to component malfunction or to defects in the current supply. If supply wires are broken or cracked internally, this results in an open-circuit, and the easiest way to check for this is to bypass the suspect wire temporarily, using a length of wire having a crocodile clip or suitable connector at each end. Alternatively, a 12-volt test lamp can be used to verify the presence of supply voltage at various points along the wire, and the break can be thus isolated.

If a bare portion of a live wire touches the bodywork or other earthed metal part, the electricity will take the low-resistance path thus formed back to the battery; this is known as a short-circuit. Hopefully, a short-circuit will blow a fuse, but otherwise, it may cause burning of the insulation (and possibly further short-circuits) or even a fire. This is why it is inadvisable to bypass persistently-blowing fuses with silver foil or wire.

Spares and tool kit

Most vehicles are supplied only with sufficient tools for wheel changing; the *Maintenance and minor repair tool kit* detailed in *Tools and working facilities*, with the addition of a hammer, is probably sufficient for those repairs that most motorists would consider attempting at the roadside. In addition, a few items which can be fitted without too much trouble in the event of a breakdown should be carried. Experience and available space will modify the list below, but the following may save having to call on professional assistance.

Drivebelt(s) - emergency type may suffice
Spare fuses
Set of principal light bulbs
Tin of radiator sealer and hose bandage
Exhaust bandage
Roll of insulating tape
Length of soft iron wire
Torch or inspection lamp (can double as test lamp)
Battery jump leads
Tow-rope
Litre of engine oil
Sealed can of hydraulic fluid

Emergency windscreen
Worm drive clips

If spare fuel is carried, a can designed for the purpose should be used, to minimise risks of leakage and collision damage. A first aid kit and a warning triangle, whilst not at present compulsory in the UK, are obviously sensible items to carry in addition to the above.

When touring abroad, it may be advisable to carry additional spares which, even if you cannot fit them yourself, could save having to wait while parts are obtained. The items below may be worth considering.

Clutch and throttle cables
Cylinder head gasket
Alternator brushes
Tyre valve core

One of the motoring organisations will be able to advise on availability of fuel etc in foreign countries.

Engine will not start

Engine fails to turn when starter operated

Flat battery (recharge or use jump leads)
Battery terminals loose or corroded
Battery earth to body defective
Engine earth strap loose or broken
Starter motor (or solenoid) wiring loose or broken
Starter switch faulty
Major mechanical failure (seizure)
Starter or solenoid internal fault (see Chapter 9)

Starter motor turns engine slowly

Partially-discharged battery (recharge or use jump leads)
Battery terminals loose or corroded
Battery earth to body defective
Engine earth strap loose
Starter motor (or solenoid) wiring loose
Starter motor internal fault

Starter motor spins without turning engine

Starter motor reduction gears stripped (where applicable)
Starter motor mounting bolts loose

Engine turns normally but fails to start

No fuel in tank (check for delivery at fuel filter)
Air in fuel
Wax formed in fuel (in very cold weather)
Poor compression
Fuel system or preheater fault
Major mechanical failure (eg camshaft drive)

Engine fires but will not run

Air leaks at injectors or inlet manifold
Fuel starvation
Preheater fault
Air in fuel
Wax formed in fuel (in very cold weather)
Other fuel system fault

Engine cuts out and will not restart

Fuel tank empty!
Fuel filter blocked
Fuel tank vent blocked (suction evident on removal of cap)
Other fuel system fault

Serious overheating
Mechanical failure

Engine overheats

Alternator (no-charge) warning light illuminated

Slack or broken drivebelt - retension or renew

Alternator (no-charge warning) light not illuminated

Coolant loss due to internal or external leakage
Thermostat defective
Low oil level
Brakes binding
Radiator clogged externally or internally
Electric cooling fan not operating correctly
Engine waterways clogged

Note: *Do not add cold water to an overheated engine while still hot, or damage may result*

Low engine oil pressure

Oil pressure warning light illuminated with engine running

Oil level low or incorrect-grade oil
Defective gauge or sender unit, as applicable
Wire to sender unit earthed
Engine overheating
Oil filter clogged or bypass valve defective
Oil pressure relief valve defective
Oil pick-up strainer clogged
Oil pump worn
Worn main or big-end bearings

Note: *Low oil pressure in a high-mileage engine at tickover is not necessarily a cause for concern. Sudden pressure loss at speed is far more significant. In any event, check the gauge or warning light sender before condemning the engine.*

Engine noises

To inexperienced ears, the diesel engine can sound alarming even when there is nothing wrong with it, so it may be prudent to have an unusual noise expertly diagnosed before making renewals or repairs.

Whistling or wheezing noises

Leaking vacuum hose
Leaking manifold gasket
Blowing head gasket

Tapping or rattling

Incorrect valve clearances
Broken piston ring (ticking noise)

Knocking or thumping

Air in fuel
Unintentional mechanical contact
Peripheral component fault (alternator, water pump, etc)
Fuel injector(s) leaking or sticking
Worn big-end bearings (regular heavy knocking, perhaps less under load)
Worn main bearings (rumbling and knocking, perhaps worsening under load)
Piston slap (most noticeable when cold)

Chapter 1 Engine

Contents

Specifications

Engine (general)

Type	Four-cylinder, in-line, overhead camshaft, compression ignition
Designation	Perkins MDi "Prima"
Number of cylinders	4
Bore	84.442 mm to 84.469 mm
Stroke	89.0 mm
Capacity.	1994 cc
Firing order	1-3-4-2 (No 1 cylinder at timing end)
Direction of crankshaft rotation	Clockwise
Compression ratio:	
Non-Turbo models	18.1 : 1
Turbo models	17.2 : 1

Compression pressure

Nominal value (engine cranking)........................	300 to 500 lbf/in²
Maximum difference between readings	50 lbf/in²

Cylinder block

Material	Cast-iron
Cylinder bore diameter:	
Standard..	84.442 to 84,469 mm
1st oversize	84.942 to 84.969 mm
Maximum cylinder bore ovality..........................	0.15 mm
Maximum cylinder bore taper............................	0.15 mm
Number of main bearings	5
Main bearing journal diameter:	
Standard..	56.99 to 57.01 mm
Undersize	0.30 mm
Main bearing journal running clearance	0.023 to 0.073 mm
Crankpin (big-end) journal diameter:	
Standard..	53.99 to 54.01 mm
Undersize	0.30 mm
Crankpin (big-end) journal running clearance....	0.023 to 0.076 mm
Crankshaft endfloat	0.03 to 0.26 mm
Crankshaft flange diameter	88.84 to 88.95 mm

Pistons and piston rings

Maximum protrusion of pistons above joint face of cylinder block:	
Non-Turbo models	0.46 to 0.65 mm
Turbo models	0.41 to 0.51 mm
Piston oversize diameter	0.50 mm
Piston ring end gaps (fitted in bore):	
Top compression ring	0.28 to 0.56 mm
Second compression ring	0.28 to 0.56 mm
Oil control ring	0.23 to 0.56 mm
Piston ring-to-groove clearance:	
Top compression ring	0.11 to 0.14 mm
Second compression ring	0.07 to 0.10 mm
Oil control ring	0.04 to 0.07 mm

Gudgeon pins

Diameter	27.995 to 28.000 mm
Clearance in piston	0.004 to 0.015 mm
Clearance in connecting rod	0.005 to 0.013 mm

Connecting rods

Length between centres.....................................	144.975 to 145.025 mm
Small-end bush diameter	28.004 to 28.010 mm

Cylinder head

Material	Aluminium alloy
Height (new)...	120.1 to 120.0 mm
Maximum regrind...	0.2 mm
Maximum acceptable gasket face distortion	0.1 mm
Valve seat angle..	45°

Camshaft

Drive	Toothed belt
Number of bearings	3
Bearing journal diameter:	
Front and rear	47.963 to 47.975 mm
Centre	47.958 to 47.975 mm
Bearing journal running clearance:	
Front and rear	0.043 to 0.094 mm
Centre	0.043 to 0.099 mm
Camshaft endfloat (maximum)	0.51 mm

Valves

Face angle	44° 30'
Head diameter:	
Inlet	37.10 to 37.25 mm
Exhaust	33.55 to 33.70 mm
Stem diameter:	
Inlet	7.41 to 7.42 mm
Exhaust	7.39 to 7.41 mm
Stem-to-guide clearance:	
Inlet	0.03 to 0.05 mm
Exhaust	0.04 to 0.07 mm
Valve head depth below cylinder head face:	
Inlet	0.90 to 1.24 mm
Exhaust	1.30 to 1.64 mm
Valve clearances (cold):	
Inlet (checking)	0.20 to 0.40 mm
Inlet (adjusting)	0.25 to 0.35 mm
Exhaust (checking)	0.30 to 0.50 mm
Exhaust (adjusting)	0.35 to 0.45 mm
Valve timing:	
Inlet opens	8° BTDC
Inlet closes	44° ABDC
Exhaust opens	50° BBDC
Exhaust closes	10° ATDC
Valve spring free length	42.5 mm
Valve guide external diameter	12.04 to 12.06 mm
Valve guide internal diameter	7.45 to 7.46 mm
Valve guide fitted height above cylinder head	10.0 mm

Lubrication system

System pressure:	
Idling	1.0 to 1.3 bars (15 to 20 lbf/in²)
Running	4.2 bars (60 lbf/in²)
Warning light switch pressure	0.6 to 0.9 bars (9.0 to 13.0 lbf/in²)
Oil pump type	Bi-rotor
Oil pump clearances:	
Outer rotor endfloat	0.05 to 0.10 mm
Inner rotor endfloat	0.030 to 0.075 mm
Outer rotor-to-body clearance	0.30 to 0.36 mm
Rotor lobe clearance	0.025 to 0.082 mm
Oil pressure relief valve opening pressure	4.2 bars (60 lbf/in²)
Oil type/specification	Multigrade engine oil, viscosity 10W/40 to 15W/50 (Duckhams Diesel, QXR, Hypergrade Plus or Hypergrade)
Oil filter	Champion B103
Oil capacity (including filter)	5.25 litres (9.0 pints)

Torque wrench settings

	Nm	lbf ft
Camshaft cover	22	16
Timing belt idler	43	32
Timing belt tensioner	43	32
Camshaft gear centre bolt	85	63
Camshaft gear hub bolts	22	16
Connecting rod big-end nuts (threads oiled)	47	35
Crankshaft pulley centre bolt	180	133
Crankshaft pulley to gear bolts	10	7
Cylinder head bolts (threads oiled):		
Stage 1	50	37
Stage 2	100	74
Stage 3	Angle-tighten by a further 90°	

Torque wrench settings (continued)

	Nm	lbf ft
Flywheel bolts	65	48
Fuel injection pump gear centre bolt	60	44
Gearbox adapter plate bolts (13 mm)	43	32
Main bearing bolts (threads oiled)	112	83
Inlet and exhaust manifold bolts	22	16
Oil pressure switch	12	9
Oil pump backplate screws	4	3
Oil pump mounting bolts:		
M6	9	6
M10	43	32
Sump bolts	12	9
Sump drain plug	30	22
Timing belt cover bolts:		
M5	3	2.2
M6	6	4.4
M8	10	7
Engine mountings (pre-1989 non-Turbo models):		
Damper to body	20	15
Damper to engine	25	18
Left-hand rear mounting bracket to rubber	25	18
Snubber	40	30
Left-hand mounting to body	40	30
Right-hand mounting bracket to rubber	40	30
Left-hand rear mounting to gearbox	45	33
Right-hand rear mounting to body and engine	45	33
Damper-to-bracket bolts	80	59
Right-hand and left-hand centre bolts	90	66
Engine mountings (Turbo and 1989 models onwards):		
Self-locking bolts on right-hand and left-hand mountings	55	41
Right-hand Hydramount lower nut	40	30
Right-hand Hydramount upper nut	50	37
Right-hand mounting snubber	28	21
Rear mounting to body	80	59
Rear mounting link	85	63
Left-hand mounting rubber to bracket	63	47
Left-hand mounting rubber centre nut	73	54
Left-hand lower mounting bracket to body	45	33

1 General description

The Rover MDi engine is a four-cylinder in-line unit, with a cast-iron block and an aluminium alloy head. Both turbocharged and normally-aspirated versions exist. The engine is made by Perkins, who call it the "Prima".

The single overhead camshaft is driven by a toothed belt, which also drives the fuel injection pump. The camshaft runs in bearings machined directly in the cylinder head and camshaft cover. The cam lobes operate inverted bucket tappets, with selective shims located inside the tappets. Eccentrics on the camshaft drive a brake servo vacuum pump and a fuel lift pump.

The pistons are fitted with two compression rings and one oil con-trol ring, and are connected to the connecting rods by fully-floating gudgeon pins.

On Turbo models, oil jets, fitted to the bottom of the cylinder bores, direct oil onto the undersides of the piston crowns. This lowers the piston crown temperatures.

The crankshaft is supported in five main bearings, and endfloat is controlled by thrustwashers on each side of the centre main bearing.

Lubrication is by a bi-rotor type oil pump mounted on the front of the cylinder block, driven by a key on the front of the crankshaft. The oil pump includes a pressure relief valve and oil pressure switch, and the oil filter is located directly on the oil pump housing. Turbo models, and all models from 1989 onwards, are fitted with an oil cooler located behind the bottom of the radiator; oil is passed through the cooler via hoses from the oil pump.

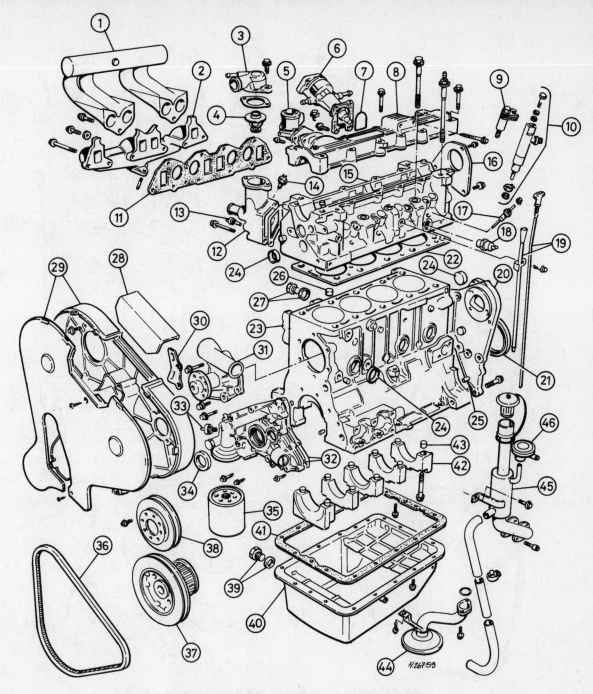

Fig. 1.1 Exploded view of the non-Turbo diesel engine (Sec 1)

1	Inlet manifold	16	Camshaft rear cover	32	Oil pump and gasket
2	Exhaust manifold	17	Glow plug	33	Oil pressure switch
3	Thermostat cover	18	Thermistor (automatic advance unit)	34	Crankshaft front oil seal
4	Thermostat	19	Engine oil level dipstick and tube	35	Oil filter
5	Fuel lift pump	20	Gearbox adapter plate	36	Alternator drivebelt
6	Brake servo vacuum pump	21	Crankshaft rear oil seal	37	Crankshaft pulley and gear
7	O-ring seal	22	Cylinder head gasket	38	Water pump pulley
8	Camshaft cover	23	Cylinder block	39	Sump drain plug and washer
9	Injector clamp	24	Core plug	40	Sump
10	Injector	25	Solid location dowel	41	Sump gasket
11	Manifold gasket	26	Ring location dowel	42	Main bearing cap
12	Thermostat housing	27	Coolant drain plug and washer	43	Ring dowel
13	Temperature sender (temperature gauge)	28	Timing belt access panel	44	Oil pick-up pipe and strainer
14	Thermistor (fast idle speed)	29	Inner and outer timing belt covers	45	Oil separator
15	Cylinder head	30	Cover retaining bracket	46	One-way valve
		31	Water pump		

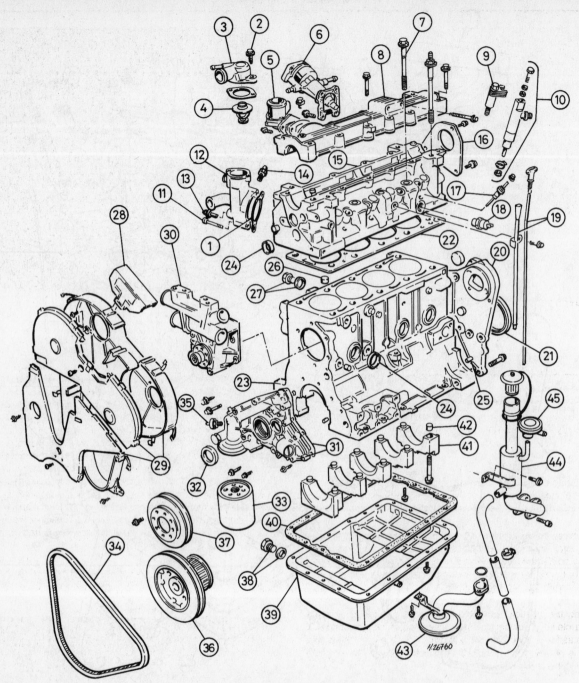

Fig. 1.2 Exploded view of the Turbo diesel engine (Sec 1)

1	Thermostat housing gasket	16	Camshaft rear cover	32	Crankshaft front oil seal
2	Thermostat cover retaining bolt	17	Glow plug	33	Oil filter
3	Thermostat cover	18	Thermistor (automatic advance unit)	34	Alternator drivebelt
4	Thermostat	19	Engine oil level dipstick and tube	35	Oil pressure switch
5	Fuel lift pump	20	Gearbox adapter plate	36	Crankshaft pulley and timing gear
6	Brake servo vacuum pump	21	Crankshaft rear oil seal	37	Water pump pulley
7	Cylinder head bolt	22	Cylinder head gasket	38	Sump drain plug and washer
8	Camshaft cover	23	Cylinder block	39	Sump
9	Injector clamp	24	Core plug	40	Sump gasket
10	Injector assembly	25	Solid location dowel	41	Main bearing cap
11	Thermostat housing retaining bolt	26	Ring location dowel	42	Ring location dowel
12	Thermostat housing	27	Coolant drain plug and washer	43	Oil pick-up pipe and strainer
13	Temperature sender (temperature gauge)	28	Timing belt access panel	44	Oil separator
14	Thermistor (fast idle speed)	29	Inner and outer timing belt covers	45	One-way valve
15	Cylinder head	30	Water pump		
		31	Oil pump and gasket		

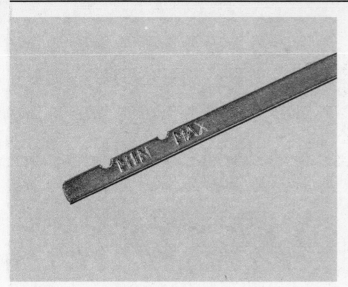

2.3 Markings on the engine oil level dipstick

2.4 Topping-up the engine with oil

2 Routine maintenance

Carry out the following procedures at the intervals given in the "Routine maintenance" Section at the start of this manual.

Check the engine oil level

1   The engine oil level is checked with a dipstick that extends through a tube and into the sump at the bottom of the engine. The dipstick is located in a tube on the front face of the engine cylinder block.

2   The oil level should be checked with the vehicle standing on level ground and before it is driven, or at least 5 minutes after the engine has been switched off. If the oil is checked immediately after driving the vehicle, some of the oil will remain in the upper part of the engine, resulting in an inaccurate reading on the dipstick.

3   Withdraw the dipstick from the tube, and wipe all the oil from the end, using a clean rag or paper towel. Insert the clean dipstick back into the tube as far as it will go, then withdraw it once more. Check that the oil level is between the upper (MAX) mark/notch and lower (MIN) mark/notch on the dipstick (photo).

4   If necessary, remove the filler cap from the top of the oil filler and breather housing, and add oil until the level is up to the upper (MAX) mark (photo). Note that 1.0 litre of oil will be required to raise the level from the lower mark to the upper mark. An oil can spout or funnel may help to reduce spillage. Always use the correct grade and type of oil, as given in "Recommended lubricants and fluids". Refit the filler cap on completion.

5   Always maintain the level between the two dipstick marks. If the level is allowed to fall below the lower mark, oil starvation may result, which could lead to severe engine damage. If the engine is overfilled by adding too much oil, this may result in oil leaks or oil seal failures.

Renew the engine oil and oil filter

6   Frequent oil and filter changes are the most important preventative maintenance procedures that can be undertaken by the D.I.Y. owner. As engine oil ages, it becomes diluted and contaminated, which leads to premature engine wear.

7   Before starting this procedure, gather together all the necessary tools and materials (photo). Also make sure that you have plenty of clean rags and newspapers handy, to mop up any spills. Ideally, the engine oil should be warm, as it will drain better and more built-up sludge will be removed with it. Take care, however, not to touch the exhaust or any other hot parts of the engine when working under the vehicle. To avoid any possibility of scalding, and to protect yourself from possible skin irritants and other harmful contaminants in used engine oils, it is advisable to wear gloves when carrying out this work. Access to the underside of the vehicle will be greatly improved if it can be raised on a lift, driven onto ramps, or jacked up and supported on axle stands. Whichever method is chosen, make sure that the vehicle remains as level as possible, as the drain plug is located in the centre rear of the sump.

8   Position a suitable container beneath the sump drain plug. Clean the drain plug and the area around it, then slacken it half a turn using a

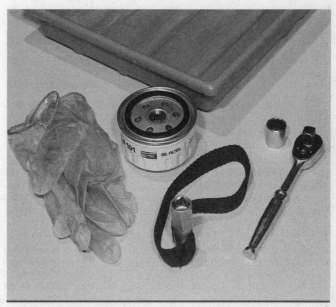

2.7 Requirements for engine oil and filter renewal

2.8   Unscrewing the engine oil drain plug

2.12   Using an oil filter wrench to loosen the oil filter

socket or spanner (photo). If possible, try to keep the plug pressed into the sump while unscrewing it by hand until the last couple of turns. As the plug releases from the threads, move it away sharply so the stream of oil issuing from the sump runs into the container, not up your sleeve!

9   Allow some time for the old oil to drain, noting that it may be necessary to reposition the container as the oil flow slows to a trickle.

10   After all the oil has drained, wipe off the drain plug with a clean rag, and renew the sealing washer if necessary. Clean the area around the drain plug opening, and refit the plug. Tighten the plug to the specified torque.

11   Move the container into position under the oil filter, which is located on the right-hand end of the engine beneath the oil pump.

12   Using an oil filter removal tool (if necessary), slacken the filter initially (photo), then unscrew it by hand the rest of the way. Empty the oil in the old filter into the container.

13   Use a clean rag to remove all oil, dirt and sludge from the filter sealing area on the oil pump. Check the old filter to make sure that the rubber sealing ring is not stuck to the oil pump. If it has, carefully remove it.

14   Apply a light coating of clean engine oil to the sealing ring on the new filter, then screw it into position on the oil pump. Tighten the filter firmly by hand only - do not use any tools (photo). Wipe clean the exterior of the oil filter.

15   Remove the old oil and all tools from under the vehicle, then lower the vehicle to the ground (if applicable).

16   Remove the oil filler cap from the oil filler and breather tube assembly on the front of the engine, and fill the engine, using the correct grade and type of oil, as described earlier in this Section. Pour the oil in slowly, otherwise it may overflow from the top of the filler tube. Check that the oil level is up to the maximum mark on the dipstick.

17   On Turbo models, disconnect the wiring from the stop solenoid, and spin the engine on the starter motor until oil pressure is registered on the oil pressure gauge (or until the low oil pressure warning light goes out). Reconnect the wiring afterwards.

18   Start the engine and run it for a few minutes, while checking for leaks around the oil filter seal and the sump drain plug.

2.14   Fitting the new oil filter

19   Switch off the engine, and wait a few minutes for the oil to settle in the sump once more. With the new oil circulated and the filter now completely full, recheck the level on the dipstick, and add more oil as necessary.

20   Dispose of the used engine oil safely with reference to *"General repair procedures"* in the preliminary Sections of this manual.

Check and adjust the valve clearances

21   Refer to Section 15 of this Chapter.

Check crankcase ventilation hoses

22   Examine the crankcase ventilation hoses for signs of cracking or deterioration. The hoses are located on the front of the engine, and are attached to the sump and filler/breather tube assembly. Renew the hoses as necessary.

Check/renew the engine breather PCV valve

23   The engine breather PCV valve is located just in front of the oil filler cap.

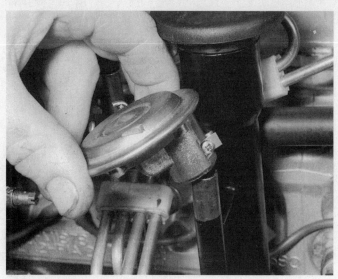

2.25 Disconnecting the engine breather PCV valve from the oil separator and breather tube

24   To check the valve, disconnect the vacuum hose from it, and connect a vacuum pump. When the vacuum is applied, a clicking noise should be heard, indicating that the breather valve is closing. If this is not the case, renew the valve as follows.

25   Loosen the clips, and disconnect the valve from the oil separator and breather tube (photo). Refitting is a reversal of the removal procedure, making sure that the vacuum hose is reconnected as well.

Renew the timing belt

26   Refer to Section 8 or 9 of this Chapter, as applicable.

3   Major operations possible with the engine in the vehicle

The following major operations can be carried out with the engine in place in the vehicle. It is recommended, however, that for reasons of cleanliness and accessibility, the operations shown with an asterisk are performed with the engine removed.

(a) Timing belt and gears removal and refitting.
(b) Camshaft oil seals renewal.
(c) Camshaft and tappets removal and refitting.
(d) Cylinder head removal and refitting.
(e) Sump removal and refitting.
(f) Oil pump removal and refitting.
(g) Big-end bearing removal and refitting*.
(h) Piston and connecting rod removal and refitting (cylinder head removed)*.
(i) Flywheel removal and refitting (after removal of the gearbox).

4   Major operations requiring engine removal

The following operation can only be carried out satisfactorily with the engine removed from the vehicle.

(a) Crankshaft and main bearings removal and refitting.

5   Engine oil cooler unit - removal and refitting

Note: *The engine oil cooler unit is fitted to all models from 1989 onwards, and to all Turbo models, and is located behind the radiator.*

Removal

1   Drain the cooling system with reference to Chapter 2.

2   Note the fitted positions of the coolant and oil hoses on the oil cooler, as the pipe runs differ between Turbo and non-Turbo models.

3   Loosen the clips and disconnect the coolant hoses from the oil cooler.

4   Unscrew the union nuts, and disconnect the oil feed and return hoses from the oil cooler unit. Also release the hoses from the support clips, where necessary. Plug the ends of the hoses to prevent the ingress of dirt and foreign matter.

5   Unscrew the mounting bolts, and remove the oil cooler from its bracket or from the front crossmember (according to model).

Refitting

6   Before refitting the oil cooler, fill it with fresh engine oil, keeping the union apertures uppermost.

7   Locate the unit near its mounting, keeping the unions uppermost, then reconnect the hoses and tighten the nuts sufficiently at this stage to prevent the oil escaping.

8   Insert and tighten the mounting bolts.

9   Fully tighten the oil hose union nuts, and refit the hoses in the support clips where necessary.

10   Reconnect the coolant hoses and tighten the clips.

11   Check and if necessary top-up the engine oil level.

12   Refill the cooling system with reference to Chapter 2.

13   **Important:** *On Turbo models, disconnect the cables from the stop solenoid, and spin the engine on the starter motor until the low oil pressure warning light goes out. Reconnect the cables to the stop solenoid before proceeding.*

14   Start the engine, and check for leaks of oil and water around the oil cooler unit. Finally check and if necessary top-up the engine oil level.

6   Timing belt cover - removal and refitting

Pre-1989 non-Turbo models

1   Apply the handbrake, then jack up the front of the vehicle and support it on axle stands. Remove the right-hand roadwheel.

2   Unscrew the screws and remove the plastic panel under the wheelarch for access.

3   Remove the water pump/alternator drivebelt with reference to Chapter 2.

4   Unbolt the pulley from the water pump drive flange.

6.8 Removing the access cover from the top of the timing cover

6.9A Unscrew the retaining screw . . .

6.9B . . . release the spring clips . . .

5   Remove the access cover from the top of the timing belt cover, carefully prising it outwards to disengage the retaining lugs, and lifting upwards.

6   Unscrew the retaining screws, release the spring clips (where fitted), and remove the timing belt cover.

7   Refitting is the reversal of removal. Refit and tension the water pump/alternator drivebelt with reference to Chapter 2.

Turbo and 1989 models onwards

Upper cover

8   Remove the access cover from the top of the timing belt cover, carefully prising it outwards to disengage the retaining lugs, and lifting upwards (photo).

9   Unscrew the retaining screw located below the access cover aperture, release the spring clips, and remove the upper cover (photos).

10   Refitting is the reversal of removal.

6.9C . . . and remove the upper timing belt cover

6.13 Removing the plastic cover from inside the right-hand wheelarch

6.16A Remove the lower bolt . . .

6.16B . . . and the two lower screws (arrowed) . . .

Lower cover

11 Remove the upper cover as previously described.

12 Apply the handbrake, then jack up the front of the vehicle and support it on axle stands. Remove the right-hand roadwheel.

13 Unscrew the screws and remove the plastic panel under the wheelarch for access (photo).

14 Remove the water pump/alternator drivebelt with reference to Chapter 2.

15 Unbolt the pulley from the water pump drive flange.

16 Undo the retaining bolts and screws, release the spring clips, and remove the lower cover (photos).

17 Refitting is the reversal of removal. Refit and tension the water pump/alternator drivebelt with reference to Chapter 2.

7 Timing belt tension - checking and adjustment

Note: *Timing pins (or 6.74 mm diameter drills), and ideally, a tension gauge (Rover tool KM 4088 AR) are required for this operation.*

Checking

1 Remove the access cover from the top of the timing belt cover, carefully prising it outwards to disengage the retaining lugs, and lifting upwards.

2 Examine the full length of the timing belt for wear and damage, particularly on the base of the teeth. Use a socket on the crankshaft pulley bolt to turn the engine through at least six complete revolutions. Check the timing belt for uneven wear, cracking and oil contamination, and if necessary renew the belt with reference to Section 8 or 9, as applicable.

3 The belt tension must be checked halfway between the camshaft gear and the fuel injection pump gear. The only accurate method of

6.16C . . . and withdraw the lower timing belt cover

7.3 Checking the timing belt tension by twisting it through 45°

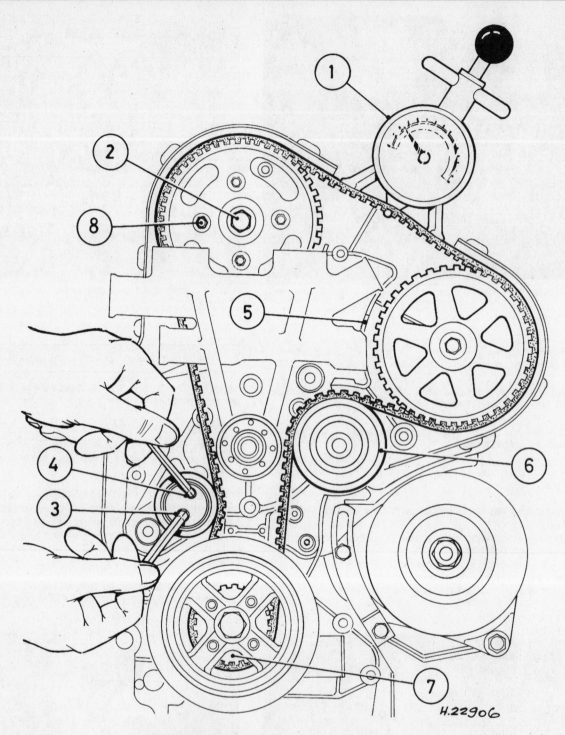

H.22906

Fig. 1.3 Checking the tension of the timing belt (Sec 7)

1	Timing belt tension checking gauge	4	Tensioner adjustment hole
2	Camshaft gear centre bolt	5	Injection pump timing marks
3	Tensioner retaining bolt	6	Idler pulley

7	Crankshaft gear
8	Camshaft gear hub bolts (hub-mounted gear)

doing this is to obtain the Rover tension gauge and check that the tension is as given below. If the gauge is not available, an approximate method of checking the tension is to twist the belt using moderate finger and thumb pressure. It should be possible to twist the belt through 45° (photo).

Used belt   *6 gauge units*
New belt   *6.5 to 7.5 gauge units*

Adjustment

4   If adjustment is necessary, proceed as follows. First disconnect the battery earth (negative) lead, then remove the timing belt covers as described in Section 6.

5   Unscrew the blanking plug from the right-hand end of the camshaft cover, then turn the crankshaft until the timing pin hole in the

7.10 Adjusting the timing belt tension at the tensioner

camshaft is aligned with the hole in the cover. In this position, No 1 piston (nearest the timing belt end of the engine) will be at TDC (Top Dead Centre) on compression.

6   Insert the timing pin (or a 6.75 mm diameter drill) through the hole in the camshaft cover, so that it engages in the hole in the camshaft.

7   Where the camshaft gear is taper-mounted, hold the camshaft gear stationary, and loosen the camshaft gear retaining bolt one or two turns. Where the camshaft gear is hub-mounted, hold the camshaft gear stationary, and loosen the four bolts securing the gear to the hub one turn each. The camshaft gear can be held against rotation using a home-made scissor-type tool, such as the one shown in photo 9.8. **Do not** rely on the timing pin alone to hold the camshaft.

8   Check that the timing hole in the cylinder block and flywheel are aligned, then insert another timing pin (or 6.75 mm diameter drill) to lock it.

9   Fit the tension gauge midway between the camshaft gear and the fuel injection pump gear.

10   Loosen the tensioner retaining bolt, then use an Allen key to turn the tensioner as required until the tension is correct (turn the tensioner clockwise to tension the belt). Finally, tighten the retaining bolt (photo). If the tensioner rotates over-centre, unscrew the tensioner bolt and insert it in the innermost of the two retaining holes. If the innermost hole was already used, renew the timing belt.

11   Remove the tension gauge.

12   Hold the camshaft gear stationary, and tighten the camshaft gear retaining bolt (taper-mounted gear) or hub bolts (hub-mounted gear) to the specified torque.

13   Check that the timing pins are still fully inserted (proving that the timing is still correct), then remove them. Refit the camshaft cover blanking plug.

14   Refit the timing covers with reference to Section 6, and reconnect the battery.

15   Check the fuel injection pump timing with reference to Chapter 3.

8   Timing belt (pre-1989 non-Turbo models) - removal and refitting

Note: *Timing pins (or 6.74 mm diameter drills) and a tension gauge (see Section 7) are required for this operation.*

Removal

1   Disconnect the battery earth (negative) lead, then remove the timing belt cover as described in Section 6.

2   Drain the cooling system as described in Chapter 2.

3   Remove the coolant hoses from the water pump.

4   Unscrew the blanking plug from the right-hand end of the camshaft cover, then turn the crankshaft until the timing pin hole in the camshaft is aligned with the hole in the cover. In this position, No 1 piston (nearest the timing belt end of the engine) will be at TDC (Top Dead Centre) on compression.

5   Insert the timing pin (or a 6.75 mm diameter drill) through the hole in the camshaft cover, so that it engages in the hole in the camshaft.

6   Using two suitable bolts, lock the injection pump gear by tightening the bolts into the injection pump mounting bracket through two diagonally-opposite unthreaded holes (the threaded holes are for pulling off the gear). Note also that the timing marks on the gear and mounting bracket are aligned with each other (refer to Chapter 3 if necessary).

7   Where the camshaft gear is taper-mounted, hold the camshaft gear stationary, and loosen the camshaft gear retaining bolt one or two turns. Where the camshaft gear is hub-mounted, hold the camshaft gear stationary and loosen the four bolts securing the gear to the hub one turn each. The camshaft gear can be held against rotation using a home-made scissor type tool as shown in photo 9.8. **Do not** rely on the timing pin alone to hold the camshaft.

8   Insert a timing pin (or 6.75 mm drill) through the gearbox adapter plate at the rear of the cylinder block and into the timing hole in the flywheel. **Warning:** *Do not turn the crankshaft with the timing belt removed and the cylinder head in position, otherwise the pistons will collide with the valves.*

9   Check if the timing belt is marked with the normal direction of rotation, and if necessary mark it with chalk.

10   Unscrew the multi-splined tensioner lockbolt, and remove the timing belt tensioner pulley.

11   Ease the timing belt progressively off the gears, and remove it.

12   Where the camshaft gear is taper-mounted, finger-tighten the centre bolt if a new timing belt is not being fitted immediately.

13   The timing belt should be stored on its edge, and must never be bent or twisted sharply, as this can damage the reinforcing fibres. Do not re-use a timing belt which has been contaminated with oil or fuel.

14   Clean all the gears, the oil pump casing and the timing covers, and wipe them dry.

Refitting

15   Check that the timing marks on the injection pump are still correctly aligned, and that the timing pins are still in position.

16   Locate the timing belt around the crankshaft and idler pulleys, making sure that the direction of rotation marks are facing the correct

9.7 Removing the complete right-hand engine mounting assembly

9.8 Loosening the crankshaft pulley centre bolt

way. Locate the belt on the injection pump and camshaft gears, and centralise it midway on the gear teeth.

17   Fit the tensioner pulley, then unscrew the bolts holding the injection pump gear.

18   Adjust the timing belt tension as described in Section 7.

19   Using a socket on the crankshaft pulley bolt, turn the crankshaft through two complete revolutions, in order to check that there is no obstruction.

20   Check and if necessary adjust the injection pump timing, with reference to Chapter 3.

21   Refit the timing belt cover as described in Section 6.

22   Refit the coolant hoses to the water pump.

23   Refill the cooling system as described in Chapter 2.

24   Reconnect the battery.

9   Timing belt (Turbo and 1989 models onwards) - removal and refitting

Note: *Timing pins (or 6.74 mm diameter drills) and a tension gauge (see Section 7) are required for this operation.*

Removal

1   Disconnect the battery earth (negative) lead, then remove the timing belt upper and lower covers as described in Section 6.

2   Drain the cooling system as described in Chapter 2.

3   Remove the cooling system expansion tank as described in Chapter 2.

4   Remove the coolant hoses from the water pump.

5   Support the weight of the engine on a trolley jack and piece of wood located under the right-hand end of the sump.

9.9A Unscrew the bolts . . .

9.9B . . . and remove the crankshaft pulley

9.10 Removing the blanking plug from the right-hand end of the camshaft cover housing

9.11 6.75 mm diameter drill inserted through the camshaft cover to lock the camshaft

6   Unscrew the bolts securing the right-hand engine mounting bracket to the wheelarch and body panel.

7   Unscrew the two bolts and two nuts securing the right-hand engine mounting to the top of the water pump, and remove the complete right-hand engine mounting assembly (photo).

8   Hold the crankshaft stationary, then unscrew and remove the crankshaft pulley centre bolt. Where the pulley incorporates holes, a home-made scissor-type tool made from two lengths of metal bar with long bolts at one end can be used to hold the crankshaft pulley (photo). If there are no holes in the pulley, one alternative method is to remove the starter motor and use a wide-bladed screwdriver engaged with the starter ring gear. The Rover tool for holding the crankshaft is bolted to the pulley using the existing four bolt holes, and if required, a similar tool may be made.

9   Using an Allen key, unscrew the bolts securing the pulley to the

crankshaft gear. Withdraw the pulley (photos).

10   Unscrew the blanking plug from the right-hand end of the camshaft cover (photo), then turn the crankshaft in a clockwise direction (temporarily refit the crankshaft pulley bolt, with washers, to turn the engine) until the timing pin hole in the camshaft is aligned with the hole in the cover. In this position, No 1 piston (nearest the timing belt end of the engine) will be at TDC (Top Dead Centre) on compression.

11   Insert the timing pin (or a 6.75 mm diameter drill) through the hole in the camshaft cover, so that it engages in the hole in the camshaft (photo).

12   Using two suitable bolts, lock the injection pump gear by tightening the bolts into the injection pump mounting bracket through two diagonally-opposite unthreaded holes (the threaded holes are for pulling off the gear). Note also that the timing marks on the gear and mounting bracket are aligned with each other (refer to Chapter 3 if necessary) (photos).

9.12A Two bolts inserted through the injection pump gear into the mounting bracket

9.12B Timing mark (Turbo model shown) on the injection pump gear

9.13 Loosening the four bolts securing the hub-mounted camshaft gear to the hub

9.14 6.75 mm drill inserted through the gearbox adapter plate at the rear of the cylinder block into the timing hole in the flywheel

13   Where the camshaft gear is taper-mounted, hold the camshaft gear stationary using the scissor-type tool used for the crankshaft pulley bolt, and loosen the camshaft gear retaining bolt one or two turns. Where the camshaft gear is hub-mounted, counterhold the camshaft gear, and loosen the four bolts securing the gear to the hub one turn each (photo). **Do not** rely on the timing pin alone to hold the camshaft.

14   Insert a timing pin (or 6.75 mm drill) through the gearbox adapter plate at the rear of the cylinder block, and into the timing hole in the flywheel (photo). **Warning:** *Do not turn the crankshaft with the timing belt removed and the cylinder head in position, otherwise the pistons will collide with the valves.*

15   Check if the timing belt is marked with the normal direction of rotation, and if necessary mark it with chalk.

16   Unscrew the multi-splined tensioner lockbolt, and remove the timing belt tensioner pulley (photos).

17   Unbolt and remove the idler pulley (photo).

18   Ease the timing belt progressively off the gears, and remove it.

19   Where the camshaft gear is taper-mounted, finger-tighten the centre bolt if a new timing belt is not being fitted immediately.

20   The timing belt should be stored on its edge, and must never be bent or twisted sharply, as this can damage the reinforcing fibres. Do not re-use a timing belt which has been contaminated with oil or fuel.

21   Clean all the gears, the oil pump casing and the timing covers, and wipe them dry.

Refitting

22   Check that the timing marks on the injection pump are still correctly aligned, and that the timing pins are still in position.

23   Refit the idler pulley, and tighten the bolt.

24   Locate the timing belt around the crankshaft and idler pulleys, making sure that the direction of rotation marks are facing the correct

9.16A Multi-splined tensioner lockbolt (arrowed)

9.16B Unscrew the lockbolt . . .

9.16C . . . and remove the tensioner

9.17 Removing the timing belt idler pulley

way. Locate the belt on the injection pump and camshaft gears, and centralise it midway on the gear teeth.

25   Fit the tensioner pulley, then unscrew the bolts holding the injection pump gear.

26   Refit the crankshaft pulley, and tighten the bolts (counterhold the crankshaft as described earlier).

27   Adjust the timing belt tension as described in Section 7.

28   Using a socket on the crankshaft pulley bolt, turn the crankshaft through two complete revolutions in order to check that there is no obstruction.

29   Check and if necessary adjust the injection pump timing with reference to Chapter 3.

30   Refit the right-hand engine mounting and the cooling system expansion tank. Lower the trolley jack from under the engine.

31   Refit the timing belt cover as described in Section 6.

32   Refit the coolant hoses to the water pump.

33   Refill the cooling system as described in Chapter 2.

34   Reconnect the battery.

---

10   Timing gears - removal and refitting

Removal

Camshaft gear (taper-mounted)

1   Remove the timing belt as described in Section 8 or 9. **Note:** *Do not remove the timing pin from the camshaft or turn the crankshaft while the timing belt is removed.*

2   Hold the camshaft gear stationary using a holding tool (tool shown in photo 9.8), then unscrew and remove the centre bolt. With-

draw the gear from the taper on the end of the camshaft. Note that there is no dowel in the end of the camshaft as fitted to the hub-mounted type.

Camshaft gear (hub-mounted)

3   Remove the timing belt as described in Section 8 or 9. **Note:** *Do not remove the timing pin from the camshaft or turn the crankshaft while the timing belt is removed.*

4   Mark the hub, gear and timing cover in relation to each other.

5   Hold the camshaft gear stationary using a suitable holding tool, then unscrew and remove the centre bolt securing the hub to the camshaft (photo). **Do not** rely on the timing pin to hold the camshaft stationary.

6   Withdraw the gear and hub from the camshaft, then unbolt the hub from the gear. If necessary, remove the location dowel from the

10.5 Unscrewing the camshaft gear/hub centre bolt

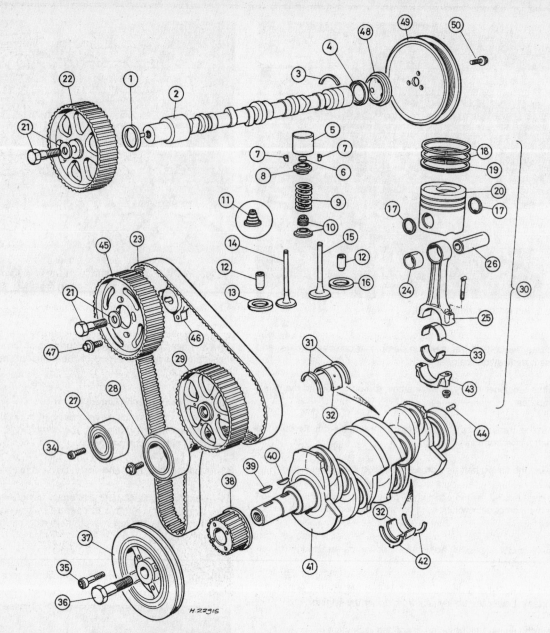

Fig. 1.4 Timing, camshaft and crankshaft components (Sec 10)

1	Camshaft front oil seal	19	Piston oil control ring	37	Crankshaft pulley
2	Camshaft	20	Piston	38	Crankshaft gear
3	Thrust ring	21	Camshaft gear bolt and washer	39	Crankshaft gear location key
4	Camshaft rear oil seal	22	Camshaft gear (taper-mounted)	40	Oil pump drive key
5	Tappet	23	Timing belt	41	Crankshaft
6	Shim	24	Small-end bush	42	Crankshaft endfloat thrustwashers
7	Collets	25	Connecting rod		(lower halves)
8	Valve spring cap	26	Gudgeon pin	43	Big-end bearing cap
9	Valve spring	27	Timing belt tensioner	44	Flywheel location dowel
10	Valve spring seat and valve stem	28	Idler pulley	45	Camshaft gear (hub-mounted)
	oil seal (early models)	29	Fuel injection pump gear	46	Hub (for hub-mounted camshaft
11	Combined valve spring and valve	30	Piston/connecting rod assembly		gear)
	stem oil seal (later models)	31	Crankshaft endfloat thrustwashers	47	Camshaft gear retaining bolt
12	Valve guide		(upper halves)		(hub-mounted)
13	Exhaust valve seat insert	32	Main bearing shells	48	Camshaft rear cover
14	Exhaust valve	33	Big-end bearing shells	49	Power steering pulley (where
15	Inlet valve	34	Timing belt tensioner retaining bolt		applicable)
16	Inlet valve seat insert	35	Crankshaft pulley-to-gear retaining	50	Power steering pulley retaining
17	Circlip		bolts		bolt (where applicable)
18	Piston compression rings	36	Crankshaft pulley bolt		

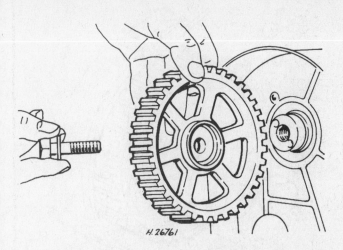

H.26761

Fig. 1.5 Removing the taper-mounted camshaft gear from the end of the camshaft (Sec 10)

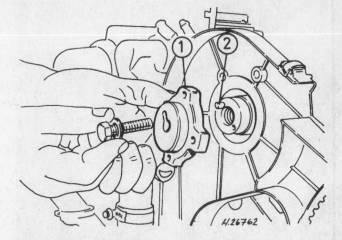

H.26762

Fig. 1.6 Removing the hub from the camshaft (hub-mounted camshaft gear) (Sec 10)

1   Hub   *2   Location dowel*

end of the camshaft (photos). Note that the four bolt holes in the camshaft gear are slotted, to allow for tensioning of the timing belt.

Fuel injection pump gear/pulley

7   Remove the timing belt as described in Section 8 or 9. **Note:** *Do not remove the timing pin from the camshaft or turn the crankshaft while the timing belt is removed.*

8   Check that the timing marks on the injection pump are aligned correctly (see Chapter 3). Note that there are two timing marks, on opposite sides of the gear - the "A" mark is for non-Turbo models, and the "B" mark is for Turbo models. It is obviously important to have the correct mark aligned; refer to Chapter 3 if necessary.

9   Hold the gear/pulley stationary using the scissor-type tool shown, then unscrew the nut from the injection pump driveshaft and remove the washer (photos).

10   To prevent the injection pump timing being lost while the gear is removed, unscrew the locking screw from the side of the pump, remove the arrow-shaped spacer, then tighten the locking screw to lock the injection pump (refer to Chapter 3 if necessary).

10.6A Removing the camshaft gear and hub assembly

10.6B Location dowel (arrowed) in the end of the camshaft

10.9A Loosening the injection pump gear/pulley retaining nut

10.9B Removing the injection pump gear/pulley retaining nut

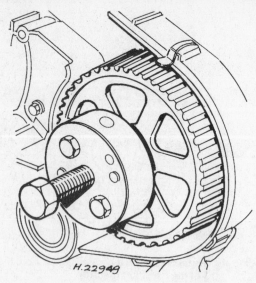

H.22949

Fig. 1.7 Using a Rover puller to remove the gear/pulley from the injection pump driveshaft (Sec 10)

11   Using a suitable puller, pull the gear/pulley off the injection pump driveshaft. The Rover tool is shown in Fig. 1.7, and consists of a circular block of metal bolted to the gear, through which a central bolt is screwed. The bolt bears against the driveshaft, and forces the gear off. Alternatively, a home-made tool may be made with reference to Chapter 3 (photos).

12   If necessary, remove the location key from the driveshaft.

Crankshaft gear

13   Remove the timing belt as described in Section 8 or 9. **Note:** *Do not remove the timing pin from the camshaft or turn the crankshaft while the timing belt is removed.*

14   On pre-1989 non-Turbo engines, hold the crankshaft stationary, then unscrew and remove the crankshaft pulley centre bolt (on other engines, the crankshaft pulley is removed with the timing belt). Where the pulley incorporates holes, a home-made scissor-type tool made from two lengths of metal bar with long bolts at one end can be used to hold the crankshaft pulley. If there are no holes in the pulley, one alternative method is to remove the starter motor and use a wide-bladed

10.11A Using a home-made puller to release the pulley/gear from the injection pump driveshaft

10.11B Removing the pulley/gear from the injection pump driveshaft

10.15 Removing the crankshaft gear

10.16 Removing the Woodruff key from the groove in the crankshaft

10.21 Inserting the camshaft gear centre bolt

screwdriver engaged with the starter ring gear. The Rover tool for holding the crankshaft is bolted to the pulley using the existing four bolt holes, and if required, a similar tool may be made. **Do not** rely on the previously-inserted timing pin to hold the crankshaft. Using an Allen key, unscrew the bolts securing the pulley to the crankshaft gear. Withdraw the pulley.

15   Slide the gear from the front of the crankshaft (photo). If it is tight, it will be necessary to use a puller.

16   If necessary, remove the Woodruff key from the groove in the crankshaft (photo).

Refitting

Camshaft gear (taper-mounted)
17   Locate the gear on the taper on the end of the camshaft, and insert the centre bolt finger-tight.

18   Refit the timing belt as described in Section 8 or 9 (the gear centre bolt is fully tightened during the belt refitting and adjustment procedure).

Camshaft gear (hub-mounted)
19   Locate the hub on the camshaft, making sure that the locating pin is correctly inserted.

20   Locate the gear on the hub, making sure that the previously-made alignment marks are in line.

21   Insert the centre bolt and bolts securing the hub to the camshaft, and tighten them sufficiently to hold the gear and hub firm (photo).

22   Counterhold the gear using the special tool used in the timing belt removal procedure, then fully tighten the centre bolt to the specified torque.

23   If necessary, re-align the marks on the hub and gear, and tighten the bolts finger-tight. The bolts are fully tightened during the timing belt refitting and adjustment procedure.

24   Refit the timing belt as described in Section 8 or 9.

Fuel injection pump gear/pulley
25   Refit the location key to the injection pump driveshaft.

26   Locate the gear/pulley on the injection pump driveshaft with the correct timing marks aligned (see Chapter 3), and refit the washer and nut. Make sure that the gear/pulley engages correctly with the key, and does not push it out of its groove. Hold the gear/pulley stationary using the special tool, and tighten the nut to the specified torque, taking care not to apply any turning force to the injection pump driveshaft.

27   Insert and tighten two bolts to lock the gear to the injection pump mounting flange. Unscrew the timing locking screw on the side of the injection pump, refit the arrow-shaped spacer, then refit the screw.

28   Refit the timing belt as described in Section 8 or 9.

Crankshaft gear
29   Refit the Woodruff key to the groove in the nose of the crankshaft, making sure that it is level.

30   Slide the gear fully onto the crankshaft. Make sure that it enters over the key correctly, and does not push it out of its groove.

31   On pre-1989 non-Turbo engines, refit the crankshaft pulley and tighten the bolts (counterhold the crankshaft as described earlier).

32   Refit the timing belt as described in Section 8 or 9.

11   Camshaft oil seals - renewal

Camshaft front (RH) oil seal
1   Remove the timing belt as described in Section 8 or 9.

2   Remove the camshaft gear as described in Section 10.

3   Using vernier calipers, measure the fitted depth of the oil seal below the surface of the cylinder head. This is necessary in order to fit the new oil seal in the correct position. If the special Rover fitting tool is available, measuring the fitted depth will not be necessary, as the depth is incorporated in the tool.

4   Rover technicians use a special extractor to remove the oil seal (using the camshaft gear retaining bolt to draw out the seal). However, the seal may be removed by drilling two small holes on opposite sides of the oil seal and inserting self-tapping screws. By pulling on the screws, the oil seal can be removed. Hooking out the oil seal with a

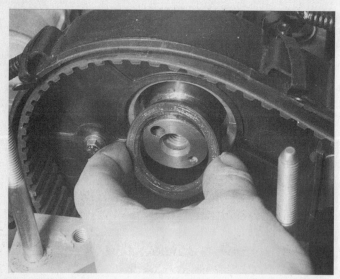

11.7 Fitting a new camshaft front (RH) oil seal

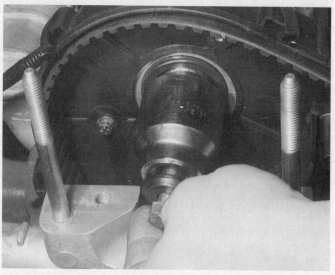

11.8 Using a socket and the camshaft gear retaining bolt to fit the new oil seal

screwdriver is not recommended, as the sealing surface on the camshaft may be damaged.

5   Clean the oil seal seating in the cylinder head and camshaft cover.

6   Oil the camshaft journal and the sealing lips of the new oil seal.

7   Position the oil seal carefully over the end of the camshaft with its closed end outwards, and press it squarely into the cylinder head by hand, so that it begins to enter the location bore (photo).

8   Using a socket or metal bar of diameter slightly less than that of the oil seal, drive the oil seal in squarely until it is at the previously-noted fitted depth. The camshaft gear retaining bolt may be used to pull the oil seal into position (photo).

9   Refit the camshaft gear as described in Section 10.

10   Refit the timing belt as described in Section 8 or 9.

Camshaft rear (LH) oil seal

11   On power steering models, remove the power steering drivebelt, pulley and drivebelt inner cover (refer to Chapter 8 if necessary).

12   Unbolt and remove the camshaft rear cover.

13   Using vernier calipers, measure the fitted depth of the oil seal below the surface of the cylinder head. This is necessary in order to fit the new oil seal in the correct position. If the special Rover fitting tool is available, measuring the fitted depth will not be necessary, as the tool incorporates the correct depth.

14   Rover technicians use a special extractor to remove the oil seal. However, it may be removed by drilling two small holes on opposite sides of the oil seal and inserting self-tapping screws. By pulling on the screws, the oil seal can be removed. Hooking out the oil seal with a screwdriver is not recommended, as the sealing surface on the camshaft may be damaged.

15   Clean the oil seal seating in the cylinder head, and the journal on the camshaft.

11.17 Fitting a new camshaft rear (LH) oil seal

11.18 Driving in a new camshaft rear (LH) oil seal

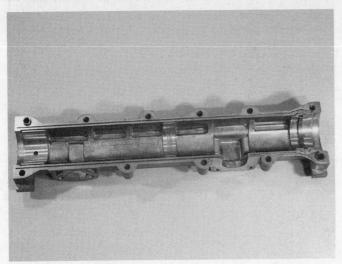

12.11 Camshaft cover

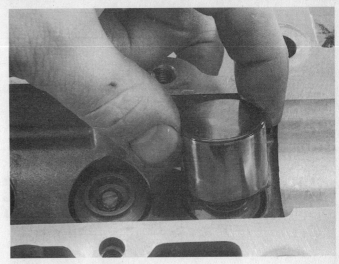

12.14A Removing the tappets . . .

16   Oil the camshaft journal and the sealing lips of the new oil seal.

17   Position the oil seal carefully over the end of the camshaft, with its closed end outwards, and press it squarely into the cylinder head by hand, so that it begins to enter the location bore (photo).

18   Using a socket or metal tube of diameter slightly less than that of the oil seal, drive the oil seal in squarely until it is at the previously-noted fitted depth (photo).

19   Refit the camshaft rear cover, and tighten the bolts.

20   On power steering models, refit the power steering drivebelt inner cover, pulley and drivebelt (refer to Chapter 8 if necessary).

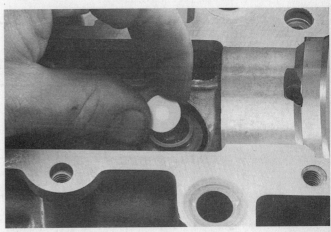

12.14B . . . and shims

12   Camshaft and tappets - removal and refitting

Note: *Three special clamps (Rover No 18G 1301A) or home-made alternatives (see Figs. 1.8 and 1.9) are required to check the valve clearances as part of this operation.*

Removal

1   Remove the timing belt as described in Section 8 or 9.

2   Remove the camshaft gear as described in Section 10.

3   Unbolt the timing belt inner cover from the camshaft cover, but do not remove the cover completely.

4   On power steering models from 1989 onwards, remove the power steering drivebelt pulley and remove the drivebelt inner cover, with reference to Chapter 8.

5   On all models not fitted with power steering and all pre-1989 models, unbolt and remove the camshaft rear cover from the cylinder head.

6   Unscrew the nut securing the accelerator cable support bracket to the camshaft cover, and move the bracket to one side.

7   Unscrew the nut securing the front cable support bracket to the cylinder head, release the bracket from the cylinder head and speedometer cable, and move the bracket to one side.

8   Unbolt the fuel lift pump and brake vacuum pump from the camshaft cover.

9   Remove the timing pin (or drill) from the camshaft cover.

10   Using vernier calipers, note the fitted depth of the oil seals at each end of the camshaft.

11   Progressively unscrew the camshaft cover retaining bolts in the reverse order to that shown in Fig. 1.10, and lift the cover from the cylinder head (photo). If the cover is stuck, use a soft-faced mallet to tap it free. Make sure that the semi-circular thrustwasher remains in the cover.

12   Lift out the camshaft, and remove the front and rear oil seals.

13   Make up a compartmented box for storing the tappets as they are removed, and mark the box compartments 1 to 8.

14   Remove the tappets and their shims from the cylinder head, and store them in the box in their correct order, remembering that No 1 is at the timing belt end of the engine (photos). The shims are not marked in any way, and they tend to wear at different rates at their top and bottom surfaces. The bottom surfaces in contact with the valve stems normally wear more than the upper surfaces in contact with the protrusion inside the tappet. For this reason, it is worth noting which way round the shims are removed, so that they can be refitted the same way round.

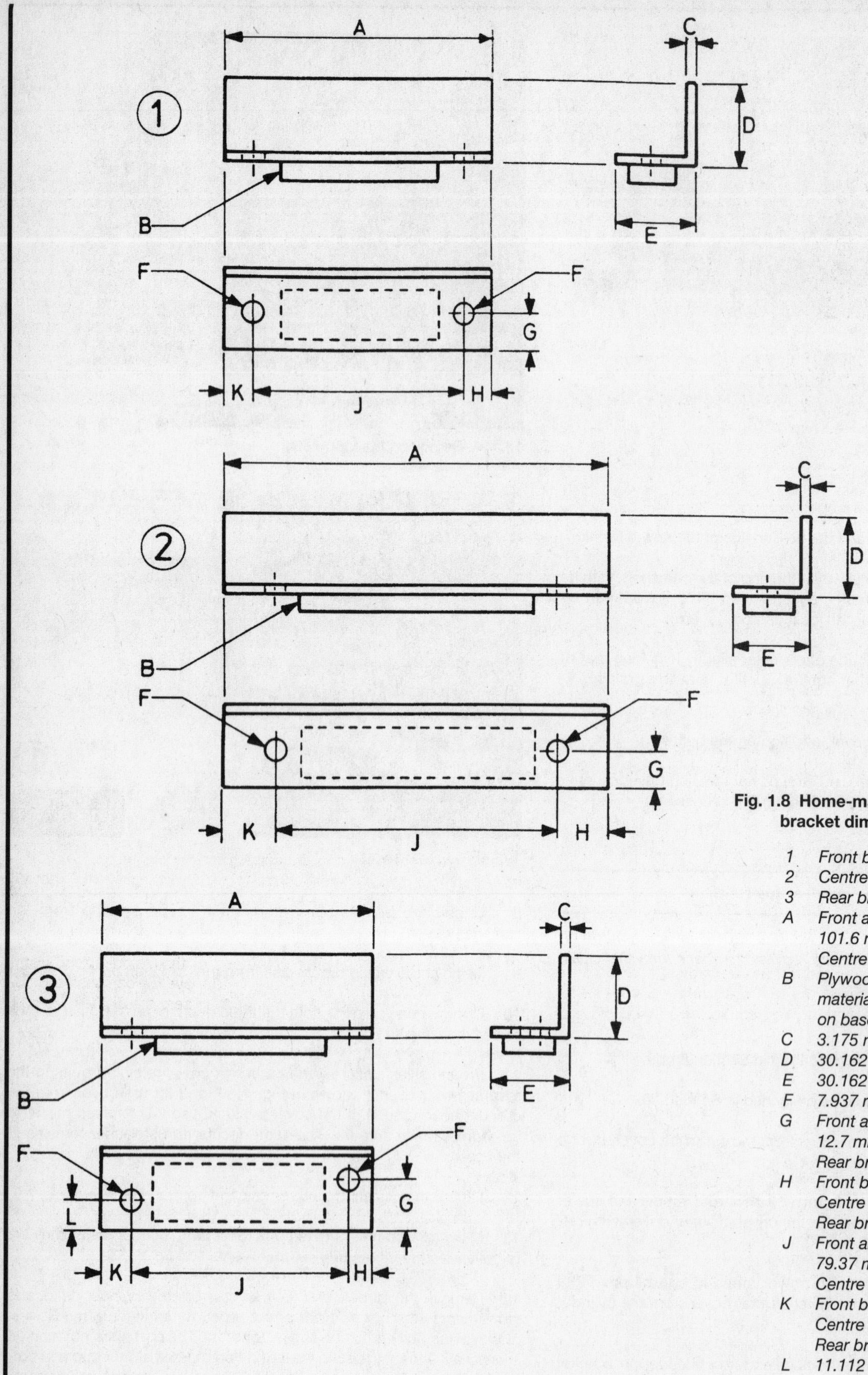

Fig. 1.8 Home-made camshaft retaining bracket dimensions (Sec 12)

1 Front bracket
2 Centre bracket
3 Rear bracket
A Front and rear bracket - 101.6 mm
  Centre bracket - 146.05 mm
B Plywood or other soft material positioned centrally on base of bracket
C 3.175 mm
D 30.162 mm
E 30.162 mm
F 7.937 mm
G Front and centre brackets - 12.7 mm
  Rear bracket - 19.05 mm
H Front bracket - 11.112 mm
  Centre bracket - 19.05 mm
  Rear bracket - 9.525 mm
J Front and rear bracket - 79.37 mm
  Centre bracket - 107.95 mm
K Front bracket - 11.112 mm
  Centre bracket - 19.05 mm
  Rear bracket - 12.7 mm
L 11.112 mm

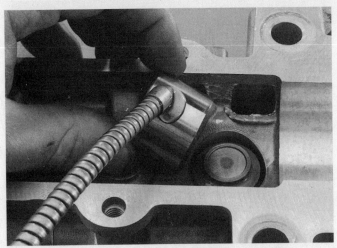

12.17 Oiling the tappets before inserting them

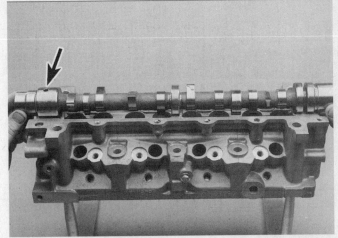

12.18 Lowering the camshaft into the cylinder head (head removed from engine) - timing hole arrowed

15   Examine the camshaft and tappets with reference to Sections 37 and 38.

Refitting

16   Before fitting the camshaft (especially if it is a new one), it is necessary to adjust the tappet clearances, to ensure that the pistons do not collide with the valve heads when the engine is rotated. First remove the flywheel timing pin (or drill) from the rear flange of the cylinder block, then turn the crankshaft just 90° anti-clockwise, to position all of the pistons halfway down their bores away from the valves.

17   Oil the shims and tappets, and locate them in their correct positions in the cylinder head (photo). If the original shims are being refitted, make sure that they are fitted the same way round as previously noted.

18   Oil the camshaft journals and cams, and lower the camshaft into the cylinder head, with the timing hole at the 12 o'clock position (photo).

19   If Rover tool 18G 1301A is available, fit the three special camshaft clamps, making sure that the pressure pads are fully unscrewed first. Tighten the clamp bolts. Check that the pressure pads are positioned so that they follow the contour of the journals, then progressively tighten the pads until the camshaft journals are seated in the cylinder

head. If the home-made brackets are being used, fit these and tighten the bolts until the camshaft is seated in the cylinder head.

20   Check and adjust the valve clearances with reference to the applicable paragraphs in Section 15, but do not refit the camshaft cover at this stage.

21   Turn the crankshaft clockwise 90° so that No 1 piston is at TDC, then refit the flywheel timing pin or drill.

22   Lower the camshaft into the cylinder head, again with the timing hole at the 12 o'clock position.

23   Clean all old sealant from the camshaft cover and cylinder head mating surfaces. Make sure that all sealant is removed from the grooves in the cover.

24   Refit the camshaft cover (together with the semi-circular thrust-washer) without applying any sealant at this stage. Insert and tighten the bolts progressively to the specified torque and in the sequence shown in Fig. 1.10.

25   Attach a dial test indicator to the end of the cylinder head, with the probe touching the end of the camshaft. Move the camshaft fully to the timing cover end of the cylinder head, and zero the dial test indica-

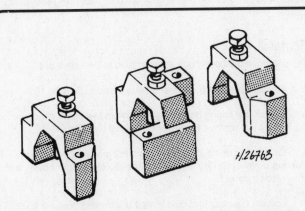

Fig. 1.9 Rover tools for retaining the camshaft (Sec 12)

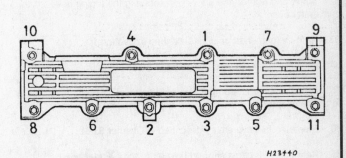

Fig.1.10 Camshaft cover bolt tightening sequence (Sec 12)

12.26 Fitting a new thrustwasher to the camshaft cover

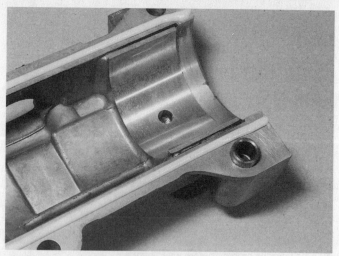

12.27A Bead of silicone sealant on the camshaft cover

tor. Now move the camshaft fully in the opposite direction, and measure the amount of endfloat.

26   If the endfloat recorded is in excess of the maximum given in the Specifications, a new thrustwasher must be fitted (photo).

27   Remove the camshaft cover again, and apply a bead of suitable silicone sealant to the grooves and outer mating surface of the camshaft cover; immediately refit the cover to the cylinder head. Progressively tighten the bolts to the specified torque, in the sequence shown in Fig. 1.10 (photos).

28   Insert the timing pin (or drill) through the camshaft cover and into the camshaft.

29   Clean the oil seal seating surfaces at the front and rear of the camshaft. Smear a little oil on the sealing lips of the new oil seals, then locate them in turn over the camshaft and drive them into position using a socket or metal tube of suitable diameter, until located at the previously-noted depth.

30   On all models not fitted with power steering and all models manufactured before 1989, refit the camshaft rear cover to the cylinder head, and tighten the bolts.

31   On power steering models from 1989 onwards, refit the drivebelt inner cover and tighten the bolts. With the timing pin (or drill) in position, refit the hub and pulley to the end of the camshaft, and tighten the bolts. Refit the power steering drivebelt with reference to Chapter 8.

32   Insert and tighten the upper bolt securing the timing cover to the camshaft cover.

33   Refit the camshaft gear as described in Section 10.

34   Refit the timing belt as described in Section 8 or 9.

35   Refit the vacuum pump (Chapter 7) and fuel lift pump (Chapter 3) to the camshaft cover.

36   Bleed the fuel system as described in Chapter 3.

37   Refit the front cable support bracket to the cylinder head.

38   Refit the accelerator cable support bracket to the camshaft cover, and tighten the nut.

39   Reconnect the battery earth (negative) lead.

12.27B Tightening the camshaft cover bolts

13 Cylinder head - removal and refitting

Note: *A torque wrench and angle-tightening tool are required for this work.*

Removal

1   Remove the timing belt as described in Section 8 or 9.

2   Remove the camshaft gear as described in Section 10.

3   Unbolt the timing belt inner cover from the camshaft cover housing, but do not remove the cover completely (photo).

4   On power steering models from 1989 onwards, remove the power steering drivebelt pulley and unbolt the drivebelt inner cover, with reference to Chapter 8.

5   Loosen the clips and disconnect the bypass hoses from the thermostat housing (photo). If necessary, the thermostat housing may be unbolted from the cylinder head, and the gasket removed.

6   Disconnect the wiring from the coolant temperature sender unit and coolant thermistor on the thermostat housing (photo).

13.3 Unscrewing the bolt securing the timing belt inner cover to the camshaft cover housing

13.5 Disconnecting the bypass hose from the thermostat housing

7   On models fitted with exhaust gas recirculation (EGR), disconnect the wiring plug from the EGR valve. Also disconnect the recirculation pipe from the exhaust manifold, and remove the gasket.

Turbo models only

8   Disconnect the inlet vacuum hoses from the turbocharger, and seal the unit with adhesive tape to prevent the ingress of dust and dirt.

9   Unscrew the boost control pipe union from the unit.

10   Loosen the outlet hose clip, then remove the outlet elbow and gaskets. Seal the unit with adhesive tape.

11   Remove the heater rail and the exhaust manifold elbow strengthening plate.

12   Unscrew the turbocharger oil feed pipe union from the oil pump, and release the pipe from the clip on the cylinder block. Also disconnect the oil return hose from the cylinder block adapter.

All models

13   Disconnect the wiring from the coolant temperature sender unit in the cylinder head, and from the No 4 glow plug.

14   Unscrew the nuts, and remove the accelerator cable and speedometer cable support brackets from the cylinder head studs.

15   Check that the timing pin (or drill) is still located in the camshaft, then unbolt the brake vacuum pump with reference to Chapter 7. Remove the O-ring if fitted.

16   Loosen the clip and disconnect the air duct from the inlet manifold.

17   Remove the air cleaner and bracket assembly as described in Chapter 3 (photo).

18   Unscrew the screw holding the fuel pipe bracket to the rear of the cylinder head.

13.6 Disconnecting the wiring from the coolant temperature sender unit

13.17 Air cleaner bracket mounting bolt (arrowed) on the cylinder head

13.24 Removing the bolt securing the engine oil level dipstick tube to the cylinder head

13.27A Unscrewing the cylinder head bolts

Turbo models only

19   Loosen the clip, and disconnect the fuel pipe located between the fuel lift pump and vapour separator.

20   Unbolt the fuel filter from the cylinder head bracket.

All models

21   Loosen the clip, and disconnect the fuel supply pipe from the fuel lift pump.

22   Hold the delivery valves stationary, then unscrew the high-pressure pipe union nuts and remove the high-pressure pipes. Detach the leak-off tube from the banjo adapter.

23   Refer to Chapter 3, and remove the injectors and glow plugs (and associated wiring) as a precaution against damaging their tips.

24   Unscrew the bolt securing the engine oil level dipstick tube to the cylinder head (photo).

25   Disconnect the exhaust downpipe from the exhaust manifold with reference to Chapter 3, and remove the gasket.

26   Except on Turbo models, remove the brake vacuum pump pipe from the connecting hose.

27   Progressively loosen the cylinder head bolts in the reverse order to that shown in Fig. 1.11. When they are all fully loosened, remove the bolts, noting the location of the long bolts with threads on their upper ends (photos).

28   Move the top of the timing belt inner cover to one side slightly, so that the end of the camshaft will clear it, then lift the cylinder head off the cylinder block and recover the cylinder head gasket (photo). Note that there are two locating dowels in the cylinder block. If the head is stuck, tap it upwards with a hide or plastic mallet to free it. Do not lever between the head and block face, or the mating surfaces may be damaged.

29   Position the cylinder head on the bench, on blocks of wood to prevent damage to the valves.

Refitting

30   Ensure that the cylinder block and head mating surfaces are perfectly clean and dry. Clean all bolt holes, making sure that any oil or

13.27B Removing a long cylinder head bolt with threaded upper section

13.27C Removing a normal hexagon-headed cylinder head bolt

13.28 Lifting the cylinder head from the cylinder block

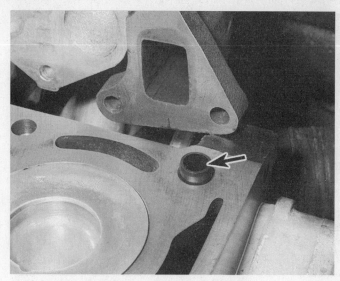

13.30 Locating dowel in the cylinder block (arrowed)

water, etc, is removed. Check that the two locating dowels are fitted in the block (photo).

31   Locate a new cylinder head gasket on the cylinder block, making sure that the holes are aligned correctly with the holes in the block (photo). The gasket can only be fitted in one position, so that the dowels and copper ring oil hole line up correctly. *Do not use any form of jointing compound on the cylinder head gasket.*

32   Make sure that the timing pin (or drill) is still located in the camshaft.

33   Move the top of the timing belt inner cover to one side slightly, then lower the cylinder head onto the cylinder block and engage it with the locating dowels.

34   Lightly oil the threads of the cylinder head bolts, then insert them in the cylinder head, making sure that the long ones with threads on their upper ends are located at each end in their previously-noted positions.

35   Progressively tighten the bolts to the specified 1st stage (pre-tighten) torque wrench setting, in the sequence shown in Fig. 1.11 (photo).

36   Tighten the bolts, one at a time and in the same sequence, to the 2nd stage torque wrench setting.

13.31 Locating a new cylinder head gasket on the block

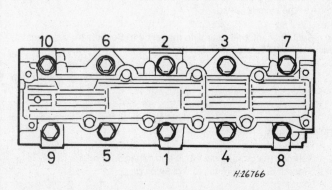

H:26766

Fig. 1.11 Cylinder head bolt tightening sequence (Sec 13)

13.35 Torque-tightening the cylinder head bolts

13.37A Angle-tightening the cylinder head bolts with a special tool

13.37B Paint dots (arrowed) on the cylinder head bolts and head prior to angle-tightening

37   Angle-tighten the bolts, one at a time and in the same sequence, by the amount given in the Specifications. To prevent angle-tightening any bolts more than once (and therefore over-tightening them) it is a good idea to draw a plan of the bolt positions on paper, and to mark them off as they are tightened. If an angle-tightening tool is not available, mark the bolt flanges and cylinder head with lines or dots at 90° to each other, then tighten the bolts until the marks are in line with each other (photos).

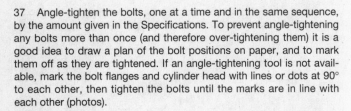

38   Reconnect the exhaust downpipe to the exhaust manifold together with a new gasket, with reference to Chapter 3.

39   Except on Turbo models, refit the brake vacuum pump pipe to the connecting hose.

40   Refit and tighten the screw holding the fuel pipe bracket to the rear of the cylinder head.

41   Refit the air cleaner bracket to the gearbox, and tighten the bolts. Reconnect the air duct to the inlet manifold, and tighten the clip.

42   Refit the accelerator cable and speedometer cable support brackets to the cylinder head studs, and tighten the nuts.

Turbo models

43   Refit the fuel filter to the cylinder head bracket, and tighten the bolts.

44   Reconnect the fuel pipe between the fuel lift pump and the vapour separator.

All models

45   Clean the mating surfaces of the brake vacuum pump and cylinder head. Apply a bead of suitable sealant to the surface of the pump, then refit the brake vacuum pump with reference to Chapter 7. If an O-ring was removed in the removal procedure, this should be discarded. **Do not** use a new O-ring instead of the sealant.

Turbo models

46   Reconnect the oil return hose to the cylinder block adapter.

47   Refit the turbocharger oil feed pipe union to the oil pump, and tighten the nut. Fit the pipe to the clip on the cylinder block.

48   Refit the exhaust manifold elbow strengthening plate and the heater rail.

49   Refit the outlet elbow together with new gaskets, and tighten the clip.

50   Refit and tighten the boost control pipe union.

51   Reconnect the inlet hose and vacuum hose.

All models

52   On models fitted with exhaust gas recirculation (EGR), refit the recirculation pipe to the exhaust manifold together with a new gasket, and reconnect the wiring plug to the EGR valve.

53   Reconnect the wiring to the coolant temperature sender and the coolant thermistor on the thermostat housing.

54   If removed, refit the thermostat housing to the cylinder head together with a new gasket, and tighten the bolts. Reconnect the bypass hoses to the thermostat housing, and tighten the clips.

55   On power steering models from 1989 onwards, refit the drivebelt inner cover and tighten the bolts. Refit the power steering drivebelt pulley, and tighten the bolts.

56   Insert and tighten the timing belt inner cover bolts securing the cover to the cylinder head.

57   Refit the camshaft gear with reference to Section 10, then refit the timing belt with reference to Section 8 or 9.

58   Reconnect the fuel supply pipe to the fuel lift pump, and tighten the clip.

59   Secure the engine oil level dipstick tube to the cylinder head, and tighten the bolt.

60   Refit the injectors, glow plugs and wiring with reference to Chapter 3. Reconnect the wire to No 4 glow plug.

61   Reconnect the wiring to the coolant temperature sender in the cylinder head.

14.4 Using a valve spring compressor tool

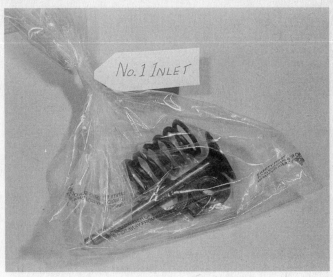

14.8 Store the valve components in a plastic bag after removal

62 Reconnect the high-pressure pipes, and tighten the union nuts while holding the delivery valves stationary.

63 Connect the leak-off tube to the banjo adapter.

64 Hold the delivery valves stationary, and tighten the high-pressure pipe union nuts. Do not overtighten the nuts, as this can distort the valves.

65 Bleed the fuel system as described in Chapter 3.

14 Cylinder head - overhaul

Dismantling

1 First remove the inlet and exhaust manifolds, with reference to Chapter 3.

2 Remove the fuel filter bracket assembly and the fuel pump.

3 Unbolt and remove the camshaft cover, then remove the camshaft and tappets with reference to Section 12. Make sure that the tappets and shims are kept in their correct order.

4 Using a valve spring compressor, compress each valve spring in turn until the split collets can be removed (photo). Release the compressor, and lift off the cap and spring. As the valves are deeply set in the cylinder head, it may be necessary to use an adapter on the valve cup in order to compress the springs, but this will depend on the type of valve compressor tool being used. A suitable length of metal tube, with two windows cut in it (for access to the split collets), may be used for this purpose.

5 If, when the valve spring compressor is screwed down, the valve spring cap refuses to free and expose the split collets, gently tap the top of the tool, directly over the cap, with a light hammer. This will free the cap.

6 On early models, carefully pull the oil seal from the top of the valve guide using a pair of pliers, and remove the spring seat. On later models, the oil seal forms part of the spring seat, and is removed together with it.

7 Withdraw the valve from the cylinder head.

8 It is essential that the valves are kept in their correct sequence, unless they are so badly worn that they are to be renewed. If they are going to be kept and used again, place them in labelled polythene bags (photo), or alternatively, insert them in a sheet of card having eight holes numbered 1 to 8, corresponding to the relative fitted positions of the valves. Note that No 1 valve is nearest the timing belt end of the engine.

9 Remove the other valves using the same procedure.

Cleaning

10 Thorough cleaning of the cylinder head and valve components, followed by a detailed inspection, will enable you to decide how much valve service work must be carried out during the overhaul.

11 Scrape away all traces of old gasket material and any sealing compound from the cylinder head.

12 Scrape away the carbon from the combustion area around the valve positions and the ports, then wash the cylinder head thoroughly with paraffin or a suitable solvent.

13 Scrape off any heavy carbon deposits that may have formed on the valves, then use a power-operated wire brush to remove deposits from the valve heads and stems. Also clean away the carbon from the glow plug and injector holes in the cylinder head.

14 With the cylinder head removed, clean the pistons and the top lips of each cylinder bore. If the pistons are still in the cylinder block, then it is essential that great care is taken to ensure that no carbon gets into the cylinder bores, as this could scratch the cylinder walls, or cause damage to the pistons and rings. To ensure this does not happen, first turn the crankshaft so that two of the pistons are at the top of their bores. Stuff rag into the other two bores, or seal them off with paper and masking tape. The waterways should also be covered with small pieces of masking tape, to prevent particles of carbon entering the cooling system and damaging the water pump. Press a little grease into the gap between the cylinder walls and the two pistons which are to be worked on. Carefully scrape away the carbon from the tops of the pistons, and from the combustion spaces in the crowns. Also scrape away the carbon from the surrounding lips of the cylinder walls. With the loose carbon removed, turn the engine so that the other pair of pistons are at the top of their bores, then wipe the grease and carbon from the bores. Repeat the procedure on the remaining pistons.

14.16 Checking the cylinder head for distortion using a straight-edge and feeler blade

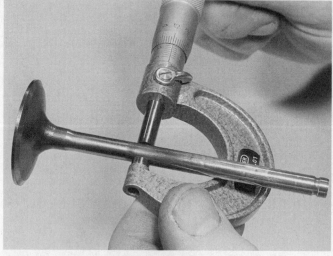

14.20 Measuring the valve stem diameter

Inspection

Note: *Be sure to perform all the following inspection procedures before concluding that the services of an engine overhaul specialist are required. Make a list of all items which require attention.*

Cylinder head

15   Inspect the head very carefully for cracks, evidence of coolant leakage, and other damage. If cracks are found, a new cylinder head should be obtained.

16   Use a straight-edge and feeler blade to check that the cylinder head surface is not distorted (photo). If it is, it may be possible to resurface it, up to the maximum amount given in the Specifications. Consult an engine overhaul specialist or engineering works.

17   Examine all of the valve seats. If they are severely pitted, cracked or burned, then they will need to be renewed or recut by an engine overhaul specialist. If they are only slightly pitted, this can be removed by grinding the valve heads and seats together with coarse, then fine, grinding paste as described below, provided the final position of the valve heads below the cylinder head surface is maintained within the tolerances given in the Specifications.

18   If the valve guides are worn, indicated by a side-to-side motion of

the valve, new guides must be fitted. This work is best carried out by an engine overhaul specialist, as it involves heating the cylinder head and using special tools. A dial gauge may be used to determine the amount of side play of the valve.

19   Use a straight-edge to check each of the cylinder head bolts. If any bolt shows a reduction in diameter on the part of the thread not engaged in the cylinder block, it should be renewed.

Valves

20   Examine the heads of each valve for pitting, burning, cracks and general wear, and check the valve stem for scoring and wear ridges. Rotate the valve, and check for any obvious indication that it is bent. Look for pits and excessive wear on the end of each valve stem. If the valve appears satisfactory at this stage, measure the valve stem diameter at several points using a micrometer (photo). Any significant difference in the readings obtained indicates wear of the valve stem. Should any of these conditions be apparent, the valve(s) must be renewed. Note that if an early type inlet valve is renewed, the later type of oil seal/spring seat must also be obtained and fitted to the new valve. If the valves are in satisfactory condition, they should be ground (lapped) into their respective seats to ensure a smooth gas-tight seal. The final position of the valve heads below the cylinder head surface must be maintained within the tolerances given in the Specifications.

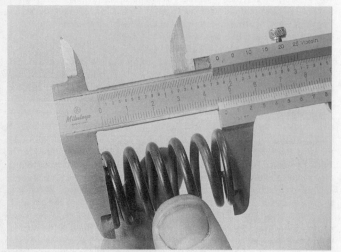

14.24 Measuring the valve spring free length

14.27 Inserting the valves in the cylinder head

14.29A Using the cap of a ballpoint pen over the valve stem as a protector for the valve stem oil seals

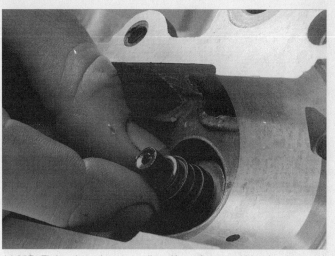

14.29B Fitting the valve stem oil seal/seat (later combined type shown)

21 Valve grinding is carried out as follows. Place the cylinder head upside-down on a bench, with a block of wood at each end to give clearance for the camshaft cover dowels.

22 Smear a trace of coarse carborundum paste on the seat face, and press a suction grinding tool onto the valve head. With a semi-rotary action, grind the valve head to its seat, lifting the valve occasionally to redistribute the grinding paste. When a dull matt even surface is produced on both the valve seat and the valve, wipe off the paste and repeat the process with fine carborundum paste. A light spring placed under the valve head will greatly ease this operation. When a smooth unbroken ring of light grey matt finish is produced on both the valve and seat, the grinding operation is complete. Be sure to remove all traces of grinding paste using paraffin or a suitable solvent before reassembly of the cylinder head.

23 After grinding-in the valves, they must be checked for depth below the cylinder head face. Use a straight-edge and feeler blades or a dial test indicator gauge to do this, and compare the results with the dimensions given in the Specifications. If any valve is lower than the maximum amount, it must be renewed. If, however, a new valve has already been fitted, then the valve seat must be renewed.

Valve components

24 Examine the valve springs for signs of damage and discoloration, and also measure their free length using vernier calipers (photo), or by comparing the existing spring with a new component.

25 Stand each spring on a flat surface, and check it for squareness. If any of the springs are damaged, distorted or have lost their tension, obtain a complete new set of springs.

26 Inspect the tappet buckets and their shims for scoring, pitting (especially on the shims) and wear ridges. Renew the components as necessary. Note that some scuffing is to be expected, and is acceptable provided that the tappets are not scored.

Reassembly

27 Lubricate the stems of the valves, and insert them into their original locations (photo). If new valves are being fitted, insert them into the locations to which they have been ground.

28 On early models, refit the spring seats over the valve guides.

29 Working on the first valve, dip the oil seal (or oil seal and seat) in engine oil, then carefully locate it over the valve and onto the guide. Take care not to damage the seal as it is passed over the valve stem; some form of protector (such as the modified cap of a ballpoint pen) should be placed on the valve stem as the oil seal is being fitted. Use a suitable socket or metal tube to press or tap the seal firmly onto the guide (photos).

30 Locate the spring and cap onto the seat (photos).

14.29C Carefully tap the oil seal/seat onto the guide

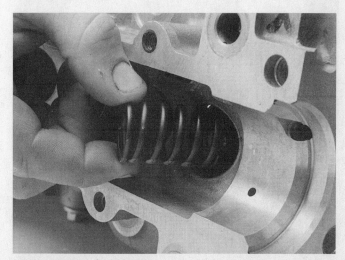

14.30A Fitting the valve spring . . .

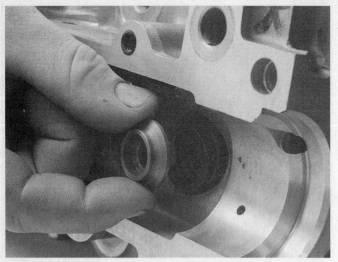

14.30B . . . and cap

14.31 Fitting the split collets

31   Compress the valve spring, locate the split collets in the recess in the valve stem, then release the valve compressor. Use a little grease to hold the collets in place during this operation (photo).

32   With all the valves installed, place the cylinder head upright on two lengths of wood (to protect the valve heads) and, using a hammer and small interposed block of wood, tap the end of each valve stem to settle the components.

33   Lubricate the tappets and shims, and refit them together with the camshaft and camshaft cover, with reference to Section 12.

34   Refit the fuel filter bracket assembly and the fuel pump.

35   Refit the inlet and exhaust manifolds together with a new gasket, with reference to Chapter 3.

15   Valve clearances - checking and adjustment

Note: *Timing pins (or 6.75 mm diameter drills), camshaft holding clamps (see Section 12), and on models not fitted with power steering, a camshaft retaining tool, are required for this operation.*

1   The valve clearances should be adjusted with the engine cold. First disconnect the battery earth (negative) lead.

2   Remove the timing belt covers as described in Section 6.

3   Unscrew the screw securing the timing belt inner cover to the camshaft cover.

4   Unscrew the blanking screw from the top of the camshaft cover, then turn the crankshaft using a socket on the crankshaft pulley bolt until the timing hole in the camshaft is aligned with the hole in the camshaft cover (this is the TDC position for No 1 piston). Insert timing pins (or 6.75 mm diameter drills) in the camshaft, and also in the flywheel through the timing hole in the cylinder block.

5   On pre-1989 models, and on models not fitted with power steering, unbolt and remove the camshaft rear cover (photos).

6   Unscrew the nut securing the accelerator cable support bracket to the camshaft cover, and move the bracket to one side.

7   On pre-1989 models, and on models not fitted with power steering, fit a camshaft retainer tool to hold the rear end of the camshaft

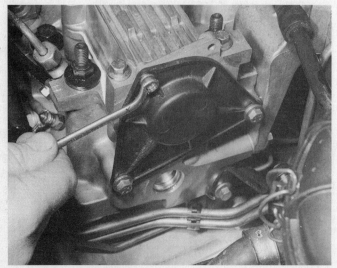

15.5A Unscrew the bolts . . .

15.5B . . . and remove the camshaft rear cover

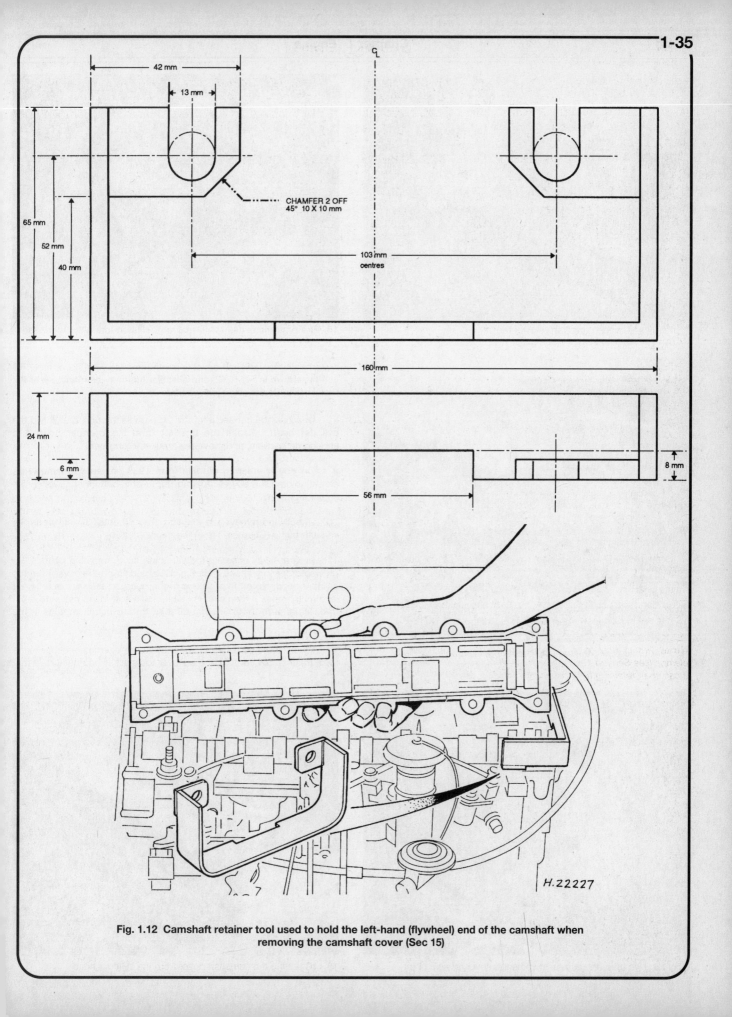

42 mm

13 mm

CHAMFER 2 OFF
45° 10 X 10 mm

65 mm

52 mm

40 mm

103 mm
centres

160 mm

24 mm

6 mm

56 mm

8 mm

H.22227

Fig. 1.12 Camshaft retainer tool used to hold the left-hand (flywheel) end of the camshaft when removing the camshaft cover (Sec 15)

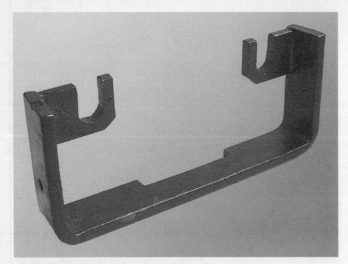

15.7A Home-made camshaft retainer tool

15.7B Home-made camshaft retainer tool fitted to the cylinder head

down while the camshaft cover is being removed. The Rover tool 18G 1548 is shown in Fig. 1.12, and a similar tool may be made out of flat metal bar to do the same job (photos).

8   Unscrew the nut securing the front cable support bracket to the cylinder head, release the bracket from the cylinder head and speedometer cable, and move the bracket to one side.

9   On power steering models from 1989 onwards, unscrew the screw holding the power steering pump drivebelt inner cover to the camshaft cover.

10   Unbolt and remove the fuel lift pump (Chapter 3) and the brake vacuum pump (Chapter 7) from the camshaft cover.

11   Progressively unscrew the camshaft cover retaining bolts in the reverse order to that shown in Fig. 1.10, and lift off the cover from the cylinder head. Note the positions of the bolts, as they are of different lengths (photos). If the cover is stuck, use a soft-faced mallet to tap it free. Make sure that the semi-circular thrustwasher remains in the cover.

12   Fit the three camshaft clamps (photo) or alternative home-made tools (refer to Section 12). If the Rover tools are used, make sure that

15.11A Unscrewing the camshaft cover retaining bolts

15.11B Two different lengths of camshaft cover retaining bolt

15.11C Lifting the camshaft cover from the cylinder head

15.12 Centre camshaft clamp in position

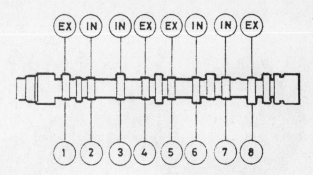

H.22233

Fig. 1.13 Valve sequence, numbered from the timing end of the camshaft (Sec 15)

the pressure pads follow the contour of the journals, and are fully un-screwed.

13   Tighten the clamp bolts or pressure pads until the camshaft journals are lightly seated in the cylinder head.

14   Remove the camshaft retainer tool where this has been fitted.

15   Draw the valve positions on a piece of paper, numbering them from 1 to 8 from the timing belt end of the engine. Mark the valve positions with an "I" if they are inlet or with an "E" if they are exhaust. The positions of the inlet and exhaust valves are as follows:

Timing belt end of engine   1 2 3 4 5 6 7 8
                              Ex In In Ex Ex In In Ex

16   Using a socket on the crankshaft pulley bolt, turn the engine until cam Nos 1 and 3 are vertical.

17   When using the Rover tools, tighten each of the pressure pads to 7 Nm, then tighten the locknuts (photos).

18   Insert a feeler gauge of the correct specified thickness between

15.17A Torque-tightening the clamp tool pressure pads

No 1 cam and No 1 valve stem, and check that it is a firm sliding fit. If not, insert different feeler gauges until the fit is correct, and record the clearance. Note that a cranked feeler gauge will make the checking easier, due to the raised camshaft cover sealing face (photo).

15.17B Tightening the locknuts on the clamp tool

15.18 Using a cranked feeler gauge to check the valve clearances

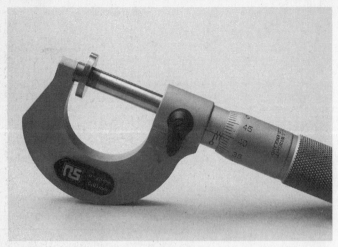

15.26 Measuring the thickness of a shim

19   Without moving the camshaft, check the clearance of No 3 valve in the same manner, and record.

20   Loosen the pressure pad bolts on the Rover tool, or slightly loosen the bolts holding the home-made tool to the cylinder head.

21   Turn the crankshaft until Nos 4 and 7 cams are vertical. Tighten the tool bolts so that the camshaft journals are seated in the cylinder head, and record the clearances for Nos 4 and 7 valves.

22   Repeat the procedure for Nos 6 and 8, then Nos 2 and 5 valves.

23   Note that it is only necessary to adjust the valve clearances if they are outside the maximum tolerances given in the Specifications. If, as may sometimes happen, the clearances have reduced by more than 0.11 mm below the standard setting, damage may have occurred to the valve seats, valves, camshaft cams and tappet faces. In this case, the cylinder head should be removed and the valves taken out for examination.

24   To adjust the valve clearances, it is necessary to completely remove the camshaft in order to remove the tappets and shims. First loosen the tool bolts, and turn the crankshaft clockwise until the camshaft timing hole is uppermost (at the 12 o'clock position). Unbolt and remove the camshaft retainer and clamps.

25   Remove the camshaft with reference to the applicable paragraphs of Section 12, but leave removal of the tappets and shims until the following paragraphs.

26   The tappet shims must now be changed in order to correct the valve clearances. Working on the first valve, remove the tappet from the cylinder head, and extract the shim from the tappet using a small screwdriver. Measure the thickness of the shim using a micrometer (photo). Select the new shim using the following formula.

$A + B - C =$ *Shim thickness required*

Where $A =$ *Valve clearance measured with feeler gauge*
  $B =$ *Thickness of shim removed*
  $C =$ *Correct valve clearance required*

27   Locate the new shim in the tappet, then oil the tappet and locate it in its correct bore in the cylinder head.

28   Change the remaining shims in the same manner, until they are all correct and the tappets are located in the cylinder head.

29   Refit the camshaft with reference to the applicable paragraphs of Section 12.

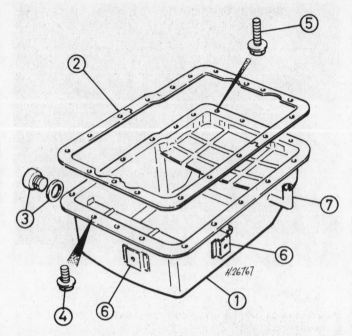

Fig. 1.14 Sump and gasket (Sec 16)

1	*Sump*	5	*Bolt (25 mm)*
2	*Two-piece gasket*	6	*Power-assisted steering*
3	*Drain plug and washer*		*pipe clip brackets*
4	*Bolt (12 mm)*	7	*Crankcase breather pipe*

16   Sump and oil pick-up tube - removal and refitting

Removal

1   If the engine is already removed from the vehicle, proceed to paragraph 7.

2   Disconnect the battery earth (negative) lead.

3   Apply the handbrake, then jack up the front of the vehicle and support on axle stands.

4   Position a suitable container beneath the engine sump. Unscrew the drain plug, and allow all of the oil to drain. Refit and tighten the drain plug on completion.

5   Disconnect the crankcase breather hose from the pipe on the front of the sump.

6   On power steering models, unscrew the bolts from the clips securing the power steering pipe to the sump.

7   Unscrew and remove the bolts securing the sump to the crankcase, but leave two diagonally-opposite bolts engaged by two or three threads at this stage. Note the position of the long bolt in the left-hand rear hole (right-hand rear bolt with engine upright on the bench) - see Fig. 1.14 (photos).

8   Free the sump from the crankcase by tapping it to one side with the palm of your hand. If this fails to free it, use a soft-headed mallet.

9   Unscrew the two remaining screws, and lower the sump from the crankcase (photo). Keep the sump beneath the crankcase for a few

16.7A Removing a short sump retaining bolt

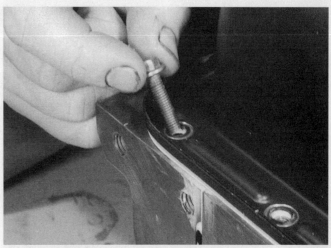

16.7B Removing the long sump retaining bolt

16.9 Removing the sump

16.10 Removing the sump gasket

16.11A Oil pick-up tube and strainer retaining bolts (arrowed)

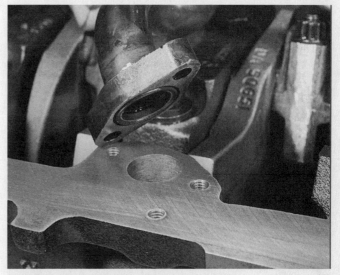

16.11B Removing the oil pick-up tube and strainer

minutes, as there will be some oil drops from the oil pump and crankcase.

10   Remove the gasket from the sump (photo).

11   With the sump removed, the oil pick-up tube and strainer may be unbolted from the crankcase and No 2 main bearing cap. Recover the O-ring (photos).

16.12 Tightening the oil pick-up tube and strainer bolts

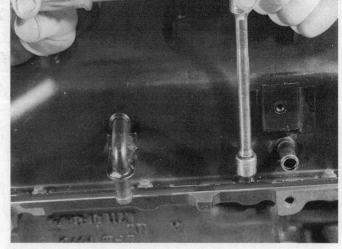

16.16 Tightening the sump bolts

Refitting

12   Wipe clean the mating surfaces of the oil pick-up tube and crankcase, then refit the tube together with a new O-ring and tighten the mounting bolts (photo).

13   Wipe clean the mating surfaces of the sump and crankcase.

14   Apply a bead of silicone sealant to the joints of the two end main bearing caps. Carry out the work in the following paragraphs as quickly as possible before the sealant starts to dry.

15   Locate the new gasket on the sump. Where applicable, apply locking fluid to the dovetail joints joining the two halves of the joint together, and lock the halves with each other.

16   Offer the sump to the crankcase, and insert two or three bolts to hold the sump in position. Check that all the bolt holes are still aligned correctly, then insert the remaining bolts and tighten all bolts progressively in diagonal sequence to the specified torque (photo). Make sure that the long bolt is located in the correct position.

17   If the engine is in the vehicle, refit the power steering pipe clips to the sump, and tighten the bolts.

18   Reconnect the crankcase breather hose to the pipe on the front of the sump.

19   Lower the vehicle to the ground.

20   Reconnect the battery earth (negative) lead.

21   Fill the engine with the specified grade and quantity of oil.

17   Oil pump - removal and refitting

Removal

1   Remove the timing belt as described in Section 8 or 9, and remove the water pump as described in Chapter 2.

17.3A Unscrewing the bolt securing the inner timing cover to the camshaft cover

17.3B Inner timing cover lower mounting bolts (arrowed)

17.3C Removing the bolt securing the inner timing cover to the oil pump

17.3D Removing the inner timing cover

2   Remove the camshaft gear, injection pump gear and crankshaft gear as described in Section 10. Also remove the key from the groove in the crankshaft.

3   Unbolt and remove the inner timing cover (photos).

4   Position a suitable container beneath the oil filter, then unscrew and remove it.

5   Disconnect the wiring from the oil pressure switch (photo), then unscrew the switch from the oil pump.

6   On Turbo models, unscrew the union nut and disconnect the turbocharger oil feed pipe union from the oil pump (photo).

7   On models fitted with an oil cooler (Turbo models, and all models from 1989 onwards), loosen the union nuts and disconnect the oil cooler pipes from the oil pump (photos).

8   Where applicable, progressively unscrew the bolts holding the deflector bracket to the oil pump, and remove the bracket.

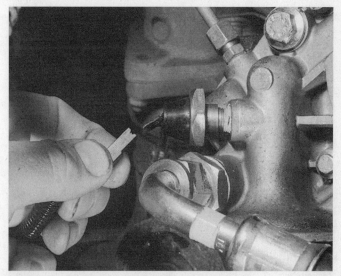

17.5 Disconnecting the oil pressure switch wiring

17.6 Loosening the turbocharger oil feed pipe union from the oil pump

17.7A Loosening the oil cooler pipe union from the rear of the oil pump

17.7B Loosening the oil cooler pipe union from the front of the oil pump

17.9A Oil pump showing retaining bolts

17.9B Removing the oil pump

17.11 Oil pump drive key in the nose of the crankshaft (note tapered end)

9   Unscrew and remove the pump retaining bolts, noting their length and locations, then withdraw the oil pump from the crankshaft (photos).

10   Remove the gasket.

11   Remove the oil pump drive key from the groove in the nose of the crankshaft (photo).

Refitting

12   Check the condition of the oil pump drive key, and if necessary renew it. When fitting it, make sure that the chamfered end of the key is facing outwards.

13   Clean the cylinder block and the No 1 main bearing cap joint faces, and check that the two oil pump locating dowels are correctly in place.

14   Apply a 3 mm bead of silicone sealant to the vertical joint faces of the No 1 main bearing cap (photo). Carry out the procedure in the following paragraphs as quickly as possible.

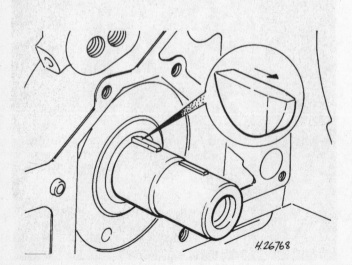

Fig. 1.15 Correct fitted position of the oil pump drive key (Sec 17)

17.14 Applying silicone sealant to the vertical joint faces of No 1 main bearing cap

17.15 Locating the oil pump gasket on the cylinder block

15   Locate the gasket on the cylinder block (photo).

16   To prevent damage to the crankshaft front oil seal in the oil pump when the pump is being fitted, it is preferable to locate a protection sleeve over the front of the crankshaft. Alternatively, wrap adhesive tape (plastic shiny type) over the crankshaft nose, in such a way that it can be removed easily after the pump is fitted. Another method is to remove the old oil seal and fit a new one once the oil pump is fitted.

17   Lubricate the protection sleeve/tape with oil, then locate the oil pump and deflector bracket (where fitted) on the cylinder block. Apply sealant to the threads of the bolt which enters the No 1 main bearing cap, and insert all of the bolts (photos).

18   Tighten the bolts to the specified torque wrench setting, in the sequence shown in Fig. 1.16 (photo).

19   Remove the protection sleeve or tape.

20   On Turbo models, reconnect the turbocharger oil feed pipe union to the oil pump, and tighten the nut.

17.17A Locating the oil pump on the cylinder block

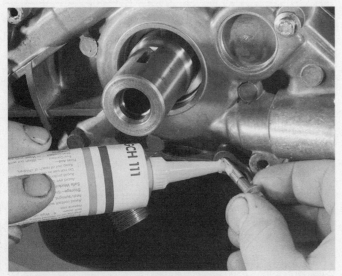

17.17B Applying sealant to the threads of the oil pump retaining bolt which enters the No 1 main bearing cap

17.18 Tightening the oil pump bolts

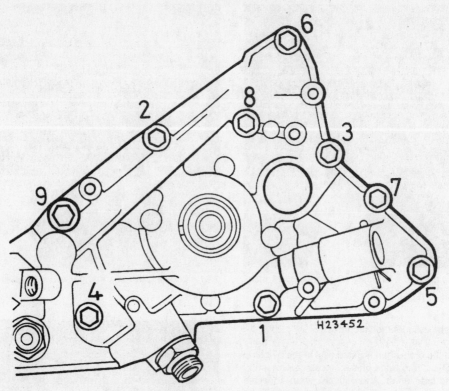

Fig. 1.16 Oil pump bolt tightening sequence (Sec 17)

21   On models fitted with an oil cooler, reconnect the oil cooler pipes to the pump, and tighten the union nuts.

22   Refit the oil pressure switch to the oil pump, and tighten it to the specified torque wrench setting. Reconnect the wiring.

23   Fit a new oil filter, tightening it by hand only (refer to Section 2 if necessary).

24   Refit the inner timing cover, and tighten the bolts.

25   Fit the key to the groove in the crankshaft.

26   Refit the crankshaft gear, injection pump gear and camshaft gear with reference to Section 10.

27   Refit the water pump as described in Chapter 2.

28   Refit the timing belt as described in Section 8 or 9.

29   Check and if necessary top-up the engine oil level.

30   On Turbo models, disconnect the wiring from the stop solenoid, and spin the engine on the starter motor until oil pressure is registered on the oil pressure gauge (or until the low oil pressure warning light goes out). Reconnect the wiring afterwards.

---

18 Oil pump - overhaul

---

1   With the oil pump removed from the engine, wipe its external surfaces clean.

2   Check that the backplate has the word "TOP" marked on it (indicating its correct fitted position) - this should be located furthest away from the straight (sump sealing) edge of the pump. If there is no mark, scribe a line on the backplate and housing.

3   Using an Torx key, unscrew the screws and remove the backplate (photos).

4   Remove the inner and outer rotors, keeping them identified for position. Note any marks or indentations on the rotors to indicate their position; on the project engine for this manual, the rotors were marked with a small square on their inner facing surfaces (photos).

5   Remove the split pin which retains the pressure relief valve, then remove the plug from the housing by pushing down on the relief valve spring with a screwdriver through the oil return hole, or by tapping the oil pump carefully on the bench. Alternatively, tap the centre of the plug so that the spring reaction forces the plug out. If this fails to remove the plug, drill a small hole in the centre of the plug, and use a

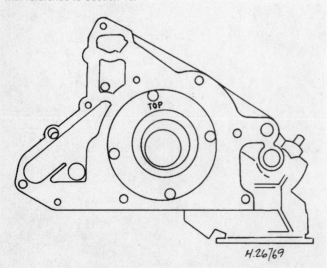

Fig. 1.17 The "TOP" marked on the oil pump backplate must be located away from the straight edge (Sec 18)

18.3A Remove the screws . . .

18.3B . . . and withdraw the oil pump backplate

18.4A Removing the oil pump inner rotor

18.4B Removing the oil pump outer rotor

18.4C Marks on the inner facing surfaces of the rotors

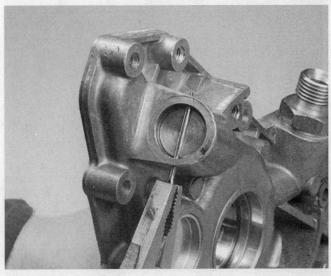

18.5A Extract the split pin . . .

18.5B . . . followed by the plug . . .

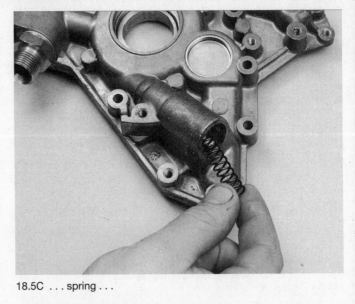

18.5C . . . spring . . .

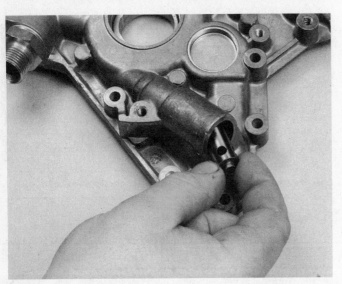

18.5D . . . and valve plunger

18.5E Oil pump with pressure relief valve components

18.8 Checking the clearance between the outer rotor and the pump body

18.9 Checking the clearance between the inner and outer rotor lobes

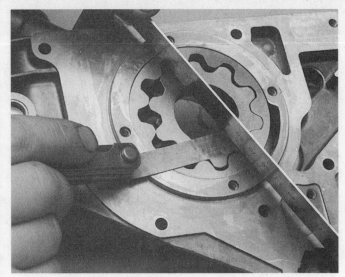

18.10 Measuring the rotor endfloat

18.13 Tightening the oil pump backplate screws

self-tapping screw to extract it. Collect the spring and valve plunger. Discard the plug O-ring seal (photos).

6   Using a screwdriver, prise the oil seal from the oil pump housing.

7   Thoroughly clean all of the components, then check the rotor endfloat and lobe clearances as follows.

8   Fit the outer rotor in the housing and, using a feeler gauge, check the clearance between the outer rotor and the pump body (photo).

9   Fit the inner rotor, and measure the inner-to-outer rotor lobe clearance (photo).

10   Measure the inner and outer rotor endfloat using a straight-edge and feeler blade (photo).

11   If any of the clearances exceed the limits given in the Specifications, the pump must be renewed.

12   Check the condition of the pressure relief valve spring. If damaged or distorted, it should be renewed.

13   Reassembly is the reverse of the dismantling procedure, making sure that each component is refitted in its correct position, as noted on dismantling. Use a new split pin to secure the pressure relief valve. Liberally lubricate the oil pump components with engine oil, fit a new O-ring on the pressure relief valve plug (and a new plug if it was drilled), and a new crankshaft front oil seal in the housing. Tighten the backplate screws to the specified torque (photo).

19   Oil pressure relief valve - removal, inspection and refitting

Removal

1   Apply the handbrake, then jack up the front of the vehicle and support on axle stands.

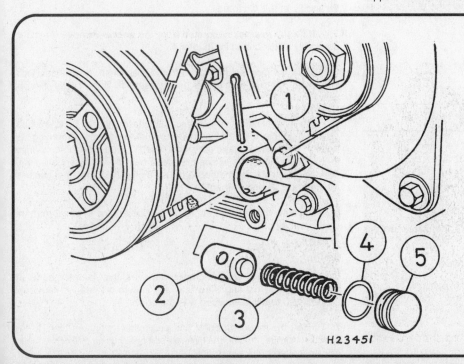

Fig. 1.18 Oil pressure relief valve components (Sec 19)

1   Split pin
2   Plunger
3   Spring
4   O-ring
5   Plug

H23451

21.4 One method of holding the flywheel stationary

21.5A Unscrew the mounting bolts . . .

2   Remove the split pin which retains the pressure relief valve, then remove the plug from the housing by tapping the centre of the plug so that the spring reaction forces it out. If this fails to remove the plug, drill a small hole in the centre of the plug, and use a self-tapping screw to extract it. Collect the spring and valve plunger. Discard the plug O-ring seal.

Inspection

3   Clean the spring, plunger and plug, and examine them for wear and damage. Check the spring for distortion, and if possible compare it with a new spring.

4   Renew the spring and plunger if necessary, and renew the plug if it was drilled. Obtain a new O-ring seal.

Refitting

5   Manipulate a new O-ring into the relief valve plug groove.

6   Lubricate the bore in the oil pump, then insert the plunger, open end first, followed by the spring and plug.

7   Retain the components with a new split pin.

8   Lower the vehicle to the ground.

20   Oil pressure switch - removal and refitting

Removal

1   Disconnect the battery earth (negative) lead.

2   Apply the handbrake, then jack up the front of the vehicle and support on axle stands.

3   Remove the right-hand roadwheel. Remove the plastic access panel from inside the wheelarch.

4   Disconnect the wiring from the oil pressure switch.

5   Unscrew the switch, and remove it from the oil pump.

Refitting

6   Make sure that the threads of the oil pressure switch are clean and not damaged.

7   Screw the switch into the oil pump housing, and tighten to the specified torque.

8   Reconnect the wiring.

9   Refit the access panel and the roadwheel.

10   Lower the vehicle to the ground, and reconnect the battery earth (negative) lead.

21   Flywheel - removal and refitting

Removal

1   The gearbox must be removed from the engine; either remove the gearbox separately as described in Chapter 5, or remove the engine and gearbox, and separate the gearbox, as described in Sections 25, 26 and 27 of this Chapter.

2   With the gearbox separated from the engine, remove the clutch assembly as described in Chapter 4.

3   Mark the flywheel in relation to the crankshaft. Note that a location dowel is fitted, so that it is only possible to fit the flywheel in one position.

4   The flywheel must now be held stationary while the bolts are loosened. To do this, locate a long bolt in one of the gearbox mounting bolt holes in the adapter plate, and either insert a wide-bladed screwdriver in the starter ring gear, or use a piece of bent metal bar engaged with the ring gear. Another method is to use a piece of metal engaged with the ring gear as shown (photo).

5   Unscrew the mounting bolts, and withdraw the flywheel from the crankshaft (photos).

Refitting

6   Clean the flywheel and crankshaft faces, then locate the unit on the crankshaft, making sure that any previously-made marks are aligned, and that it is engaged with the dowel.

7   Insert the mounting bolts, and progressively tighten them to the specified torque, holding the flywheel stationary using one of the methods described previously (photo).

21.5B . . . and withdraw the flywheel

21.7 Tightening the flywheel mounting bolts

8   Refit the clutch assembly as described in Chapter 4.

9   Refit the gearbox and the engine with reference to Sections 26 and 27 of this Chapter, or refit the gearbox with reference to Chapter 5.

22 Crankshaft front (RH) and rear (LH) oil seals - renewal

Front (RH) oil seal

1   Remove the timing belt, crankshaft gear and key as described in Sections 8 or 9, and 10.

2   Using vernier calipers, measure the fitted depth of the oil seal in the oil pump housing. This is necessary in order to fit the new oil seal in the correct position. However, if the special Rover fitting tool is available, then this measurement is not necessary. On the project engine used for this manual, the oil seal was flush with the oil pump housing.

3   Rover technicians use a special extractor to remove the oil seal, but it may be removed by carefully drilling two small holes on diago-

nally-opposite sides of the oil seal and inserting self-tapping screws. By pulling on the screws, the oil seal can be removed. Hooking out the oil seal with a screwdriver is not recommended, as the sealing surface on the crankshaft may be damaged.

4   Clean the oil seal seating in the oil pump, and the journal on the crankshaft.

5   Oil the crankshaft journal and the sealing lips of the new oil seal.

6   To prevent damage to the oil seal as it is being located over the nose of the crankshaft, it is preferable to use a protection sleeve (plastic or metal) during the fitting procedure. Alternatively, wrap adhesive tape over the crankshaft nose, in such a way that it can be removed easily after the oil seal is fitted.

7   Lubricate the protection sleeve/tape with oil, then locate the oil seal over the front of the crankshaft, and press it squarely into the oil pump housing by hand, so that it begins to enter the location bore.

8   Using a socket of diameter slightly less than that of the oil seal, drive the oil seal in squarely until it is at the previously-noted fitted depth. Alternatively, the crankshaft gear and pulley, together with the old seal, may be used to press on the new oil seal squarely (photos).

22.8A Locate the oil seal over the front of the crankshaft . . .

22.8B . . . then use an old oil seal and the crankshaft pulley . . .

22.8C . . . to press the oil seal into position

22.11A Carefully drill the rear (LH) oil seal . . .

9   Refit the crankshaft gear and timing belt, as described in Sections 8 or 9, and 10.

Rear (LH) oil seal

10   Remove the flywheel as described in Section 21.

11   Carefully drill two small holes on opposite sides of the oil seal, and insert self-tapping screws. By pulling on the screws, the oil seal can be removed (photos). Hooking out the oil seal with a screwdriver is not recommended, as the sealing surface on the crankshaft may be damaged.

12   Clean the oil seal seating in the gearbox adapter plate, and the area on the crankshaft which contacts the oil seal.

13   Locate a thin piece of plastic on the crankshaft to act as a guide for the new oil seal, then oil the crankshaft and the sealing lips of the new oil seal.

14   Locate the oil seal over the rear of the crankshaft with the closed side facing outwards, and press it squarely into the gearbox adapter plate, so that it begins to enter the location bore. Remove the plastic guide.

15   If the sealing surface on the crankshaft is good, or if a new crankshaft has been fitted, the new oil seal should be fitted flush with the outer surface of the gearbox adapter plate. However, if the sealing surface is worn, the oil seal should be fitted to a depth of 3.0 mm in the adapter plate.

16   Using a metal tube (or similar) of diameter slightly less than that of the oil seal, drive the oil seal in squarely until it is at the required depth.

17   Refit the flywheel as described in Section 21.

---

23   Engine mountings - removal and refitting

Removal

Right-hand mounting (pre-1989 non-Turbo models)

1   Apply the handbrake, then jack up the front of the vehicle and support on axle stands.

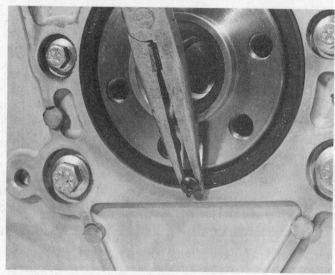

22.11B . . . insert a self-tapping screw, and withdraw the oil seal

2   Disconnect the battery earth (negative) lead.

3   Refer to Chapter 3 and remove the inlet and exhaust manifolds.

4   Release the fuel pipe from the mounting clip.

5   Position a trolley jack and block of wood beneath the sump, then take the weight of the engine with the jack.

6   Loosen the right-hand engine mounting through-bolt, and remove the bolts and spacers securing the mounting bracket to the body and support plate.

7   Unbolt the mounting arm from the engine, and remove the mounting assembly from under the thermostat housing.

8   Withdraw the bracket and snubber washers from the right-hand mounting arm.

Rear mounting (pre-1989 non-Turbo models)

9   Apply the handbrake, then jack up the front of the vehicle and support on axle stands.

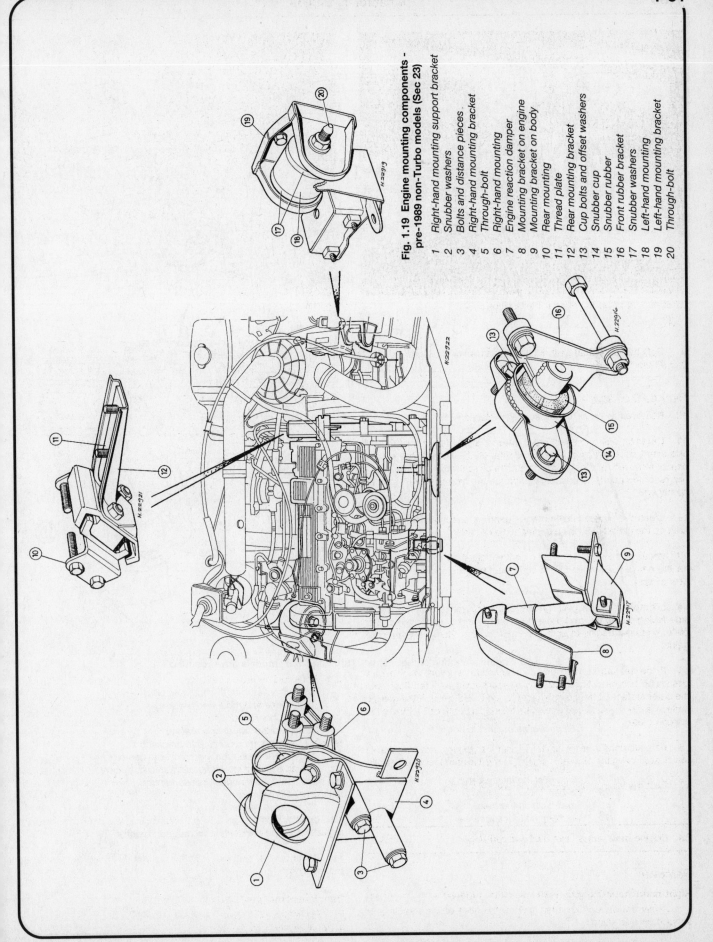

Fig. 1.19 Engine mounting components - pre-1989 non-Turbo models (Sec 23)

1 Right-hand mounting support bracket
2 Snubber washers
3 Bolts and distance pieces
4 Right-hand mounting bracket
5 Through-bolt
6 Right-hand mounting
7 Engine reaction damper
8 Mounting bracket on engine
9 Mounting bracket on body
10 Rear mounting
11 Thread plate
12 Rear mounting bracket
13 Cup bolts and offset washers
14 Snubber cup
15 Snubber rubber
16 Front rubber bracket
17 Snubber washers
18 Left-hand mounting
19 Left-hand mounting bracket
20 Through-bolt

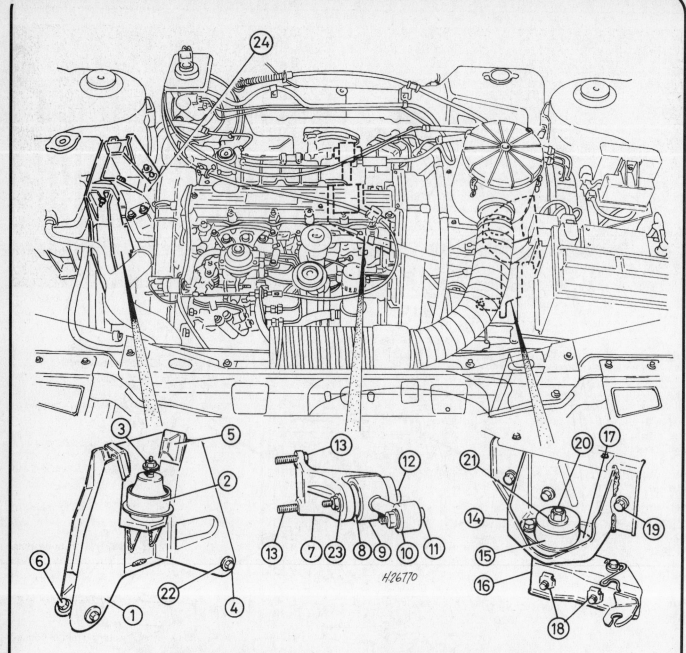

Fig. 1.20 Engine mounting components - Turbo and 1989 models onwards (Sec 23)

1	Right-hand mounting bracket	13	Bracket to body mounting bolts
2	Rubber Hydramount	14	Left-hand mounting bracket
3	Nut (mounting to support bracket)	15	Rubber mounting
4	Bolt (mounting bracket to body)	16	Gearbox mounting bracket
5	Rubber snubber	17	Left-hand mounting to bracket bolt
6	Bolt (mounting bracket to body)	18	Left-hand mounting bracket to gearbox bolt
7	Tie-bar bracket	19	Left-hand mounting bracket to body bolt
8	Large bush on the tie-bar	20	Rubber mounting securing nut
9	Tie-bar	21	Slip washer
10	Small bush on the tie-bar	22	Large washer
11	Mounting bolt for subframe	23	Insert
12	Mounting bolt for bracket	24	Right-hand mounting support bracket

23.28A Right-hand engine mounting nuts and bolts

23.28B Right-hand engine mounting location studs on the water pump

10   Disconnect the battery earth (negative) lead.

11   Support the weight of the gearbox with a trolley jack.

12   Unscrew and remove the two through-bolts holding the engine rear mounting bracket to the gearbox; also unscrew and remove the two bolts holding the bracket to the subframe.

13   Withdraw the mounting bracket assembly from under the gearbox, and remove the bracket from the mounting.

Left-hand mounting (pre-1989 non-Turbo models)

14   Disconnect the battery earth (negative) lead.

15   Disconnect the clutch cable from the gearbox with reference to Chapter 4.

16   Support the weight of the gearbox on a trolley jack and piece of wood.

17   Unscrew and remove the through-bolt securing the mounting bush to the body bracket.

18   Unscrew the remove the bolts securing the mounting to the gearbox, and withdraw the mounting. Recover the snubber washers.

Front snubber (pre-1989 non-Turbo models)

19   Unscrew and remove the two through-bolts securing the snubber bracket to the gearbox adapter plate, and withdraw the bracket.

20   Unbolt the snubber cup bracket from the front crossmember.

Engine front damper (pre-1989 non-Turbo models)

21   Unscrew and remove the two through-bolts securing the damper to the mounting brackets, then lever the damper free.

22   The damper may be checked for smooth operation by mounting it upright in a vice, and pulling the upper end through both full and short strokes. If there is any tendency of jerky or uneven operation, the damper should be renewed.

Right-hand mounting (Turbo and 1989 models onwards)

23   Drain the cooling system as described in Chapter 2.

24   Remove the cooling system expansion tank as described in Chapter 2.

25   Remove the timing belt upper cover as described in Section 6.

26   Support the weight of the engine on a trolley jack and piece of wood located under the right-hand end of the sump.

27   Unscrew the bolts securing the right-hand engine mounting bracket to the wheelarch and body panel.

28   Unscrew the two bolts and two nuts securing the right-hand engine mounting to the top of the water pump, and remove the complete right-hand engine mounting assembly (photos).

29   Unscrew and remove the nut securing the mounting rubber to the upper support bracket, and lift off the bracket.

30   Unscrew the lower nut, and remove the mounting rubber from the mounting bracket.

Tie-bar and mounting bracket (Turbo and 1989 models onwards)

31   Apply the handbrake, then jack up the front of the vehicle and support on axle stands.

32   Support the weight of the gearbox using a trolley jack and piece of wood.

33   Unbolt and remove the tie-bar assembly.

34   Unscrew the mounting bracket nuts and bolts, and withdraw the tie-bar.

35   Recover the large and small bushes, and also the insert.

Left-hand mounting (Turbo and 1989 models onwards)

36   Remove the air cleaner and air duct with reference to Chapter 3.

37   Using a trolley jack and piece of wood, support the left-hand side of the gearbox.

23.38 Left-hand engine mounting, showing nut securing the rubber mounting to the gearbox mounting bracket

23.39 Removing the left-hand rubber mounting and bracket

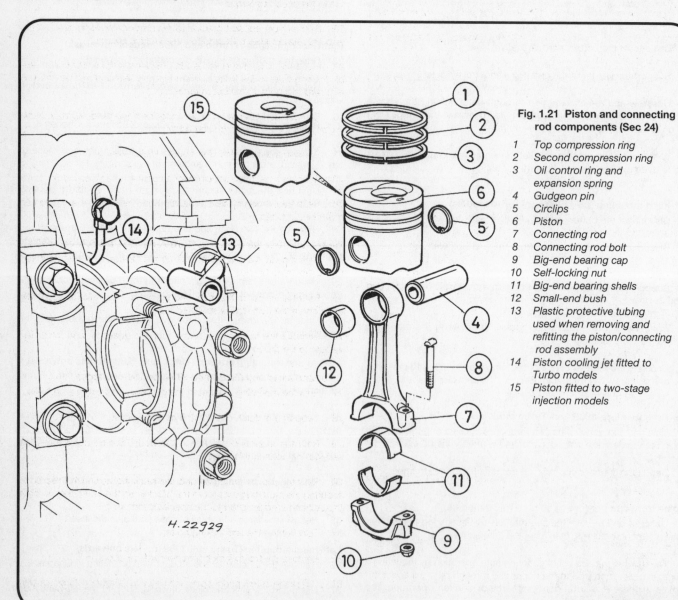

Fig. 1.21 Piston and connecting rod components (Sec 24)

1 Top compression ring
2 Second compression ring
3 Oil control ring and expansion spring
4 Gudgeon pin
5 Circlips
6 Piston
7 Connecting rod
8 Connecting rod bolt
9 Big-end bearing cap
10 Self-locking nut
11 Big-end bearing shells
12 Small-end bush
13 Plastic protective tubing used when removing and refitting the piston/connecting rod assembly
14 Piston cooling jet fitted to Turbo models
15 Piston fitted to two-stage injection models

H.22929

38   Unscrew and remove the nut securing the rubber mounting to the gearbox mounting bracket (photo).

39   Unscrew and remove the self-locking bolts holding the mounting bracket to the body. Also remove the bolts securing the bracket to the gearbox mounting bracket. Withdraw the rubber mounting and the bracket (photo).

40   Release the clutch cable from the mounting clip.

41   Unscrew the bolts and remove the mounting bracket from the gearbox.

Refitting

Right-hand mounting (pre-1989 non-Turbo models)
42   Refit the snubber washers and bracket to the right-hand mounting arm, leaving the through-bolt finger-tight at this stage.

43   Locate the mounting assembly under the thermostat housing, and insert and tighten the bolts securing the mounting arm to the engine.

44   Refit the mounting bracket to the support plate and body, using the same spacers as removed. Align the mounting using a suitable small screwdriver or rod through the side tab and the unused weld nut before tightening the bolts.

45   Lower the jack, then tighten the through-bolt to the specified torque.

46   Refit the inlet and exhaust manifolds with reference to Chapter 3.

47   Secure the fuel pipe to its mounting clip.

48   Reconnect the battery earth (negative) lead.

49   Lower the vehicle to the ground.

Rear mounting (pre-1989 non-Turbo models)
50   Refit the bracket to the mounting.

51   Locate the mounting bracket assembly under the gearbox, and insert the two bolts holding the bracket to the subframe. Insert the two through-bolts holding the engine rear mounting bracket to the gearbox. Tighten all of the bolts to the specified torque.

52   Remove the trolley jack from under the gearbox.

53   Reconnect the battery earth (negative) lead.

54   Lower the vehicle to the ground.

Left-hand mounting (pre-1989 non-Turbo models)
55   Fit the snubber washers to the mounting bush, and fit the bush in the body bracket and gearbox mounting.

56   Insert the through-bolt securing the mounting bush to the body bracket, and tighten finger-tight at this stage.

57   Locate the mounting on the gearbox, and tighten the bolts.

58   Lower the trolley jack, then tighten the mounting bush through-bolt to the specified torque.

59   Reconnect the clutch cable with reference to Chapter 4.

60   Reconnect the battery earth (negative) lead.

Front snubber (pre-1989 non-Turbo models)
61   Refit the snubber cup bracket to the front crossmember, leaving the bolts finger-tight at this stage.

62   Engage the snubber rubber in the cup, and refit the bracket to the gearbox adapter plate.

63   Centralise the cup in the snubber rubber so that it is free of any load, then tighten the securing bolts to the specified torque.

Engine front damper (pre-1989 non-Turbo models)
64   Locate the damper in the mounting brackets, with the bell end at the top.

65   Insert the two through-bolts, and tighten them to the specified torque.

Right-hand mounting (Turbo and 1989 models onwards)
66   Clean the old locking fluid out of the bolt threads in the water pump housing using a tap of the correct size.

67   Fit the rubber mounting to the mounting bracket, and tighten the nut to the specified torque.

68   Fit the upper support bracket to the rubber mounting, and secure with the retaining nut tightened to the specified torque.

69   Place the mounting assembly in position on the water pump. Apply locking fluid to the bolts and studs, then refit and tighten the two nuts and two bolts to the specified torque.

70   Refit and tighten the bolts securing the right-hand engine mounting bracket to the wheelarch and body panel.

71   Remove the trolley jack from under the engine.

72   Refit the timing belt upper cover as described in Section 6.

73   Refit the cooling system expansion tank and refill the system as described in Chapter 2.

Tie-bar and mounting bracket (Turbo and 1989 models onwards)
74   Refit the large and small bushes to the tie-bar, and refit the insert to the mounting bracket.

75   Refit the tie-bar to the mounting brackets, then refit the assembly and tighten the bolts to the specified torque.

76   Remove the trolley jack from under the gearbox, and lower the vehicle to the ground.

Left-hand mounting (Turbo and 1989 models onwards)
77   Refit the mounting bracket to the gearbox, and tighten the bolts.

78   Support the clutch cable in the mounting clip.

79   Refit the mounting bracket to the body, but do not tighten the self-locking bolts at this stage.

80   Refit the rubber mounting and the retaining nut. Insert the bolts securing the mounting bracket to the bracket on the body, then tighten the bolts and retaining nut to the specified torque.

81   Fully tighten the self-locking bolts.

82   Remove the trolley jack from under the gearbox.

83   Check the clutch pedal operation (refer to Chapter 4 if necessary).

84   Refit the air cleaner and air duct with reference to Chapter 3.

24.10A   Loosen the big-end bearing cap nuts . . .

;24.10B   . . . unscrew the nuts . . .

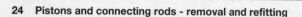

24   Pistons and connecting rods - removal and refitting

Note: *Ideally, the pistons and connecting rods should be removed with the engine on the bench. This method is easier for the home mechanic, and there will be less chance of foreign matter entering internal oilways, etc. However, if there is no reason to remove the engine, the work may be carried out with the engine remaining in the vehicle.*

Removal

1   If the engine is on the bench, proceed to paragraph 5.

2   Disconnect the battery earth (negative) lead, then drain the cooling system as described in Chapter 2.

3   Apply the handbrake, then jack up the front of the vehicle and support on axle stands.

4   Drain the engine oil into a suitable container.

5   Remove the cylinder head with reference to Section 13.

6   Turn the crankshaft so that all pistons are halfway down their bores, then place cloth rags in each bore. Scrape off all carbon from the tops of the cylinder bores, and use fine emery tape soaked in oil to thoroughly clean the surfaces. Remove the cloth rags and wipe clean the cylinder bores.

7   Remove the sump and oil pick-up tube with reference to Section 16.

8   Rotate the crankshaft so that No 1 big-end cap (nearest the timing end of the engine) is at the lowest point of its travel. If the big-end cap and rod are not already numbered, mark them with a centre-punch on the thrust side (cylinder block drain plug side). Mark both cap and rod in relation to the cylinder they operate in, noting that No 1 is nearest the timing end of the engine.

9   Before removing the big-end caps, use a feeler blade to check the amount of side play between the caps and the crankshaft webs.

10   Unscrew and remove the No 1 big-end bearing cap nuts, and withdraw the cap, complete with shell bearing, from the connecting rod (photos). If only the bearing shells are being attended to, push the connecting rod up and off the crankpin, and remove the upper bearing

24.10C   . . . and remove the caps together with the shell bearings

shell. Keep the bearing shells and cap together in their correct sequence if they are to be refitted.

11   Push the connecting rod up, and remove the piston and rod from the top of the bore. To prevent the big-end cap bolts damaging the bore or crankshaft journal as the piston is being removed, it is a good idea to fit plastic tubing over them (photo).

12   If not already done, remove the upper bearing shell from the connecting rod at this stage (photo).

13   Keep the cap, shell bearings and piston/connecting rod assemblies together in sets (photo).

14   Repeat the procedure for No 4 piston/connecting rod assembly, then turn the crankshaft through half a turn, and remove Nos 2 and 3 pistons and connecting rods.

15   Keep all the assemblies in sets and identified for position, so that they can be refitted to their correct bores.

16   Note that later models with two-stage injection have pistons without shallow cut-outs in their crowns. These pistons may be fitted to earlier models, but they must always be fitted in sets of four.

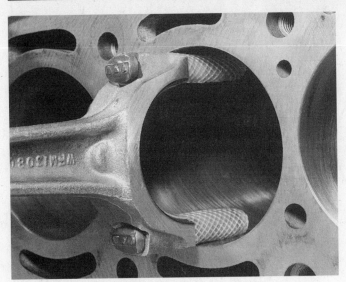

24.11 Plastic tubing fitted over the big-end cap bolts to prevent damage to the cylinder bores

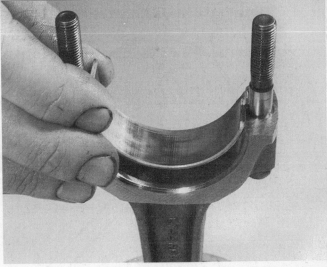

24.12 Removing an upper bearing shell from the connecting rod

Refitting

17   Clean the backs of the big-end bearing shells and the recesses in the connecting rods and big-end caps. If new shells are being fitted, ensure that all traces of the protective grease are cleaned off using paraffin. Wipe the shells and connecting rods dry with a lint-free cloth.

18   Press the big-end bearing shells into the connecting rods and caps in their correct positions. Make sure that the location tabs are engaged with the cut-outs in the connecting rods.

Big-end bearing running clearance check

19   Lubricate No 1 piston and piston rings, and position the gaps as follows. The oil control ring gap should be on the thrust side of the piston, and the compression ring gaps should be spaced at 90° to each other on the opposite side of the piston.

20   Fit a ring compressor to No 1 piston, then insert the piston and connecting rod into No 1 cylinder. With No 1 crankpin at its lowest point, drive the piston carefully into the cylinder with the wooden handle of a hammer, and at the same time guide the connecting rod onto the crankpin (photo). Make sure that the arrow on the piston crown

faces the timing end of the engine. If there is no arrow, refer to Fig. 1.22.

21   Remove the plastic tubing from the big-end cap bolts.

22   To measure the big-end bearing running clearance, refer to the information contained in Section 31, as the same general procedures apply. If the Plastigage method is being used, ensure that the crankpin journal and the big-end bearing shells are clean and dry, then engage the connecting rod with the crankpin. Lay the Plastigage strip on the crankpin, fit the bearing cap in its previously-noted position, then tighten the bolts to the specified torque. Do not rotate the crankshaft during this operation. Remove the cap and check the running clearance by measuring the Plastigage as previously described.

23   Repeat the above procedures on the remaining piston/connecting rod assemblies.

Final connecting rod refitting

24   Having checked the running clearance of all the crankpin journals, and taken any corrective action necessary, clean off all traces of Plastigage from the bearing shells and crankpin.

24.13 Connecting rod and big-end bearing components

24.20 Using a hammer handle to drive the piston through the ring compressor and into the cylinder

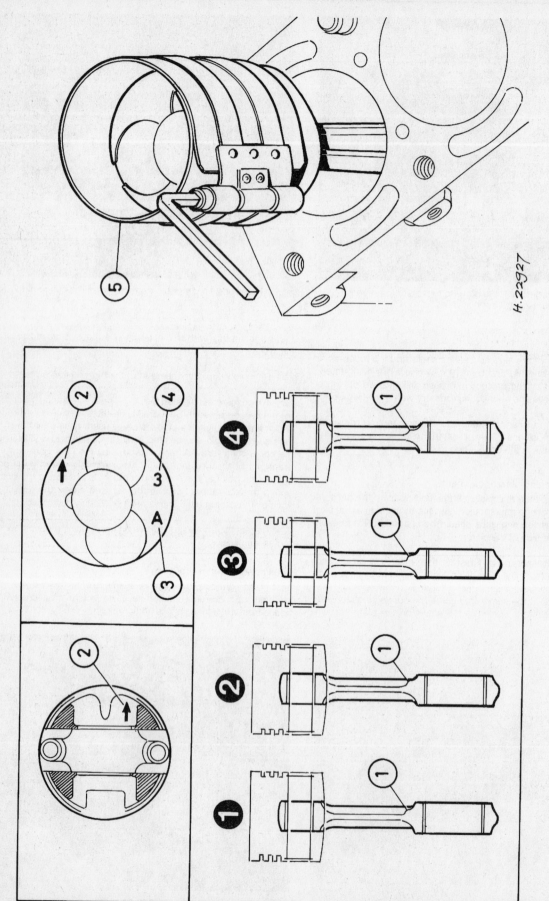

H.22927

Fig. 1.22 Refitting the pistons and connecting rods (Sec 24)

1 Boss on the connecting rods
2 Location of arrows on the pistons
3 Piston diameter grade
4 Piston height grade
5 Piston ring compressor

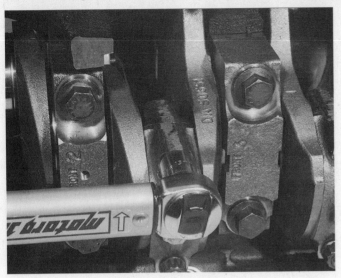

24.25 Tightening the big-end bearing cap nuts

24.26 Checking the piston protrusion above the cylinder block

25 Liberally lubricate the crankpin journals and big-end bearing shells, and refit the bearing caps once more, ensuring correct positioning as previously described. Tighten the bearing cap nuts to the specified torque, and turn the crankshaft each time to make sure that it is free before moving on to the next assembly (photo).

26 Using a dial test indicator, check that the piston protrusion above the joint face of the cylinder block is not in excess of the amount given in Specifications (photo).

27 If the engine is in the vehicle, carry out the work in the remaining paragraphs.

28 Refit the oil pick-up pipe and strainer, together with a new O-ring, and tighten the bolts.

29 Refit the sump with reference to Section 16.

30 Refit the cylinder head with reference to Section 13.

31 Lower the vehicle to the ground.

32 Fill the engine with the correct grade and quantity of oil.

33 Reconnect the battery earth (negative) lead.

34 Refill the cooling system with reference to Chapter 2.

25 Engine - removal method

The engine and gearbox assembly can be lifted from the vehicle as a complete unit, as described in the following Section, or the gearbox may first be removed, as described in Chapter 5. It is not possible to remove the engine on its own, owing to space restrictions in the engine compartment.

26 Engine and gearbox - removal and refitting

Removal

1 Remove the battery and battery tray (photos).

2 Drain the cooling system with reference to Chapter 2.

26.1A Removing the battery clamping bolt

26.1B Battery tray

26.10A Disconnecting the fuel return hose . . .

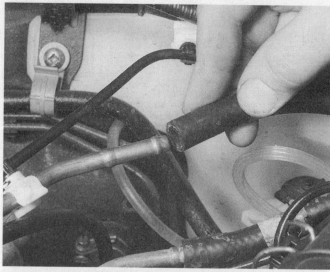

26.10B . . . and the fuel hose to the vapour separator

3   Remove the bonnet, and plug the washer pump outlet.

4   Disconnect the crankcase ventilation breather hose at the non-return valve.

5   Disconnect the brake vacuum pump inlet hose.

6   Remove the air cleaner assembly, complete with the hoses.

7   Disconnect the clutch cable from the release fork and support clip.

8   Unscrew the bolt securing the speedometer cable retaining plate to the gearbox. Withdraw the plate, and lift out the speedometer cable and pinion assembly. Place the cable to one side.

9   Disconnect the accelerator cable from the throttle lever and support plate, and place to one side.

10   Loosen the clips and disconnect the fuel inlet and return hoses, also the hose connecting the fuel lift pump outlet pipe to the vapour separator (photos).

11   Unscrew the nut and disconnect the battery positive cable from the starter motor.

12   Disconnect the engine harness connectors from the following components, and position the harness to one side (photo).

    (a) Starter motor.
    (b) Reversing light switch.
    (c) Oil pressure switch.
    (d) Temperature sensors.
    (e) Fuel injection pump.
    (f) No 4 heater glow plug.
    (g) Stop/start and automatic advance solenoids.
    (h) Alternator.
    (i) Throttle potentiometer and EGR valve (where fitted).
    (j) Fast idle solenoid.
    (k) Coolant thermistor.

13   Disconnect and plug the fuel inlet and spill return hoses.

14   Loosen the clips and remove the radiator top and bottom hoses completely.

26.12 Disconnecting the alternator wiring

15   Unscrew and remove the coolant expansion tank mounting bolts, and move the tank to one side.

16   Loosen the clips and disconnect the heater pipes from the water rail.

17   Disconnect the pipes from the fuel filter, and disconnect the wiring harness from the throttle potentiometer. The fuel filter head may also be removed by disconnecting the pipes and unbolting the unit from the cylinder head (photos).

18   Disconnect the pipes from the oil cooler, where fitted. Plug the pipes and apertures to prevent the ingress of dirt and foreign matter.

19   Apply the handbrake, then jack up the front of the vehicle and support on axle stands.

20   Drain the engine oil and gearbox oil into a suitable container. Refit and tighten the drain plugs on completion.

21   Remove the cover band, then tap out the roll pin securing the gearchange rod to the gearchange shaft. Unscrew the small bolt and

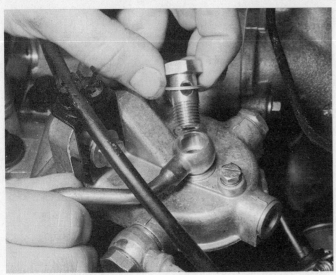

26.17A Disconnect the pipes . . .

26.17B . . . and remove the filter head

remove the dished washer, steady bar and flat washer from the gearbox case. Slide the gearchange rod rearwards and off the shaft.

22 Disconnect the exhaust downpipe from the exhaust manifold, and recover the flange gasket.

23 Remove both front roadwheels.

24 Remove the access panels from inside both front wheel arches.

25 Disconnect the steering tie-rod ends from the levers on the swivel hubs on both sides.

26 Unscrew and remove the bolts securing the front suspension struts to the swivel hubs. Note which way round the bolts are fitted.

27 Using a wide-bladed screwdriver or flat bar as a lever, release the driveshaft inner constant velocity joints from the final drive assembly. Once the joints have been released, tip the swivel hub outwards at the top, as far as possible without straining the brake hoses unduly. Do not remove the inner ends of the driveshafts out of the final drive completely, as this can be more easily done when the engine mountings have been removed.

28 Attach a suitable hoist to the engine. If available, attach lifting brackets to the studs of numbers 7 and 9 cylinder head bolts. Raise the hoist to just take the weight of the engine.

29 On pre-1989 non-Turbo models, unbolt the front snubber bracket from the gearbox adapter plate, and remove the front damper complete with its brackets. Refer to Section 23 if necessary.

30 Refer to Section 23, and remove the engine rear mounting complete with its bracket from the suspension crossmember and gearbox.

31 Remove the left-hand engine mounting from the gearbox and body, with reference to Section 23.

32 Remove the right-hand engine mounting with reference to Section 23.

33 Make a final check that everything attaching the engine and gearbox to the vehicle have been disconnected and moved well clear.

34 Move the gearbox end of the assembly forwards in the engine compartment, then lift the assembly approximately 50 mm so that the driveshafts may be disconnected from the final drive.

35 Raise the engine and gearbox assembly carefully, moving them slightly to clear any protrusions. When the unit has been raised sufficiently, draw the hoist forward to bring the engine and gearbox over the front body panel, then lower the assembly to the floor.

Refitting

36 Refitting is a reversal of the removal procedure, but note the following additional points.

   (a) *Refit all of the engine mounting bolts loosely, then tighten them in the following sequence - right-mounting and support bracket, left-hand mounting, rear mounting, and snubber bracket (where applicable). When all of the mountings have been tightened, centralise the snubber cup around the snubber rubber, and tighten the cup bolts (except Turbo and 1989 models onwards).*
   (b) *After refitting the driveshafts, check that the retaining circlips are fully engaged by attempting to pull out the driveshafts from the final drive by hand.*
   (c) *Refill the engine and gearbox with the recommended grade and quantity of oil. On Turbo models, disconnect the wiring from the stop solenoid, and spin the engine on the starter motor until the oil pressure warning light goes out before attempting to start the engine.*
   (d) *Refill the cooling system as described in Chapter 2.*

27 Engine - separation from gearbox

1 With the engine and gearbox removed from the vehicle, unscrew the starter motor retaining bolts and nuts, and remove the starter motor from the gearbox bellhousing.

2 Unscrew and remove the bolts and nuts securing the gearbox to the engine, noting the length of the bolts to ensure correct refitting.

3 Take the weight of the gearbox, and withdraw it directly off the engine adapter plate. If the location dowels are tight, it may be necessary to move the gearbox from side to side to start with, in order to free them.

28 Engine - dismantling (general)

1 It is best to mount the engine on a dismantling stand, but if this is

30.2A Removing the clutch disc and cover

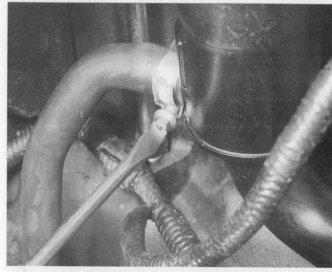

30.2B Disconnecting the crankcase ventilation hose from the top . . .

30.2C . . . and bottom of the oil filler tube

30.2D Unbolt the oil filler tube from the cylinder block . . .

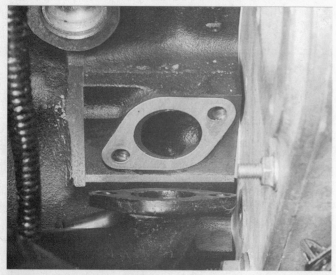

30.2E . . . and remove the gasket

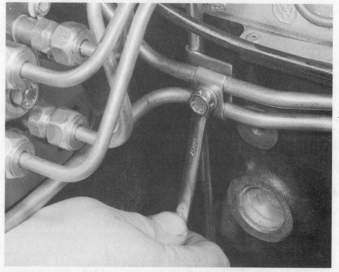

30.2F Unbolting the fuel supply and return pipes from the cylinder block

not available, then stand the engine on a strong bench, so as to be at a comfortable working height.

2   During the dismantling process, the greatest care should be taken to keep exposed parts free of dirt. As an aid to achieving this, it is a sound scheme to thoroughly clean down the outside of the engine, removing all traces of oil and congealed dirt.

3   When cleaning the engine, use paraffin or a good grease solvent. The latter compound will make the job easier, as, after the solvent has been applied and allowed to stand for a time, a vigorous jet of water will wash off the solvent and all the grease and filth. If the dirt is thick and deeply embedded, work the solvent into it with a stiff paint brush.

4   Finally wipe down the exterior of the engine with a rag, and only then when it is quite clean should the dismantling process begin. As the engine is stripped, clean each part in a bath of paraffin.

5   Never immerse parts with oilways in paraffin (eg the crankshaft); to clean, wipe down carefully with a paraffin-moistened rag. Oilways can be cleaned out with nylon pipe cleaners. If an air line is available, all parts can be blown dry and the oilways blown through as an added precaution.

6   Re-use of old engine gaskets is a false economy, and can give rise to oil and water leaks, if nothing worse. To avoid the possibility of trouble after the engine has been reassembled, always use new gaskets throughout.

7   Do not throw the old gaskets away, as it sometimes happens that an immediate replacement cannot be found, and the old gasket is then very useful as a template. Hang up the old gaskets on a suitable hook or nail as they are removed.

8   When purchasing engine gaskets, be particularly careful to state the chassis number of the vehicle. The standard Rover cylinder head gasket set includes a set of valve stem oil seals for early models, and if the engine being worked on is the later type, it will be necessary to obtain the later type of valve spring seats which include integral oil seals.

9   To strip the engine, it is best to work from the top down. The oil sump and suitable wood packing provides a firm base on which the engine can be supported in an upright position. When the stage where the sump must be removed is reached, the engine can be turned on its side, and all other work carried out with it in this position.

10   Whenever possible, refit nuts, bolts and washers finger-tight from wherever they were removed. This helps to avoid later loss and muddle. If they cannot be refitted, lay them out in such a fashion that it is clear from where they came.

29   Engine - dismantling procedure

1   If the engine has been removed from the car for major overhaul or repair, first read through all the information contained in the previous Section.

2   Prior to major dismantling, the engine ancillary components should be removed as described in Section 30.

3   Once the ancillary components have been removed, refer to the previous Sections of this Chapter for removal and refitting procedures, but ignore any references to work that needs to be carried out with the engine in the car.

4   With the engine dismantled as necessary, refer to the later Sections of this Chapter covering examination and renovation prior to refitting.

30   Ancillary components - removal and refitting

1   With the engine removed from the vehicle and thoroughly cleaned, the externally-mounted ancillary components should now be removed before any major dismantling begins.

2   Depending on the extent of the dismantling, the following items should be removed (photos).

   (a) *Brake vacuum pump (Chapter 7).*
   (b) *Alternator (Chapter 9).*
   (c) *Water pump (Chapter 2).*
   (d) *Fuel injection pump (Chapter 3) and mounting bracket (note the bracket has two dowels on its mounting bolts).*
   (e) *Fuel injectors (Chapter 3).*
   (f) *Glow plugs (Chapter 3).*
   (g) *Clutch unit (Chapter 4).*
   (h) *Oil filter (Section 2 of this Chapter).*
   (i) *Inlet/exhaust manifolds and where applicable, the turbocharger unit (Chapter 3).*
   (j) *Engine mounting brackets (Section 23 of this Chapter).*
   (k) *Oil filler tube.*
   (l) *Fuel supply and return pipes from the cylinder block, and the fuel filter head and bracket (Chapter 3).*

3   On completion of engine reassembly, the ancillary components should be refitted with reference to the applicable Chapters of this manual.

31   Crankshaft and main bearings - removal and refitting

Removal

1   The engine must be removed from the vehicle, and the gearbox separated from it. Also remove the sump, oil suction pipe, clutch, flywheel, crankshaft gear, and oil pump. It is not strictly necessary to remove the pistons, although in most cases the crankshaft removal will be carried out during a complete engine overhaul.

2   Progressively loosen the bolts securing the gearbox adapter plate to the rear of the cylinder block, then remove the bolts and withdraw the plate. Remove the gasket (photos).

31.2A Unscrew the securing bolts (arrowed) . . .

31.2B . . . and remove the gearbox adapter plate . . .

31.2C . . . and gasket

31.4 Checking the crankshaft endfloat using a dial gauge

3   If necessary, note the fitted depth of the crankshaft rear oil seal, then press it out of the adapter plate. Note that the oil seal is fitted flush with the outer surface at the factory, but may have been re-positioned during a subsequent overhaul, to avoid contact with an excessively-worn surface on the crankshaft.

4   Before the crankshaft is removed, check the endfloat using a dial gauge in contact with the end of the crankshaft (photo). Push the crankshaft fully one way, and then zero the gauge. Push the crankshaft fully the other way, and check the endfloat. The result can be compared with the specified amount, and will give an indication as to whether new thrustwashers are required. Note that the total endfloat must be divided by two to give the correct thickness of each thrustwasher, since new washers must be of equal thickness.

5   If a dial gauge is not available, feeler blades can be used. First push the crankshaft fully towards the flywheel end of the engine, then slip the feeler blade between the web of No 3 crankpin and the thrustwasher of the centre main bearing (photo).

6   Identification numbers are cast onto the base of Nos 2, 3 and 4 main bearing caps, together with the word "FRONT" indicating the timing end of the engine (photo). Nos 1 and 5 main bearing caps can only be fitted one way round, but mark them with a centre-punch if necessary, to avoid any confusion.

31.5 Checking the crankshaft endfloat using feeler blades

31.6 Identification on the main bearing caps (arrowed)

31.8A Unscrewing the main bearing cap bolts

31.8B Removing the centre main bearing cap

7   If the pistons are not being removed from the cylinder block, disconnect the big-end caps at this stage, with reference to Section 24.

8   Unscrew and remove the main bearing cap retaining bolts, and withdraw the caps, complete with lower bearing shells. Keep the shells with their respective bearing caps (photos).

9   Carefully lift the crankshaft from the crankcase (photo).

10   Remove the thrustwashers from each side of the centre main bearing, then remove the bearing shell upper halves from the crankcase. Place each shell with its respective bearing cap.

Refitting

Main bearing running clearance check

11   Clean the backs of the bearing shells and the bearing recesses in both the cylinder block and main bearing caps.

12   If the original main bearing shells are being re-used, these must be refitted to their original locations in the block and caps.

13   Press the bearing shells with oil holes and grooves into the recesses in the cylinder block, noting that the centre main bearing shell is wider than the others (photo). Make sure that the tags locate in the cut-outs.

31.8C Removing the rear main bearing cap

31.9 Lifting the crankshaft from the crankcase

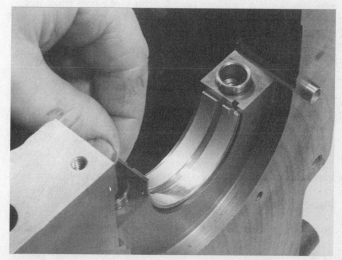

31.13 Fitting the main bearing shells into the cylinder block

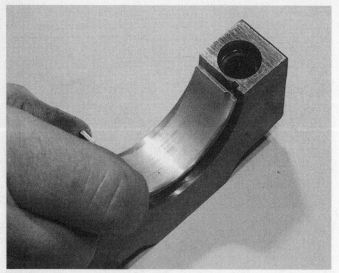

31.14A Fitting the main bearing shells into the caps

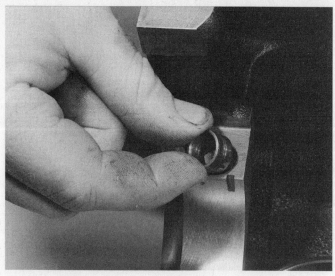

31.14B Inserting a main bearing cap location dowel in the block

14   Press the plain bearing shells into the caps, ensuring that the tag on the shell engages in the notch in the cap. Check that the location dowels are all fitted in the cylinder block (photos).

15   Using a little grease, stick the thrustwashers each side of the centre main bearing, both on the crankcase and cap, making sure that the oil grooves are facing outwards from the bearing.

16   Before the crankshaft can be permanently installed, the main bearing running clearance should be checked; this can be done in either of two ways. One method is to fit the main bearing caps to the cylinder block, with the bearing shells in place, before fitting the crankshaft. With the cap retaining bolts tightened to the specified torque, measure the internal diameter of each assembled pair of bearing shells using a vernier dial indicator or internal micrometer. If the diameter of each corresponding crankshaft journal is measured and then subtracted from the bearing internal diameter, the result will be the main bearing running clearance. The second (and more accurate) method is to use an American product known as Plastigage. This consists of a fine thread of perfectly-round plastic, which is compressed between the bearing cap and the journal. When the cap is removed, the plastic is deformed, and can be measured with a special card gauge supplied with the kit. The running clearance is determined from this gauge. Plastigage is sometimes difficult to obtain in the UK, but enquiries at one of the larger specialist chains of quality motor factors should produce the name of a stockist in your area. The procedure for using Plastigage is as follows.

17   With the upper main bearing shells in place, carefully lay the crankshaft in position. Do not use any lubricant; the crankshaft journals and bearing shells must be perfectly clean and dry.

18   Cut several pieces of the appropriate-size Plastigage (they should be slightly shorter than the width of the main bearings), and place one piece on each crankshaft journal axis.

19   With the bearing shells in position in the caps, fit the caps to their numbered or previously-noted locations. Take care not to disturb the Plastigage. Do not put any sealant on the front and rear main bearing caps at this stage.

20   Starting with the centre main bearing and working outward, tighten the main bearing cap bolts progressively to their specified torque setting. Don't rotate the crankshaft at any time during this operation.

21   Remove the bolts and carefully lift off the main bearing caps, keeping them in order. Don't disturb the Plastigage or rotate the crankshaft. If any of the bearing caps are difficult to remove, tap them from side-to-side with a soft-faced mallet.

22   Compare the width of the crushed Plastigage on each journal to the scale printed on the Plastigage envelope to obtain the main bearing running clearance.

23   If the clearance is not as specified, the bearing shells may be the wrong size (or excessively-worn, if the original shells are being re-used). Before deciding that different size shells are needed, make sure that no dirt or oil was trapped between the bearing shells and the caps or block when the clearance was measured. If the Plastigage was wider at one end than at the other, the journal may be tapered.

24   Carefully scrape away all traces of the Plastigage material from the crankshaft and bearing shells, using your fingernail or something similar which is unlikely to score the shells.

Final crankshaft refitting

25   Carefully lift the crankshaft out of the cylinder block once more.

26   Check that the thrustwashers are correctly fitted to each side of the centre main bearing.

27   Liberally lubricate each bearing shell in the cylinder block (photo), and lower the crankshaft into position.

28   Check that the horizontal sealing grooves of the front and rear main bearing caps are clean.

29   Lubricate the bearing shells in the main bearing caps, then fit all the caps in their numbered, or previously-noted, locations.

30   Lightly oil the threads of the main bearing cap bolts, then insert them and tighten progressively to the specified torque (photo).

31   Inject silicone sealant into the horizontal grooves in the front and rear main bearing caps until it oozes from the sides and top (photo). The grooves must be completely full of sealant.

32   Check that the crankshaft is free to turn, then check the endfloat as described earlier in this Section.

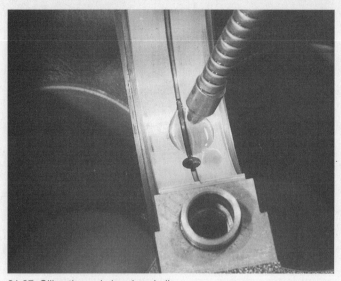

31.27 Oiling the main bearing shells

31.30 Tightening the main bearing cap bolts

33   If the pistons were not removed, the big-end caps may be refitted at this stage, with reference to Section 24.

34   Clean the mating faces of the gearbox adapter plate and rear of the cylinder block. Wipe clean the crankshaft flange.

35   Apply a 1.5 mm bead of silicone sealant to the adapter plate, as shown in Fig. 1.23. Also fill the cavities on the sides of the rear main bearing cap with sealant (photo).

36   Locate the adapter plate on the rear of the cylinder block, together with a new gasket, making sure that the location dowels are in position. Insert the retaining bolts, and tighten them in diagonal sequence to the specified torque.

37   Fit a new crankshaft rear oil seal with reference to Section 22.

38   If removed, refit the pistons with reference to Section 24.

39   Refit the oil pump, crankshaft gear and timing belt, flywheel, clutch, oil suction pipe, and sump with reference to the relevant Sections of this Chapter, then reconnect the gearbox and refit the engine/gearbox assembly to the vehicle.

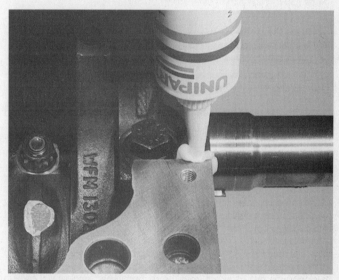

31.31 Injecting silicone sealant in the horizontal grooves in the front main bearing cap

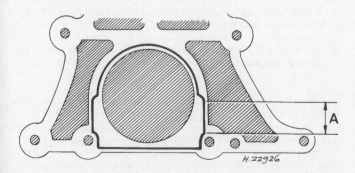

Fig. 1.23 Sealant bead position on the gearbox adapter plate (Sec 31)

A = 35 mm

31.35 Filling the cavities on the sides of the rear main bearing cap with sealant

33.2A Lay the length of Plastigage on the journal to be measured, parallel to the crankshaft centre-line

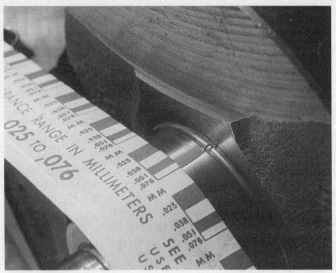

33.2B Check the width of the filament against the scale

32 Engine components - examination and renovation (general)

1   With the engine completely dismantled, all components should be cleaned and examined as detailed in the following Sections.

2   Most components can be cleaned with rags, a soft brush and paraffin, or some other solvent. Do not immerse parts with oilways in solvent, since it can be very difficult to remove, and if left, will contaminate the oil. Clean oilways and water channels with a piece of wire, and blow through with compressed air if available.

3   When faced with a borderline decision as to whether to renew a particular part, take into consideration the expected future life of the engine, and the degree of trouble or expense which will be caused if the part fails before the next overhaul.

4   If extensive overhauling is required, estimate the likely cost, and compare it with the cost of a complete reconditioned engine. The difference may not be great, and the reconditioned engine will have a guarantee.

33 Crankshaft - examination and renovation

1   Examine the bearing surface of the crankshaft for scratches or scoring and, using a micrometer, check each journal and crankpin for ovality. Where the ovality or wear is found to be in excess of 0.0254 mm (0.001 in), the crankshaft will have to be reground, and undersize bearings fitted.

2   An accurate method of determining bearing wear is by the use of Plastigage (refer to Section 31 as well). The crankshaft is located in the main bearings (and big-end bearings if necessary), and the Plastigage filament located across the journal, which must be dry. The cap is then fitted, and the bolts/nuts tightened to the specified torque. On removal of the cap, the width of the filament is checked against a scale which shows the bearing running clearance. The clearance can then be compared with that given in the Specifications (photos).

3   Check the sealing surfaces of the front and rear oil seals. It is normally possible to reposition the new oil seal so that it contacts an unworn area on the crankshaft, but if the surface is worn excessively, it may be reduced by 0.25 mm to provide a new surface.

4   Crankshaft regrinding should be carried out by a suitable engineering works, who will normally supply the matching undersize main and big-end shell bearings.

5   Note that undersize bearings may already have been fitted, either in production or by a previous repairer. Check the markings on the backs of the old bearing shells, and if in doubt, take them along when buying new ones.

6   If the crankshaft endfloat is more than the maximum specified amount, new thrustwashers should be fitted to the centre main bearing. These are usually supplied together with the main and big-end bearings on a reground crankshaft.

7   Before taking the crankshaft for regrinding, also check the cylinder bores and pistons, as it may be advantageous to have the whole engine reconditioned together.

34 Crankshaft main and big-end bearing shells - examination and renovation

1   With careful servicing and regular oil and filter changes, bearings will last for a very long time, but they can still fail for unforeseen reasons. With big-end bearings the indication is a regular rhythmic knocking from the crankcase. The frequency depends on engine speed, and is particularly noticeable when the engine is under load. This symptom is accompanied by a fall in oil pressure, although this is not normally noticeable unless an oil pressure gauge is fitted. Main bearing failure is usually indicated by serious vibration, particularly at higher engine revolutions, accompanied by a more significant drop in oil pressure and a "rumbling" noise.

2   Bearing shells in good condition have bearing surfaces with a smooth, even matt silver/grey colour all over. Worn bearings will show patches of a different colour when the bearing metal has worn away and exposed the underlay. Damaged bearings will be pitted or scored. It is always well worthwhile fitting new shells, as their cost is relatively low. If the crankshaft is in good condition, it is merely a question of obtaining another set of standard size shells. A reground crankshaft will need new bearing shells as a matter of course.

3   Squirt clean engine oil through the crankshaft oilways, to ensure that they are clear, and clean of any machining swarf.

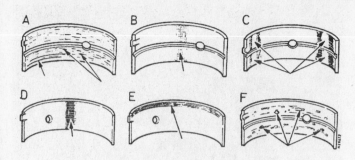

Fig. 1.24 Typical bearing shell failures (Sec 34)

A   *Scratched by dirt; dirt embedded into bearing material*
B   *Lack of oil; overlay wiped out*
C   *Improper seating; bright (polished) sections*
D   *Tapered journal; overlay gone from entire surface*
E   *Radius ride*
F   *Fatigue failure; craters or pockets*

35.7A Oil jet nozzle fitted to the base of each cylinder bore on Turbo models

35 Cylinder block and crankcase - examination and renovation

1   A new cylinder is perfectly round, and the walls parallel throughout its length. The action of the piston tends to wear the walls at right-angles to the gudgeon pin, due to side thrust. This wear takes place principally on that section of the cylinder swept by the piston rings.

2   It is possible to get an indication of bore wear by removing the cylinder head with the engine still in the vehicle. With the piston down in the bore, first signs of wear can be seen and felt just below the top of the bore where the top piston ring reaches, and there will be a noticeable lip. If there is no lip, it is fairly reasonable to expect that bore wear is not severe, and any lack of compression or excessive oil consumption is due to worn or broken piston rings or pistons (see the next Section).

3   If it is possible to obtain a bore-measuring micrometer, measure the bore in the thrust plane below the lip, and again at the bottom of the cylinder in the same plane. If the difference is greater than 0.015 mm, it will necessary to have the cylinders rebored and oversize pistons fitted. Again, this work must be carried out by a specialist firm, who will decide how much metal must be ground off the cylinder bores, and will supply a set of oversize pistons and piston rings to suit.

4   If new standard size pistons and/or rings are being fitted and the cylinders have not been rebored, it is essential to slightly roughen the hard glaze on the sides of the bores with fine emery, so the new piston rings will have a chance to bed-in properly. The top piston ring will also have to be of the "stepped" type, to avoid fouling the unworn ridge at the top of the cylinder bore.

5   Examine the crankcase for cracks and leaking core plugs. To renew a core plug, drill a hole in its centre, and tap a thread in it. Screw in a bolt and, using a distance piece, tighten the bolt and extract the core plug. When fitting the new plug, smear its outer edge with gasket cement.

6   Squirt clean engine oil through the various oil galleries, using a pump-action oil gun, to ensure that the oilways are clear. Also check that the coolant galleries are clear.

7   Turbo models have oil jet nozzles fitted at the base of each cylinder bore, and their function is to cool the underside of the pistons by spraying them with oil (photos). Ensure that the nozzles are clean and, if removed, renew their retaining bolt washers. If there is any possibility

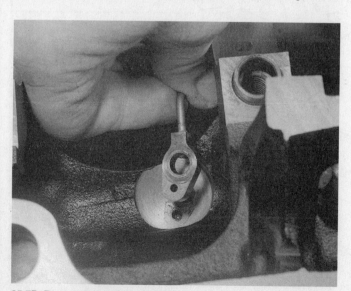

35.7B Removing the oil jet nozzles

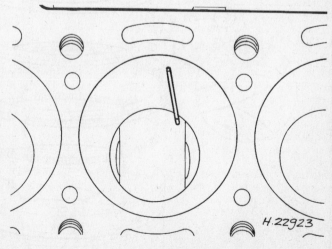

Fig. 1.25 1.5 mm alignment rod inserted in the piston cooling jet (Sec 35)

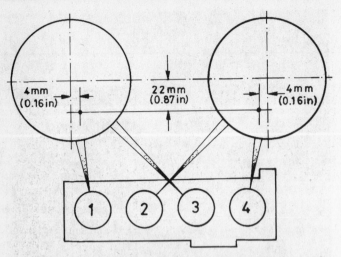

Fig. 1.26 Points at which the piston cooling jet alignment rod should extend out of the top of the cylinder (Sec 35)

36.1 Sliding the gudgeon pin from the piston and connecting rod

of the nozzles having been misaligned, they can be checked for alignment as follows. Obtain a perfectly-straight length of 1.5 mm diameter metal rod, and insert it into the nozzles in turn so that it extends out of the top of the cylinder bore. The top of the rod must be within 5.00 mm of the points shown in Fig. 1.24. If this is not the case, the nozzles should be carefully bent.

36 Pistons/connecting rod assemblies - examination and renovation

1   Using a pair of circlip pliers, remove the circlips from the piston, and slide out the gudgeon pin from the piston and connecting rod small-end bearing (photo). If the gudgeon pin is a tight fit, immerse the piston in hot water. The gudgeon pin should then slide out quite easily. Mark the connecting rod in relation to the piston, so that it may be refit-

ted in exactly the same way. Where the pistons have markings on them, note their relationship with any markings or lugs on the connecting rods. If the assembly is held with the boss on the connecting rod uppermost, note that the glow plug cut-out on the piston crown is on the right-hand side.

2   To remove the piston rings, slide them carefully over the top of the piston, taking care not to scratch the aluminium alloy of the piston. Never slide them off the bottom of the piston skirt. It is very easy to break piston rings if they are pulled off roughly, so this operation should be done with extreme caution. It is helpful to use an old feeler gauge to facilitate their removal, as follows.

3   Lift one end of the piston ring to be removed out of its groove, and insert the end of the feeler gauge under it (photo).

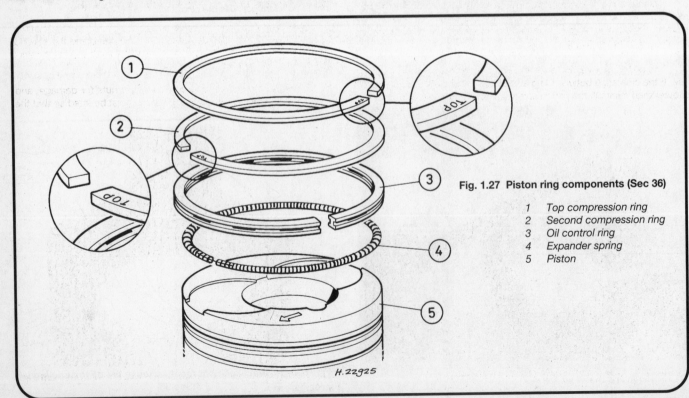

Fig. 1.27 Piston ring components (Sec 36)

1   Top compression ring
2   Second compression ring
3   Oil control ring
4   Expander spring
5   Piston

H.22925

36.3 Removing a piston ring using an old feeler gauge

36.5 Checking the piston ring gap

4   Turn the feeler gauge slowly round the piston; as the ring comes out of its groove, it rests on the land above. It can then be eased off the piston, with the feeler gauge stopping it from slipping into any empty grooves, if it is any but the top piston ring that is being removed. The oil control ring may be removed in the same manner, but care must be taken not to damage the expander spring, which must be removed after the main ring has been removed.

5   Piston ring wear can be checked by first removing the rings from the pistons as described previously. Place each ring in the cylinder bores individually from the top, and push them down the bores approximately 38 mm using the head of a piston, so that they rest square in the cylinder. Then measure the gap at the ends of the rings with a feeler gauge (photo). If the gap exceeds the figures given in the Specifications, the rings will need renewal.

6   Clean out the piston ring grooves using a piece of old piston ring as a scraper. Be careful not to scratch the aluminium surface of the pistons. *Protect your fingers - piston ring edges are sharp.* Also probe the groove oil return holes.

7   The piston grooves in which the rings locate become enlarged in use. If the clearance between ring and piston in the piston ring groove is other than minimal, the piston and rings must be renewed (photo).

8   Examine the connecting rods carefully. They are not subject to wear, but in extreme cases, such as partial engine seizure, they could be distorted. Such conditions may be visually apparent, but if doubt exists they should be renewed, or checked for alignment by engine reconditioning specialists. If new gudgeon pin bushes are required, this job should also be entrusted to a specialist, as the new bushes have to be reamed to fit the gudgeon pins.

9   If new pistons are being fitted, they will be supplied with the rings already assembled. If new rings are to be fitted to existing pistons, follow the manufacturer's fitting instructions supplied with the rings. Note that when fitting new standard size pistons and/or rings to partially-worn cylinders, the top ring will need to be of a "stepped" type, to avoid fouling the unworn ridge at the top of the cylinder bore. When fitting the oil control ring, make sure that the locating pin is fully entered in the spring, and position the outer ring gap 180° to the spring joint. The outer ring gap should be on the thrust side of the piston.

10   New Rover compression rings are colour-coded to identify their fitted position - the top ring is marked with red paint, and the second ring with green paint. With the piston held at eye level, the paint marks must be fitted to the left of the ring gaps.

11   Check the big-end bearing cap bolts and nuts for damage, and renew them if necessary. Note that the bolts must be fitted so that the

36.7 Checking the piston ring-to-groove clearance

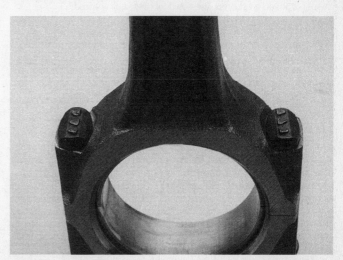

36.11 The big-end bearing cap bolt arrows must point away from the connecting rod

arrow or manufacturer's identification points away from the connecting rod (photo).

12   Refitting the piston to the connecting rod is the reverse sequence to removal, ensuring that the two components are refitted the same way as noted during dismantling.

37 Camshaft - examination and renovation

1   Examine the camshaft for signs of wear and damage, especially on the cam lobes themselves.

2   The camshaft bearing surfaces in the cylinder head and camshaft cover should be examined for signs of scoring and pitting. If they are worn excessively, it will be necessary to renew the cylinder head complete, together with a new camshaft.

38 Tappets - examination and renovation

1   Examine the tappets and shims for excessive wear, and make sure that the tappets are free to slide and rotate in their bores.

2   The faces of the tappets which bear on the camshaft lobes should show no signs of pitting, scoring or other forms of wear. Thoroughly clean them out, removing all traces of sludge. It is most unlikely that the sides of the tappets will prove worn, but if they are a very loose fit in their bores and can be rocked readily, then they should be renewed.

39 Timing belt and gears - examination and renovation

1   Examine the timing belt for cracks, fraying, and damage to the teeth. Pay particular attention to the roots of the teeth. If any damage is evident, or if the belt is contaminated with oil, it must be renewed (and any oil leak rectified).

2   Examine the timing gears for any damage to their teeth.

40 Flywheel - examination and renovation

1   Examine the clutch disc mating surface of the flywheel. If this is deeply grooved or scored, the flywheel must be renewed.

2   If the teeth on the starter ring gear are badly worn, then it will be necessary to remove the ring gear. The old ring can be removed from the flywheel by cutting a notch between two teeth with a hacksaw, and then splitting it with a cold chisel. Take suitable precautions to avoid flying fragments, paying particular attention to protection of your eyes. Note which way round the ring gear is fitted.

3   To fit a new ring gear requires heating the ring to 400°F (204°C), and it is recommended that this work is carried out by a Rover dealer or engineering works. The following procedure is given for those wishing to do this work themselves. The temperature can be determined by polishing four equally spaced sections on the ring gear, laying it on a suitable heat-resistant surface (such as fire bricks) and heating it evenly with a blow torch or lamp until the polished areas turn a light yellow tinge. Alternatively, it is possible to obtain temperature-sensitive crayons which change colour when heated (obtain the crayons from a motor accessory shop). *Do not overheat,* or the hardwearing properties will be lost. When hot enough, place the gear in position quickly, tapping it home if necessary, and let it cool naturally without quenching in any way.

41 Sump - examination

1   Wash out the oil sump, and wipe dry.

2   Inspect the exterior for signs of damage. If evident, a new sump must be obtained.

3   To ensure an oil-tight joint, when refitting, scrape away all traces of the old gasket from the sump and cylinder block mating faces.

42 Engine - reassembly (general)

1   To ensure maximum life with minimum trouble from a rebuilt engine, not only must everything be correctly assembled, but everything must be spotlessly-clean, all the oilways must be clear, locking washers and spring washers must always be fitted where indicated, and all bearing and other working surfaces must be thoroughly lubricated during assembly.

2   Before assembly begins, renew any bolts or studs if their threads are in any way damaged.

3   In addition to the normal range of good-quality socket spanners and general tools which are essential, the following must be available before assembly begins.

   (a) *Complete set of new gaskets and oil seals.*
   (b) *Supply of clean rag.*
   (c) *Clean oil can full of engine oil.*
   (d) *Torque wrenches.*
   (e) *All new parts as necessary.*
   (f) *Tube of silicone sealant.*

43 Engine - initial start-up after major overhaul or repair

1   With the engine refitted to the car, make a visual check to see that everything has been reconnected, and that no loose rags or tools have been left within the engine compartment.

2   Make sure that the battery is fully charged, and that all coolant and lubricants are fully replenished.

3   On Turbo models, disconnect the wiring from the stop solenoid, and spin the engine on the starter motor until the low oil pressure warning light goes out. Reconnect the wiring afterwards.

4   Prime the fuel system as described in Chapter 3, then start the engine.

5   As the engine fires and runs, keep it going at a fast idle only (no faster), and allow it to reach normal working temperature.

6   As the engine warms up, there will be odd smells and some smoke from parts getting hot and burning off oil deposits. The signs to look for are leaks of water or oil, which will be obvious if serious. Check also the exhaust pipe and manifold connections, as these do not always find their exact gas-tight position until the heat and vibration have acted on them - if necessary tighten them further with the engine stopped.

7   When normal operating temperature has been reached, stop the engine, and adjust the engine idle speed as described in Chapter 3.

8   Stop the engine, and wait a few minutes to see if any coolant or lubricant is dripping out when the engine is stationary.

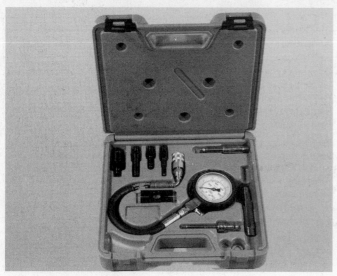

44.1A Compression tester set

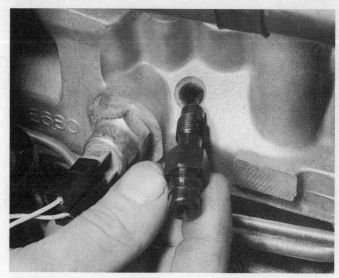

44.1B Fitting the compression tester adapter to a glow plug hole

9   Road test the vehicle to check that the engine is giving the necessary smoothness and power. Do not race the engine - if new bearings and/or pistons have been fitted, it should be treated as a new engine, and run-in at a reduced speed for the first 1000 miles.

44 Compression test - description and interpretation

1   A compression test involves measuring the pressure developed in each cylinder when the engine is being cranked by the starter motor. It can be a valuable aid in fault diagnosis. A special compression tester will be needed, with an adapter to connect it to an injector hole (or glow plug hole) (photos). Rather than buy such a tester, it may be cheaper to let a Rover dealer or other specialist do the test.

2   The engine must be at normal operating temperature, the battery well-charged, and the valve clearances correct.

3   Switch off the engine, then clean the area around the injectors (or glow plugs), and remove them with reference to Chapter 3.

4   Disconnect the wiring from the stop/start solenoid.

5   Screw in the adapter and compression tester into one of the holes. Crank the engine on the starter, and record the maximum pressure indicated on the tester (photo).

6   Repeat the operations on the other three cylinders, and record the pressures developed.

7   Compare the pressures with those given in the Specifications.

8   A low reading in one cylinder may be due to burnt or poorly-seating valves, piston/bore wear, a blown head gasket or a cracked head. To check for worn pistons/bores, the compression test can be repeated after injecting a teaspoonful of clean engine oil into each cylinder. If this improves the compression temporarily, worn pistons or

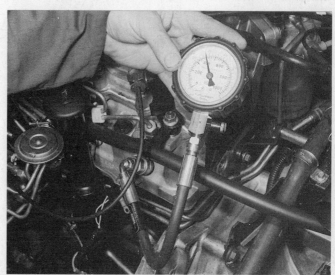

44.5 Using the compression tester

bores are indicated. **Do not** inject more than a teaspoonful of oil for the test.

9   If the compressions are low with or without injecting the oil, then the valves and seats may be in poor condition, or the cylinder head gasket may be blown.

10   A low reading obtained for two adjacent cylinders suggests strongly that the head gasket has blown between them.

11   Further tests (eg cooling system pressure tests) may be needed to determine the likely causes of poor compression.

12   When the tests are complete, refit the injectors (or glow plugs) with reference to Chapter 3, and reconnect the wiring to the stop/start solenoid.

45 Fault diagnosis - engine

Symptom	Reason(s)
Engine will not turn over when attempting to start	Battery discharged Loose battery connections Faulty starter motor or solenoid Earth strap broken or disconnected Fault in starting circuit wiring
Engine turns over but will not start	Low cranking speed Poor compression No fuel in tank Air in fuel system Major mechanical failure Valve clearances incorrect Fuel system fault
Low cranking speed	Battery discharged Inadequate battery capacity Incorrect grade of oil Starter motor fault
Engine lacks power	Accelerator linkage not moving through full travel (cable slack or pedal obstructed) Air cleaner dirty Valve timing incorrect Valve clearances incorrect Poor compression Fuel system fault
Low oil pressure	Oil level too low Oil grade or quality incorrect Oil filter clogged Oil pump pick-up strainer clogged Faulty or worn oil pump Oil pressure relief valve sticking Crankshaft bearings worn
High oil pressure	Oil grade or quality incorrect Oil pressure relief valve stuck shut
Engine knocks	Injector faulty Fuel injection pump timing incorrect Air in fuel system Valve springs weak or broken Valve clearances incorrect Piston rings broken or worn Pistons and/or bores worn Crankshaft bearings worn or damaged Small-end bearings worn Camshaft worn
Crankcase pressure excessive (oil being blown out)	Blockage in crankcase ventilation system Piston rings broken or sticking Pistons or bores worn Cylinder head gasket blown

Chapter 2 Cooling system

Contents

Specifications

System type .... Pressurised, with front-mounted radiator and electric cooling fan

Coolant

Type/specification .... Ethylene glycol-based antifreeze with non-phosphate corrosion
inhibitors, suitable for mixed-metal engines, containing no methanol
and meeting specifications BS6580 and BS5117 (Duckhams Universal
Antifreeze and Summer Coolant)

Capacity .... 7.5 litres
Recommended concentration of antifreeze .... 50% by volume

Antifreeze properties:	**Begins freezing**	**Frozen solid**
33% antifreeze by volume	-19°C	-36°C
50% antifreeze by volume	-36°C	-48°C

Thermostat

Type	Wax
Opening temperature	88°C

Expansion tank cap pressure .... 1.0 bar

Drivebelt deflection .... 7.0 to 12.0 mm, midway between crankshaft and alternator pulleys, under load of 44 N (10 lbf)

Torque wrench settings

	Nm	lbf ft
Temperature sender unit	10	7
Water pump mounting bolts	22	16
Water pump pulley-to-flange bolts	9	6

1 General description

The cooling system is of the pressurised type. The system consists of the radiator, water pump, thermostat, electric cooling fan, expansion tank, and associated hoses. The impeller-type water pump is mounted on the timing end of the engine and, in conjunction with the alternator, is belt-driven from the crankshaft pulley.

The system functions as follows. Cold coolant in the bottom of the radiator left-hand tank passes through the hose to the water pump, where it is pumped around the cylinder block and head passages. After cooling the cylinder bores, combustion surfaces and valve seats, the coolant reaches the underside of the thermostat (which is initially closed), and is diverted through the heater inlet hose to the heater. After passing through the heater, the coolant travels through the water jacket of the inlet manifold before returning to the water pump inlet

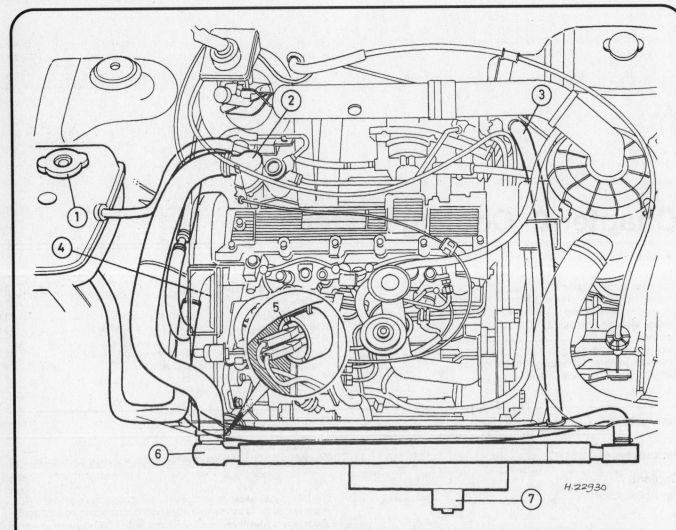

Fig. 2.1 Cooling system components for non-Turbo models and all models manufactured before November 1988 (Sec 1)

1 Expansion tank filler cap	4 Water pump	6 Radiator
2 Thermostat housing	5 Cooling fan thermostatic	7 Electric cooling fan and
3 Heater hose	switch	motor

Fig. 2.2 Coolant level indicator post inside the expansion tank (Sec 2)

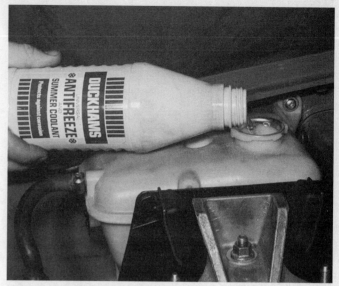

2.5 Topping-up the cooling system

hose. When the engine is cold, the thermostat remains closed and the coolant only circulates around the engine, heater and inlet manifold. When the coolant reaches a predetermined temperature, the thermostat opens and the coolant passes through the top hose to the radiator right-hand tank. As the coolant circulates around the radiator, it is cooled by the inrush of air when the vehicle is in forward motion. Air flow is supplemented by the action of the electric cooling fan when necessary. Upon reaching the left-hand side of the radiator, the coolant is now cooled and the cycle is repeated.

When the engine is at normal temperature, the coolant expands, and some of it is displaced into the expansion tank. This coolant collects in the tank, and is returned to the radiator when the system cools.

The electric cooling fan mounted in front of the radiator is controlled by a thermostatic switch located in the radiator right-hand side tank. At a predetermined coolant temperature the switch contacts close, thus actuating the fan.

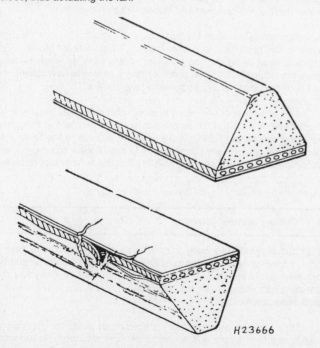

Fig. 2.3 Check the V-type drivebelt for signs of wear like these - if the belt looks worn, renew it (Sec 2)

2 Routine maintenance

Carry out the following procedures at the intervals given in the "Routine maintenance" Section at the start of this manual.

Check the coolant level

1   When checking the level, take great care to avoid scalding if the system is hot. Place a thick cloth over the expansion tank cap, and turn the cap anti-clockwise slowly to the first stop. Wait for any steam to be released, then depress the cap, turn it further anti-clockwise and remove it completely.

2   Look into the expansion tank and check that the coolant just covers the indicator post.

3   Topping-up should only be necessary at very infrequent intervals. If this is not the case and frequent topping-up is required, it is likely there is a leak in the system.

4   With the cap removed, clean it thoroughly with a rag. Also clean the filler neck on the tank. The presence of rust or corrosion in the filler neck indicates that the coolant should be changed.

5   If topping-up is required, add antifreeze/corrosion inhibitor of the correct type and concentration (photo), then refit and tighten the expansion tank cap.

Check the drivebelt condition and tension

6   Examine the full length of the drivebelt for cracks and deterioration. It will be necessary to turn the engine in order that the belt can be inspected thoroughly. Twist the belt between the pulleys so that both sides can be viewed. Also check for fraying, and glazing (which gives the belt a shiny appearance). Check the pulleys for nicks, cracks, distortion and corrosion.

7   Refer to Section 13 of this Chapter to check the tension.

Renew the coolant

8   Refer to Sections 4, 5 and 6 of this Chapter.

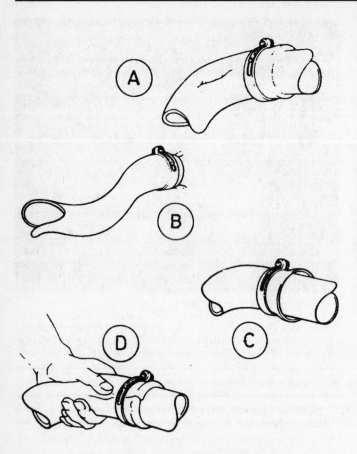

Fig. 2.4 Coolant hose inspection (Sec 2)

A   *Check hose for chafed or burned areas; these may lead to sudden and costly failure.*
B   *A soft hose indicates inside deterioration, leading to contamination of the cooling system and clogging of the radiator.*
C   *A hardened hose can fail at any time; tightening the clamps will not seal the joint or prevent leaks.*
D   *A swollen hose or one with oil-soaked ends indicates contamination from oil or grease. Cracks and breaks can be easily seen by squeezing the hose.*

Check all coolant hoses and connections

9   Check all hoses and joint faces for any staining, or actual wetness, and rectify if necessary. If no leaks can be found, yet the coolant level drops, it is advisable to have the system pressure-tested, as the leak could possibly be internal. It is a good idea to keep a check on the engine oil level, as a serious internal leak can often cause the oil level in the sump to rise, thus confirming suspicions.

10   Carefully inspect all hoses, hose clips and visible joint gaskets for cracks, corrosion, deterioration or leakage. Renew any hoses and clips that are suspect, and also renew any gaskets, if necessary.

3   Pressure test - description and interpretation

1   In cases where leakage is difficult to trace, or some other malfunction of the cooling system is suspected, a pressure test can prove helpful. The test involves pressurising the system by means of a hand pump and an adapter which is fitted to the expansion tank in place of the filler cap. The resourceful home mechanic may be able to impro-

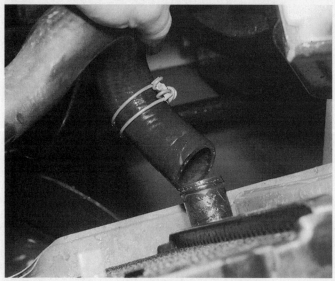

4.3 Disconnecting the radiator bottom hose

vise something from (eg) a spare filler cap and tyre inflation equipment; alternatively, the test can be performed by a Rover dealer or most other garages.

2   Bring the engine to normal operating temperature, then switch it off.

3   Place a thick cloth over the expansion tank cap. Turn the cap anti-clockwise to the first stop, and wait for any pressure to be released. Depress the cap and turn it further anti-clockwise to remove it. Take care to avoid scalding.

4   Connect the pressure test equipment to the expansion tank filler hole. Apply the specified test pressure, and check that it is held for at least ten seconds. If the pressure drops within ten seconds, check for leaks. Release the pressure and disconnect the equipment.

5   Besides leaks from hoses, pressure can also be lost through leaks in the radiator and heater matrix. A blown head gasket, or a cracked head or block, can give rise to "invisible" leakage. Usually there are other clues to this condition, such as coolant contamination of the oil or combustion gases entering the coolant.

6   The condition of the filler/pressure relief valve cap must not be overlooked. Normally, it is tested with similar equipment to that used for the pressure test. The release pressure is given in the Specifications, and is also usually stamped on the cap. Renew the cap if it will not hold the specified pressure, or if its condition is otherwise doubtful.

4   Cooling system - draining

1   It is preferable to drain the cooling system when the engine is cold. If the engine is hot, the pressure in the cooling system must be released before attempting to drain the system. Place a cloth over the pressure cap of the expansion tank, and turn the cap anti-clockwise until it reaches its stop.

2   Wait until the pressure has escaped, then press the cap downwards and turn it further in an anti-clockwise direction. Release the downward pressure on the cap very slowly and, after making sure that all the pressure in the system has been released, remove the cap.

3   Place a suitable container beneath the left-hand side of the radiator. Slacken the hose clip and carefully ease the bottom hose off the radiator outlet (photo). Allow the coolant to drain into the container.

4   If the cooling system is to be flushed after draining, refer to the next Section; otherwise, refit the bottom hose, then fill the system as described in Section 6.

5   Cooling system - flushing

1   After some time, the radiator and engine waterways may become restricted or even blocked with scale or sediment, which reduces the efficiency of the cooling system. When this occurs, the coolant will appear rusty and dark in colour, and the system should then be flushed. Begin by draining the cooling system as described in Section 4.

2   Disconnect the top hose at the thermostat housing (pre-1989 non-Turbo models), or water pump (Turbo and 1989 models onwards) and leave the bottom hose disconnected at the radiator outlet.

3   Insert a garden hose into the top hose, and allow water to circulate through the radiator until it runs clear from the outlet. Also insert the hose in the expansion tank, and let the water run until it emerges clear from the bottom hose.

4   Disconnect the heater inlet hose at the thermostat housing or heater rail. Insert the hose, and allow water to circulate through the heater matrix and manifold, and out through the bottom hose, until clear.

5   In severe cases of contamination, the system should be reverse-flushed. To do this, remove the radiator as described in Section 8, invert it, and insert the garden hose in the bottom outlet. Continue flushing until clear water runs from the top hose outlet.

6   The engine should also be flushed. To do this, remove the thermostat as described in Section 9, and insert the hose into the cylinder head. Flush the system until clear water runs from the bottom hose.

7   The use of chemical cleaners should only be necessary as a last resort. Regular renewal of the coolant should prevent further contamination of the system.

6   Cooling system - filling

1   If the system has been flushed out, refit any hoses or components that were removed for this purpose.

2   Fill the system through the expansion tank with the appropriate mixture of water and antifreeze (see Section 7) until the tank is half-full. Do not refit the expansion tank cap at this stage.

3   Start the engine, and run it at a fast idle for approximately one minute. During this time, compress the top and bottom hoses several times to release any air pockets in the system.

4   Stop the engine, top-up the expansion tank to the indicated level, then refit the filler cap.

7   Antifreeze mixture - general

Note: *Antifreeze is toxic, and must not be allowed to contact the skin.*

Precautions must also be taken to prevent the mixture contacting the bodywork and clothing.

1   The antifreeze mixture (coolant) should be renewed at the intervals specified in "Routine maintenance" at the start of this manual. This is necessary not only to maintain the antifreeze properties, but mostly to prevent corrosion which would otherwise occur as the properties of the inhibitors become progressively less effective.

2   Always use the antifreeze recommended in the Specifications.

3   Before adding the antifreeze, the cooling system should be completely drained and flushed, and all hoses checked for condition and security.

4   The quantity of antifreeze and levels of protection are indicated in the Specifications.

5   After filling with antifreeze, a label should be attached to the radiator, stating the type and concentration of antifreeze used and the date installed. Any subsequent topping-up should be made with the same type and concentration of antifreeze.

6   Do not use engine antifreeze in the windscreen/tailgate washer system, as it will cause damage to the vehicle paintwork. A screen-wash additive such as Turtle Wax High Tech Screen Wash should be added to the washer system, in the recommended quantities.

8   Radiator - removal, inspection, cleaning and refitting

Note: *If the reason for removing the radiator is coolant leakage, note that minor leaks can be cured without removing the radiator, by using a radiator sealer such as Holts Radweld.*

Removal

1   Disconnect the battery earth (negative) lead, and remove the inlet air ducting.

2   Drain the cooling system as described in Section 4. Leave the bottom radiator hose disconnected.

3   Unscrew the upper screws, and lift the radiator grille from the lower rubber grommets (photos).

8.3A Remove the screws . . .

8.3B . . . and lift the radiator grille from the lower rubber grommets

8.4 Disconnecting the radiator top hose

4   Loosen the retaining clip and detach the radiator top hose (photo).

5   Detach the electrical connectors from the radiator cooling fan thermostatic switch (photo).

6   Disconnect the cooling fan motor wiring multi-plug (photo).

7   Unscrew and remove the three bolts each side securing the front body crossmember panel in position. Where applicable, release the air cleaner cold air intake hose from the panel, then withdraw the panel and place it to one side, leaving the bonnet release cable still attached. Note that the upper mounting pegs on the radiator are located in the rubber grommets in the panel. If preferred, the panel may be completely removed by unbolting the locking catch and disconnecting the bonnet release cable and spring (photos).

8   Where applicable, release the radiator upper retaining clips and the two plastic panel support clips from the left-hand side of the radiator.

9   Carefully lift the radiator from the lower mounting rubber grommets (photos).

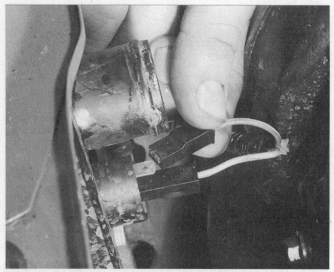

8.5 Disconnecting the wiring from the radiator cooling fan thermostatic switch

8.6 Disconnecting the cooling fan motor wiring multi-plug

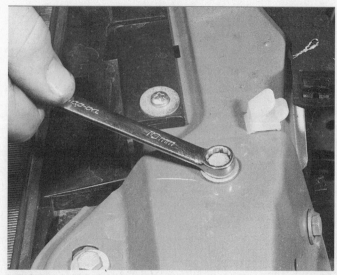

8.7A Unscrew the bolts . . .

8.7B . . . lift the crossmember from the radiator . . .

8.7C . . . then unbolt the bonnet locking catch . . .

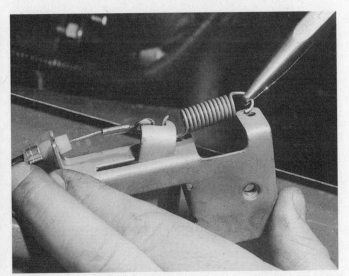

8.7D . . . unhook the return spring . . .

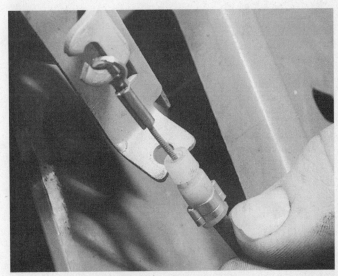

8.7E . . . and disconnect the bonnet release cable

8.9A Removing the radiator

8.9B Lifting the radiator from the lower mounting rubber grommets

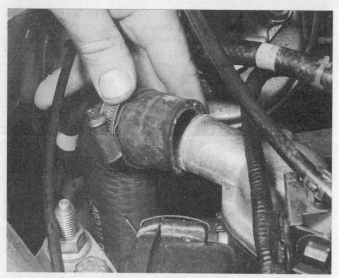

9.2 Disconnecting the hose from the thermostat water outlet elbow

9.3A Lift off the water outlet elbow . . .

Inspection and cleaning

10   If the radiator has been removed because of suspected blockage, reverse-flush it as described in Section 5.

11   Clean dirt and debris from the radiator fins, using an air jet or water and a soft brush. Be careful not to damage the fins, or cut your fingers.

12   A radiator specialist can perform a "flow test" on the radiator, to establish whether an internal blockage exists.

13   A leaking radiator must be referred to a specialist for permanent repair. Do not attempt to weld or solder a leaking radiator, as damage may result.

Refitting

14   Refitting is a reversal of the removal procedure, but make sure that the lower mounting lugs engage in the rubber grommets. Fill the cooling system as described in Section 6.

9   Thermostat - removal, testing and refitting

Removal

1   Drain the cooling system as described in Section 4.

2   Slacken the clips, and detach the hose from the thermostat water outlet elbow (photo).

3   Unscrew and remove the two bolts securing the water outlet elbow to the thermostat housing. Lift off the elbow and recover the gasket (photos).

4   Withdraw the thermostat from its seat in the housing (photo).

Testing

5   To test whether the unit is serviceable, suspend it on a string in a saucepan of cold water, together with a thermometer. Do not allow the thermostat or thermometer to touch the bottom of the pan. Heat the

9.3B . . . and remove the gasket

9.4 Withdrawing the thermostat from its seat

9.7 Jiggle pin (arrowed) and markings on the thermostat

water, and note the temperature at which the thermostat begins to open. Continue heating the water until the thermostat is fully open, then remove the unit from the water.

6   The temperature at which the thermostat should start to open is given in the Specifications. If the unit does not start to open at the specified temperature, or if it does not close when removed from the water, then it must be discarded and a new one fitted.

Refitting

7   Refitting is a reversal of the removal procedure. Make sure that all traces of old gasket are removed from the mating faces of the water

outlet elbow and thermostat housing. Check that the jiggle pin is free to move in the thermostat flange; there is no requirement to position it uppermost, as the unit is mounted horizontally (photo). Use a new gasket, and tighten the retaining bolts securely. On completion, refill the cooling system with reference to Section 6.

10   Water pump - removal and refitting

Removal

1   Disconnect the battery earth (negative) lead.

2   Apply the handbrake, then jack up the front of the vehicle and support on axle stands. Remove the right-hand roadwheel.

3   Drain the cooling system as described in Section 4.

4   Reconnect the bottom hose to the radiator, and tighten the clip.

5   Remove the timing belt together with the water pump pulley, as described in Chapter 1.

6   Disconnect the hose(s) from the water pump; however, on 1989 and later models, do not disconnect the hose from the thermostat at this stage.

Pre-1989 non-Turbo models

7   Unscrew and remove the bolt attaching the timing belt rear cover to the water pump.

8   Progressively unscrew and remove the water pump mounting bolts, noting the locations of the various sizes of bolt. Recover the timing cover bracket (held by the two rearmost bolts).

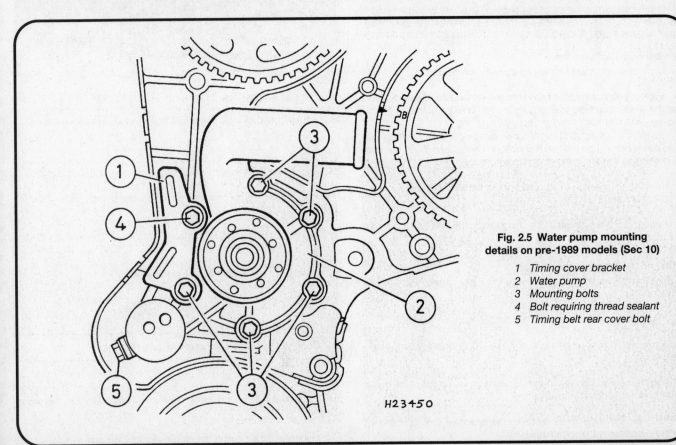

Fig. 2.5 Water pump mounting details on pre-1989 models (Sec 10)

1   *Timing cover bracket*
2   *Water pump*
3   *Mounting bolts*
4   *Bolt requiring thread sealant*
5   *Timing belt rear cover bolt*

H23450

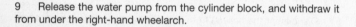
10.10 Water pump and mounting bolts (arrowed)

10.11 Removing the water pump

9   Release the water pump from the cylinder block, and withdraw it from under the right-hand wheelarch.

Turbo and 1989 models onwards

10   Unscrew and remove the water pump mounting bolts (photo), noting the locations of the various sizes of bolt.

11   Release the water pump from the cylinder block, disconnect the thermostat hose, and withdraw the pump from the engine compartment (photo).

Refitting

12   Clean the mating faces of the water pump and cylinder block. Also clean out the threaded holes in the block (and timing cover hole on early models) using a tap.

Pre-1989 non-Turbo models

13   Apply thread sealant to one of the short mounting bolts.

14   Apply a bead of suitable sealant to the water pump joint face, inside of the mounting bolt holes.

15   Locate the water pump on the cylinder block, then position the timing cover bracket on the two rearmost bolt holes, and insert the bolt with the thread sealant in the uppermost hole.

16   Insert the remaining bolts, and tighten them all progressively to the specified torque.

17   Refit and tighten the bolt attaching the timing belt rear cover to the water pump.

Turbo and 1989 models onwards

18   Reconnect the thermostat hose to the water pump, and tighten the clip.

19   Apply thread sealant to the threads of the mounting bolts.

20   Apply a 3 mm bead of silicone sealant to the water pump joint face (photo).

21   Locate the water pump on the cylinder block, and insert the bolts in their previously-noted locations.

22   Progressively tighten the bolts to the specified torque, starting with the inner ring and working outwards.

10.20 3 mm bead of sealant applied to the water pump joint face

All models

23   Reconnect the hoses to the water pump, and tighten the clips.

24   Refit the timing belt together with the water pump pulley, with reference to Chapter 1.

25   Refit the right-hand roadwheel, and lower the vehicle to the ground.

26   Reconnect the battery earth (negative) lead.

27   Refill the cooling system, with reference to Section 6.

---

11   Cooling fan assembly - removal and refitting

Removal

1   Remove the inlet air ducting from the engine compartment front panel.

2   Disconnect the cooling fan motor wiring multi-plug.

11.3 Cooling fan assembly on the rear of the radiator (removed for clarity)

3   Unscrew the three nuts securing the fan cowl to the radiator, and withdraw the assembly from its location (photo).

4   If required, the fan may be removed by pulling it off the motor shaft. Mark the outer face to ensure correct refitment. To remove the fan motor, drill off the rivet heads, tap out the rivets securing the motor to the cowl, and lift away the motor.

Refitting

5   Refitting is a reversal of the removal procedure.

12   Cooling fan thermostatic switch - testing, removal and refitting

Testing

1   The radiator cooling fan is operated by a thermostatic switch located on the right-hand side of the radiator. When the coolant exceeds a predetermined temperature, the switch contacts close and the fan is activated.

2   If the operation of the fan or switch is suspect, run the engine until normal operating temperature is reached, and then allow it to idle. If the fan does not cut in within a few minutes, switch off the engine and disconnect the wiring plug from the thermostatic switch. Bridge the two terminals in the wiring plug with a length of wire, and switch on the ignition. If the fan now operates, the thermostatic switch is faulty and must be renewed. If the fan still fails to operate, check that battery voltage is present at the plug terminals. If not, check for a blown fuse or wiring fault. If voltage is present but the fan does not operate, the fan motor is faulty.

Removal

3   To remove the switch, disconnect the battery negative terminal, then drain the cooling system as described in Section 4.

4   Disconnect the wiring plug, release the retaining plate, and withdraw the switch and seal from the radiator.

Refitting

5   Refitting is a reversal of the removal procedure, but use a new seal on the switch; refill the cooling system as described in Section 6.

13.4 Loosen the alternator pivot and adjustment link bolts (arrowed) . . .

13   Drivebelt - removal, refitting and adjustment

Removal

1   Apply the handbrake, then jack up the front of the vehicle and support on axle stands. Remove the right-hand roadwheel.

2   Remove the plastic engine access panel from inside the wheelarch.

3   Disconnect the battery earth (negative) lead.

4   Loosen the alternator pivot and adjustment link bolts (photo).

5   Swivel the alternator towards the engine, and slip the drivebelt off the crankshaft, water pump and alternator pulleys (photo).

Refitting and adjustment

6   Locate the drivebelt on the pulleys, then lever the alternator away from the engine until the drivebelt is moderately tight. The alternator must only be levered with care at the drive end bracket.

13.5 . . swivel the alternator towards the engine and remove the drivebelt

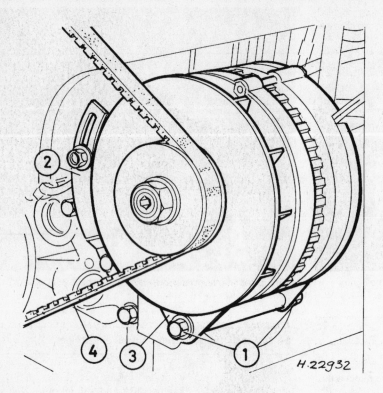

Fig. 2.6 Drivebelt adjustment (Sec 13)

1   *Pivot bolt*
2   *Adjustment link*
3   *Drive end bracket*
4   *Drivebelt deflection*
      checking point

7   Hold the alternator in this position and tighten the adjustment link bolt.

8   If the drivebelt is new, the engine should now be run at a fast idle for approximately five minutes in order to stretch it to its normal operating length.

9   Check that the deflection of the drivebelt midway between the crankshaft and alternator pulleys is as given in the Specifications. Ideally, a Rover tension gauge should be used to apply the correct load, but moderate pressure with finger or thumb will normally be sufficient to make the check (photo). If the Rover tension gauge is being used, check that the tension is as given below.

Used belt	5 gauge units
New belt	7 gauge units

10   If necessary, loosen the adjustment link bolt, readjust the tension, then tighten both the link bolt and the pivot bolt securely.

11   Reconnect the battery earth (negative) lead.

12   Refit the access panel inside the wheelarch, then refit the roadwheel and lower the vehicle to the ground.

14   Temperature gauge sender unit - removal and refitting

Removal

1   The temperature gauge sender is located on the rear of the thermostat housing, on the right-hand end of the cylinder head. The sender contains an element, the resistance of which alters according to coolant temperature.

2   Remove the expansion tank filler cap. If the engine is hot, place a cloth over the cap, and release it slowly to allow the pressure to escape.

3   Place a suitable container beneath the radiator bottom hose outlet. Disconnect the hose, drain approximately 2.5 litres of the coolant, then refit the hose and tighten the clip.

4   Disconnect the wiring from the sender unit, then unscrew the unit from the thermostat housing.

Refitting

5   Refitting is a reversal of the removal procedure. Tighten the sender unit to the specified torque, and refill the cooling system with reference to Section 6.

13.9 Checking the drivebelt deflection

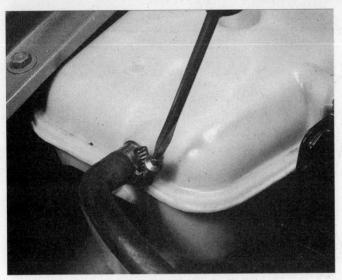

15.2 Disconnecting the vent hose from the expansion tank

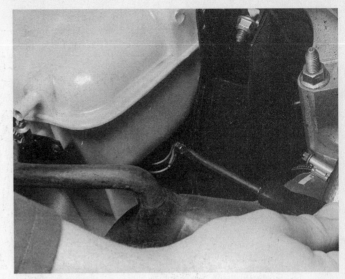

15.3 Disconnecting the supply hose from the expansion tank

15 Expansion tank - removal and refitting

Removal

1   Drain the cooling system as described in Section 4.

2   Loosen the clip and disconnect the small vent hose from the front of the expansion tank (photo).

3   Loosen the clip and disconnect the supply hose from the bottom of the expansion tank (photo).

4   Remove the screws and withdraw the support bracket from the front of the tank (photo).

5   Unscrew and remove the rear mounting screw (photo).

6   Remove the expansion tank by twisting it through 90° (photo).

Refitting

7   Refitting is a reversal of the removal procedure; refill the cooling system with reference to Section 6.

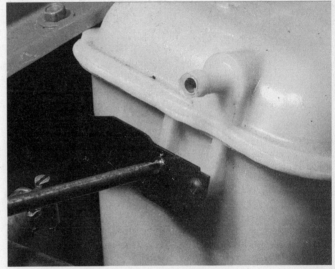

15.4 Removing front mounting bracket screws

15.5 Rear mounting screw

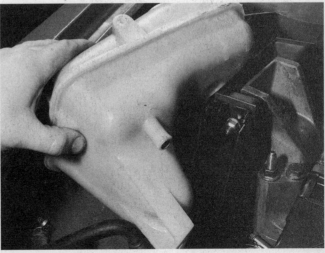

15.6 Withdrawing expansion tank (twisting through 90°)

16   Fault diagnosis - cooling system

Symptom	Reason(s)
Overheating	Low coolant level (this may be the result of overheating for other reasons)
	Faulty expansion tank pressure cap
	Thermostat sticking shut
	Drivebelt slipping or broken
	Clogged radiator matrix (internal or external), or grille restricted
	Faulty fan unit or thermostatic switch
	Cylinder head gasket blown (combustion gases in coolant)
	Cylinder head or block cracked
	Expansion tank pressure cap faulty
Overcooling	Thermostat jammed open, missing, or of incorrect rating
Slow warm-up	Thermostat sticking open
Coolant loss	Damaged or deteriorated hose
	Leaking water pump or thermostat housing gasket
	Leaking radiator (or heater matrix)
	Pressure cap defective or incorrect rating
	Cylinder head or block cracked
	Core plug leak
Corrosion	Infrequent draining and flushing
	Incorrect antifreeze mixture or inappropriate type of antifreeze

Chapter 3
Fuel, exhaust and emission control systems

Contents

Specifications

General .... Rear-mounted fuel tank, fuel lift pump operated from camshaft, fuel vapour separator tank (on some models only), fuel filter, injection pump. Glow plug pre-heating. Normally-aspirated or turbocharged

Fuel

Fuel type .... Commercial diesel fuel for road vehicles (DERV)

Fuel capacity:

    Except Van .... 50 litres (11 gallons)

    Van .... 54 litres (12 gallons)

Air filter
Air filter .... Champion W227

Fuel filter
Fuel filter .... Champion L111

Fuel lift pump
Type .... AC/YD
Static pressure (no delivery) .... 41 to 69 kPa (6 to 10 lbf/in²)

Glow plugs
Type .... Champion CH88 or CH137
Tip starts to glow .... 5 seconds
Initial current draw .... 25 amps
Current draw after 20 seconds .... 12 amps
Nominal operating voltage .... 11 volts

Fuel injection pump
Type .... Bosch EPVE

Turbocharger
Type .... Garret AiResearch T2
Boost pressure at 4500 rpm (full load) .... 89 to 96 kPa (12.9 to 13.9 lbf/in²)

Injectors
Type:
   Maestro 500 and 700 Van (1986 to 1988) .... CAV 4-hole
   Maestro 500 and 700 Van (1989-on):
      Non-Turbo .... CAV 4-hole
      Turbo .... CAV 5-hole
   Montego Turbo (1989 to 1991) .... CAV 5-hole
   Maestro Hatchback (1990 to 1992) .... CAV 4-hole, two-stage
   Montego Turbo (from VIN 606579 RHD, VIN 606709 LHD)
   (1991-on) .... Bosch 4-hole, two-stage
   Maestro Turbo and Montego (from VIN 635617) (1992-on) .... Bosch 5-hole, two-stage

Adjustment data
Static injection pump timing (with No 1 piston at TDC on compression):
   Maestro 500 and 700 Van (1986 to 1988) .... 1.37 mm (0.054 in) plunger lift
   Maestro 500 and 700 Van (1989-on):
      Non-Turbo .... 1.37 mm (0.054 in) plunger lift
      Turbo .... 1.00 mm (0.040 in) plunger lift
   Montego Turbo with single-stage injectors (1989 to 1991) .... 1.00 mm (0.040 in) plunger lift
   Maestro Hatchback (1990 to 1992) .... 1.00 mm (0.040 in) plunger lift
   Montego Turbo with two-stage injectors (from VIN 606579 RHD,
   VIN 606709 LHD) (1991-on) .... 1.20 mm (0.050 in) plunger lift
   Maestro Turbo and Montego (from VIN 635617) (1992-on) .... 1.20 mm (0.050 in) plunger lift
Idle speed:
   Maestro 500 and 700 Van (1986 to 1988) .... 900 to 950 rpm
   All other models .... 800 to 850 rpm
Fast idle speed:
   Maestro 500 and 700 Van (1986 to 1988) .... 1050 to 1075 rpm
   All other models .... 950 to 975 rpm
Maximum no-load speed (all models) .... 4500 rpm

Torque wrench settings

	Nm	lbf ft
Fuel filter banjo bolt	30	22
Injection pump gear/pulley nut	60	44
Fuel lift pump	22	16
Glow plugs	20	15
Injector high-pressure pipe union nuts	22	16
Injector clamp bolts	43	32
Manifold bolts	22	16
Air cleaner to bracket	13	10
Air cleaner strut to bracket	60	44
Air cleaner strut to cylinder head	30	22
EGR valve-to-EGR pipe screws	22	16
EGR valve-to-inlet manifold screws	22	16
EGR pipe-to-exhaust manifold nuts	22	16

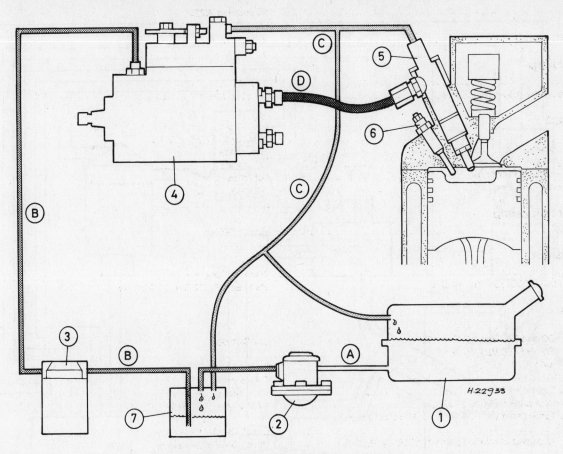

Fig. 3.1 Diagram of the fuel injection system (Sec 1)

1	Fuel tank	5	Injector	A	Suction
2	Fuel lift pump	6	Glow plugs	B	Lift pump pressure
3	Fuel filter	7	Vapour separator tank	C	Leak-off
4	Fuel injection pump		(where fitted)	D	Injection pressure

1 General description and precautions

Fuel from the rear-mounted fuel tank passes through a strainer within the tank to the vapour separator (where fitted) located on the left-hand side of the engine compartment, then to the fuel filter which extracts dirt and water from the fuel. From the filter, the fuel passes to the Bosch EPVE injection pump, where an internal pump and control valve increases and regulates the pressure in relation to the engine speed. The fuel then passes (via the stop/start solenoid valve) to the pump plunger, which forces the exact metered quantity of fuel at high pressure to the injectors at the correct instant. Excess fuel cools and lubricates the pump components, and is returned to the fuel tank.

The CAV multi-hole injectors are operated by the pressure of the fuel delivered by the injection pump, and they are designed to commence and cease delivery at precise pressures, in order to provide complete combustion. The nozzles on the injectors deliver the fuel to the combustion chambers in the form of a fine spray.

Fuel injection is direct into the combustion chambers which are formed in the piston crowns. The injectors fitted to all models from VIN 606579 (right-hand drive models) or VIN 606709 (left-hand drive models) are of the two-stage type, giving very smooth and quiet combustion. Prior to these VIN numbers, the injectors are of single-stage type. Preheating is by glow plugs, with automatic control of preheating time, and an afterglow period.

The glow plugs are fitted to assist cold starting. One plug is used per cylinder, and the plugs are wired in parallel, so that failure of one plug will not affect the operation of the others. The tips of the glow plugs become red-hot after a few seconds when battery voltage is applied to them. When the incoming fuel spray swirls into contact with the hot plug, the fuel ignites. The glow plug circuit incorporates a ballast resistor (photo).

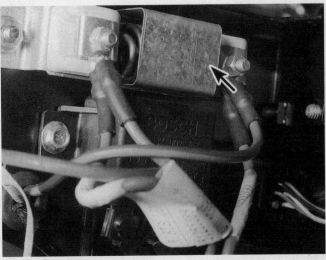

1.4 Ballast resistor (arrowed) for the glow plug circuit

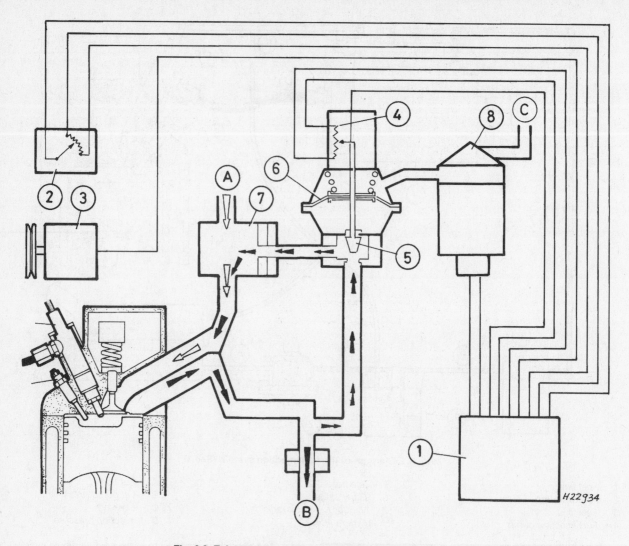

Fig. 3.2 Exhaust gas recirculation (EGR) system (Sec 1)

1	Control unit	4	EGR valve lift potentiometer
2	Throttle potentiometer	5	EGR valve
3	Engine speed signal taken from alternator	6	EGR valve diaphragm
		7	Inlet manifold

8	Modulator valve
A	Intake air
B	Exhaust gas
C	Vacuum

The time for which the glow plugs need to be energised before the engine can be started will depend on engine temperature and ambient air temperature. The glow plugs are controlled by a timer unit, start relay and resistor. The timer unit has two electrical supplies. When the ignition switch is turned to position "II", 12 volts is supplied to the timer unit, completing the circuit to the start relay. The warning light is illuminated until the glow plugs reach the predetermined temperature; the glow plugs will continue to operate after the warning light goes out because the alternator supplies an earth path for the ignition switch supply. At this stage, the resistor is bypassed. When the ignition switch is turned to position "III" (starting), the electrical supply comes from from position "III"; once the engine is running and the alternator is turning, the earth path for the ignition switch circuit is lost, and the relay is then switched off. The only complete circuit is now through the resistor, and this means that the glow plugs produce less heat. The timer automatically switches off the glow plugs 13 seconds after the engine has started.

Glow plugs may last the life of the engine, or one may fail after only a few thousand miles. An engine on which one glow plug has failed can normally still be started without too much trouble, except in

1.10 Throttle potentiometer located on the top of the injection pump

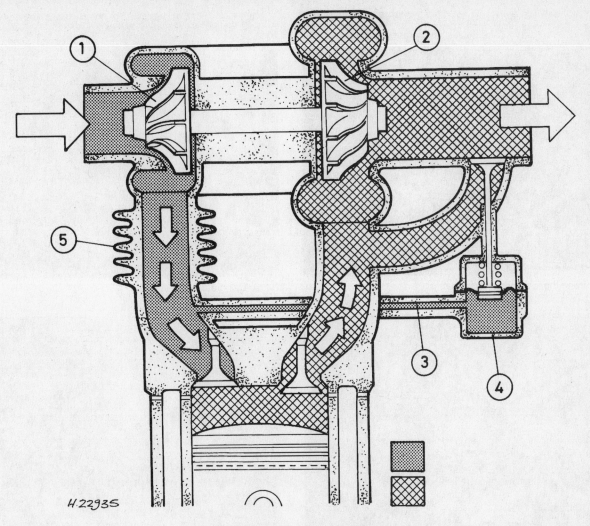

H.2293S

Fig. 3.3 Turbocharging principles (Sec 1)

1 Compressor
2 Turbine
3 Pressure control pipe

4 Wastegate
5 Cooling (when necessary according
   to installation)

very cold weather. With two glow plugs failed, cold starting will be difficult or impossible. It is therefore worth checking the glow plugs at major service intervals, in case one has failed unnoticed.

A cold start device is fitted to the injection pump. It is operated by a 12-volt supply from the ignition switch position "II" through fuse C5 and the coolant thermistor to the solenoid. With the engine cold, the resistance of the thermistor is high, and the solenoid is prevented from operating. At this point, the fuel pressure in the injection pump is high and the timing point is advanced. During the engine warm-up phase, the thermistor resistance decreases until the point is reached where the supply is sufficient to operate the unit. The fuel pressure and injection timing then return to normal.

A fast idle unit is fitted to the injection pump, to increase the idle speed when starting from cold. It is operated by a 12-volt supply from the ignition switch position "II" through the thermistor located on the thermostat housing. With the engine cold, the resistance of the thermistor is low, and a full 12 volts is applied to the solenoid, which moves the plunger and injection pump control lever to the fast idle position. As the engine temperature increases, the thermistor resistance also increases, and the electrical supply to the solenoid is reduced until the point is reached where the injection pump control lever is allowed to return to its normal idle position.

All Maestro Hatchback models from VIN 696263 and Montego Estate models from VIN 635617 are fitted with a modulated closed-loop exhaust gas recirculation (EGR) system. The system reduces the emission of nitrogen oxides (NOx) by passing a controlled volume of exhaust gas into the combustion chambers. EGR is not required under all engine operating conditions, and a control unit is fitted to regulate the EGR valve.

The EGR control unit is supplied with engine speed, engine load and EGR valve lift information, and from this it determines the signal to send to the vacuum modulator, which in turn controls the amount of vacuum applied to the EGR valve. Engine speed information is taken from the alternator, and throttle position is monitored by a potentiometer (photo). The control unit also determines the rate of change of engine speed, so that the EGR function may be stopped at engine speed accelerations greater than 55 rpm per second. The EGR valve incorporates a potentiometer, so that the control unit is continually aware of the degree of valve lift and can compare it with the desired lift. Any adjustment to the lift is therefore made instantly.

A turbocharger is fitted to some models. It uses the energy of the escaping exhaust gas to drive a turbine which pressurizes the air in the inlet manifold. The air is forced into the cylinders instead of being sim-

2.6 Removing the fuel filter

2.11A Using a screwdriver . . .

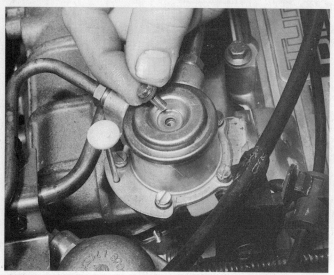

2.11B . . . remove the screw retaining the fuel lift pump cover

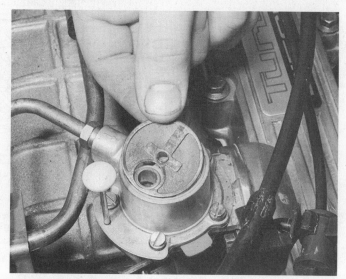

2.12 Removing the strainer

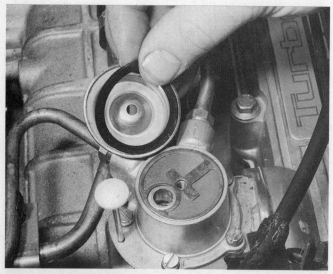

2.13 Renewing the cover sealing washer

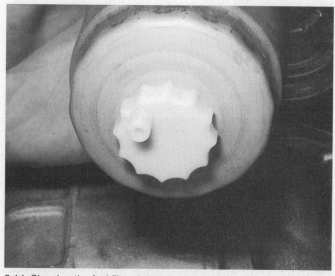

2.14 Showing the fuel filter drain tap

ply sucked in. If more air is present, more fuel can be burnt and more power developed from the same size engine.

The turbocharger turbine shaft is pressure-lubricated by a feed from the oil pump. When the engine is running, the shaft "floats" on a cushion of oil.

On turbocharged models, a manifold pressure compensation system is fitted. The compensation unit is located on the top of the injection pump, and it reacts to the inlet manifold pressure generated by the turbocharger, adjusting the full-load fuel delivery to the same pressure.

The turbocharger operates at extremely high speeds and temperatures. Certain precautions must be observed to avoid premature failure of the turbo, or injury to the operator.

Do not operate the turbo with any parts exposed. Foreign objects falling onto the rotating vanes could cause damage and (if ejected) injury. Loose rags, small tools or other objects can be drawn into the turbo air intake when the engine is running.

Do not run the engine without an air cleaner element fitted. Even if no large foreign objects pass through and damage the turbo, dust and grit in the air can damage the turbo at operating speeds.

Do not race the engine immediately after start-up, especially if it is cold. Give the oil a few seconds to circulate. This is particularly important after an oil change. If the turbo oil feed has drained, it is advisable to prime it by cranking the engine on the starter motor (with the pump stop solenoid disconnected) until the oil pressure warning light goes out.

Do not switch off the engine before it has returned to idle speed. After a high-speed run, allow the engine to idle for a minute or so before switching off. **Do not** blip the throttle and then switch off, as this will leave the turbo spinning without lubrication.

When working in contact with diesel fuel, observe the recommendations given in *"Safety first!"* at the beginning of this manual.

2 Routine maintenance

Check fuel hoses, fuel pipes and vacuum hoses

1   Check all fuel and vacuum hoses and pipes in the engine compartment for security, leakage and damage.

2   Raise the rear of the vehicle and support on axle stands, then check the fuel tank and all connections for security, leakage, damage and corrosion.

Check exhaust system

3   Refer to Section 23.

Check EGR system

4   Check the security of the EGR components, vacuum hoses and wiring. Refer to Sections 18, 19 and 20 if necessary.

Renew fuel filter

5   Wipe clean the area around the filter head.

6   Position rags beneath the filter to absorb spilt fuel, then unscrew the filter from the head using a chain or strap wrench. Keeping the filter upright, withdraw it from the head, then drain the fuel into a suitable container (photo).

7   Smear the seal on the new filter with clean fuel. If sufficient fuel is readily available, fill the new filter with fuel. Fit the filter, and tighten it by hand only.

8   Bleed the fuel system as described in Section 7.

Check smoke emissions

9   This check should be made by a Rover dealer or diesel specialist, who will have the expertise and equipment necessary to make the check.

Renew air cleaner element

10   Refer to Section 3.

Clean fuel lift pump strainer

11   Unscrew the retaining screw and remove the lift pump cover (photos); be prepared for some fuel spillage.

12   Remove the strainer and clean it (photo). Also clean the sediment chamber. Refit the strainer.

13   Refit the cover, using a new sealing washer if necessary (photo). Bleed the fuel system at the filter head with reference to Section 7.

Drain water from the fuel filter

14   Place a small container under the filter. Slacken the bleed screw on the filter head and the drain tap on the base (photo).

15   Allow roughly 100 ml (a quarter of a pint) of fuel to drain, then tighten the drain tap and the bleed screw. Dispose of the drained fuel safely.

3 Air cleaner and element - removal and refitting

Removal

1   To remove the element, release the spring clips and lift off the air cleaner cover (photo). Note that on non-Turbo models, the outlet hose remains on the cover stub.

3.1 Releasing the air cleaner cover spring clips

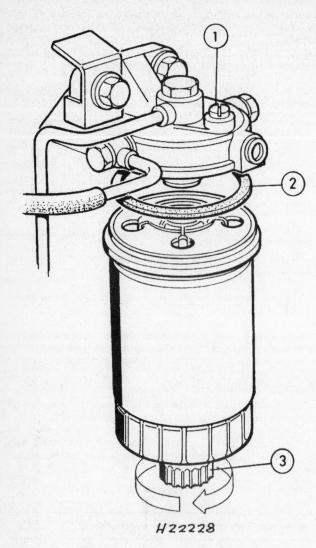

3.2 Removing the air cleaner element

Fig. 3.4 Fuel filter details (Sec 2)

1   Bleed screw   3   Water drain
2   Seal   tap

3.3 Disconnecting the air cleaner outlet hose

3.4A Disconnecting the crankcase ventilation hose - Turbo models

3.4B Heater hose support clips and bolts (arrowed) - Turbo models

3.5 Bolts (arrowed) securing the air cleaner body to the mounting bracket - Turbo models

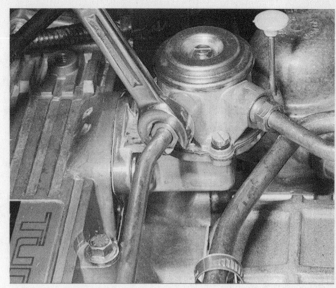

4.3A Loosen the union nut . . .

2   Lift out the element from the air cleaner body (photo).

3   To remove the air cleaner body, loosen the clips and disconnect the inlet and outlet hoses (photo).

4   On Turbo models, loosen the clip and disconnect the crankcase ventilation hose from the outlet elbow. Also unbolt the heater hose support clips from the mounting bracket (photos).

5   On Turbo models, unscrew the bolts securing the air cleaner body to the mounting bracket (photo).

6   Lift the air cleaner body from the mounting bracket. On non-Turbo models, the body is located by two pegs in mounting rubbers.

Refitting

7   Locate the air cleaner body on its mounting bracket. On non-Turbo models, make sure that the two pegs locate in the mounting rubbers.

8   On Turbo models, insert and tighten the air cleaner mounting bolts.

9   On Turbo models, reconnect the crankcase ventilation hose to the outlet elbow, and tighten the clip.

10   Reconnect the inlet and outlet hoses, and tighten the clips.

11   Wipe clean the interior surfaces of the air cleaner, then insert a new element.

12   Locate the cover on the air cleaner body, and secure with the spring clips.

4.3B . . . and disconnect the outlet pipe from the fuel lift pump

2   Unscrew and remove the timing blanking screw from the right-hand end of the camshaft cover housing, then turn the engine using a socket on the crankshaft pulley bolt until the TDC timing hole in the camshaft is aligned with the hole in the cover. This procedure is necessary to position the eccentric on the camshaft away from the fuel lift pump. Refit and tighten the timing screw.

3   Unscrew the union nuts, and disconnect the inlet and outlet pipes from the pump (photos). A little fuel will escape as the pipes are disconnected, so position some rag beneath them first. Plug the ends of the pipes, to prevent dust and dirt entering the fuel system.

---

4   Fuel lift pump - removal and refitting

Removal

1   Disconnect the battery earth (negative) lead.

4   Unscrew the mounting bolts, and withdraw the fuel lift pump from

4.4A Unscrew the mounting bolts . . .

4.4B . . . and remove the fuel lift pump

the camshaft cover housing. Recover the gasket (photos).

Refitting

5   Clean the mounting faces of the pump and camshaft cover housing.

6   Locate the fuel lift pump on the camshaft cover housing, making sure that the operating lever locates on the camshaft eccentric correctly.

7   Apply a little locking fluid to the threads of the mounting bolts.

8   Hold the fuel lift pump square to the camshaft cover housing face with a new gasket in position, then insert the mounting bolts and tighten them progressively to the specified torque.

9   Reconnect the fuel inlet and outlet pipes, and tighten the union nuts.

10   Loosen the bleed screw on the fuel filter, then operate the plunger on the fuel pump until fuel emerges free from air bubbles. Tighten the bleed screw.

11   Reconnect the battery earth (negative) lead.

5   Injectors - testing on engine

Warning: *Never expose the hands, face or any other part of the body to injector spray, since the high working pressure can cause the fuel to penetrate the skin, with potentially-fatal results.*

1   A faulty injector which is causing knocking noises can be identified as follows.

2   Clean around the injector fuel pipe unions. Run the engine at a fast idle so that the knock can be heard. Using a suitable split ring spanner, slacken and retighten each injector union in turn. (Cover the union with a piece of rag to absorb the fuel which will be spilt.)

3   When the union supplying the defective injector is slackened, the knock will disappear. Stop the engine and remove the injector for inspection.

4   The balance between injectors can be checked in a similar way, provided an accurate tachometer is available. With the engine idling, each union is slackened in turn and the drop in rpm noted. Any injector which produces a much larger or smaller drop in rpm when its union is slackened should be viewed with suspicion.

5   With equipment such as Dieseltune's Injector Tester, it is possible to check injector opening pressures and leakage without removing the injectors from the engine. This is obviously a time-saving measure if it is simply wished to verify that the pressures are correct, or to locate one defective injector.

6   Testing the spray pattern, by cranking or running the engine with an injector out of its hole and connected to its fuel pipe, should **not** be attempted. It is tempting to use this method because it is quick and requires no special equipment, but the risks of fire and blood poisoning from the injector spray mean that it cannot be recommended.

6   Injectors - removal and refitting

Removal

1   Disconnect the battery earth (negative) lead.

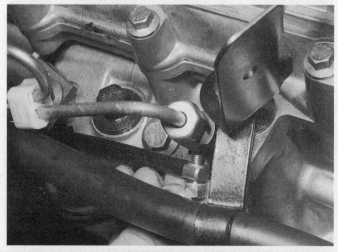

6.2 Removing the fuel leak-off pipes from the injectors

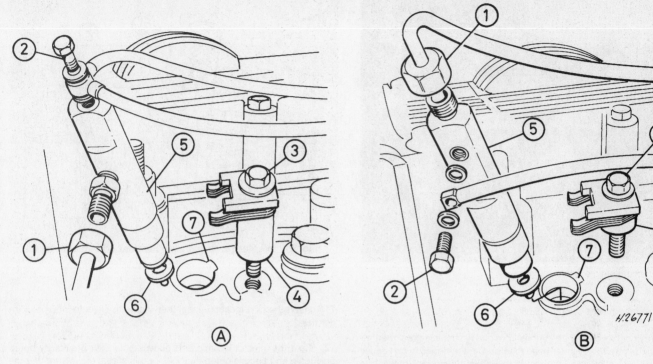

Fig. 3.5 Single-stage (A) and two-stage (B) injectors (Sec 6)

1 Injector pipe union
2 Leak-off (return) pipe banjo union bolt
3 Clamp bolt assembly
4 Pedestal

5 Injector
6 Seat washer
7 Locating ring

2   Unscrew and remove the banjo bolts securing the leak-off pipes to the injectors (photo). Recover the sealing washers. Note that when removing No 2 or No 3 injector, the leak-off pipe must be removed from both injectors.

3   Counterhold the delivery valves on the injection pump, and loosen the high-pressure pipe unions. Note that the delivery valves will be dis-

torted if they are not counterheld when loosening the unions. Also take care not to bend the pipes.

4   Unscrew the unions at the injectors, and remove the high-pressure pipes.

5   Note the fitted position of the injector clamps and pedestals, then unscrew the bolts and remove the clamps and pedestals (photos).

6.5A Unscrew the bolt . . .

6.5B . . . and remove the injector clamp and pedestal components

6.6 Removing an injector

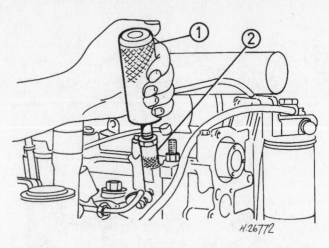

H.26772

Fig. 3.6 Injector-removing slide hammer (1) and adapter (2) (Sec 6)

6   Brush or blow away any debris from around the injectors, then re-move them from the cylinder head (photo). Carbon deposits can cause the injector to stick in its recess; in this case, an injector puller or a small slide hammer can be used, or it may be possible to free the injec-tor by careful levering. **Do not** attempt to free a sticking injector by cranking the engine; it could be ejected with enough force to cause damage or serious injury.

7   Prise out the locating rings and seat washers from the bottom of the injector hole (photos).

8   Examine the clamps for damage, in particular the retaining arms. If any one of these is damaged, the clamp must be renewed.

9   Wipe clean the injector seatings in the cylinder head.

Refitting

10   Locate new seat washers in the bottom of the injector holes.

11   Insert the new locating rings, then locate the injectors in the cylin-der head.

12   Refit the injector clamps and pedestals in their previously-noted positions, and finger-tighten the bolts at this stage. Make sure that the clamp arms are located squarely on the injector shoulders.

13   Refit the high-pressure pipes, and tighten the unions at the injec-tion pump to the specified torque. Make sure that the delivery valves are counterheld. Leave the unions at the injector ends loose at this stage.

14   Tighten the clamp bolts to the specified torque.

15   Bleed the fuel system as described in Section 7.

16   Refit the leak-off pipes to the injectors using new sealing wash-ers, and tighten the banjo bolts securely.

17   Reconnect the battery earth (negative) lead.

18   Start the engine, and check for fuel leaks.

6.7A Removing an injector locating ring . . .

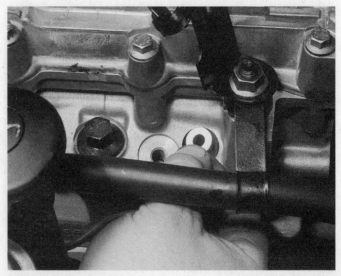

6.7B . . . and seat washer

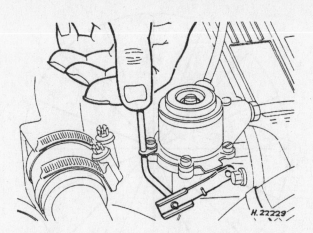

Fig. 3.7 Hand-priming lever on the fuel lift pump (Sec 7)

7.2 Loosening the bleed screw on the fuel filter head

7 Fuel system - bleeding

Warning: *Do not attempt to bleed the fuel system by towing the vehicle. The injection pump will be seriously damaged if it is turned without fuel in it.*

1 Check if the hand-priming plunger on the fuel lift pump can be moved through its full stroke. If not, turn the crankshaft through one complete turn, using a socket on the crankshaft pulley bolt. This will reposition the fuel pump lever on its operating cam, thus allowing the plunger to move through its full stroke.

2 Using a screwdriver or spanner, loosen the bleed screw on the fuel filter head (photo).

3 Operate the hand-priming plunger on the fuel lift pump (photo). When fuel free of air bubbles emerges from the bleed screw, tighten the bleed screw.

4 Loosen the feed pipe union bolt on the injection pump, then continue to operate the hand-priming plunger until fuel free of air bubbles emerges. Tighten the union bolt securely.

5 Loosen all of the high-pressure union nuts at the injectors, sufficient to allow fuel to escape.

6 Fully depress the accelerator pedal, then spin the engine on the starter motor until fuel free of air bubbles emerges from the high-pressure unions.

7 Tighten the union nuts to the specified torque, then mop up all spilt fuel with rags.

8 Start the engine and let it run until it is running on all cylinders.

8 Idle speed - checking and adjustment

1 The type of tachometer (rev counter) which senses ignition system HT pulses via an inductive pick-up cannot be used on diesel engines, unless a device such as the Sykes-Pickavant timing light adapter is available (photo). Alternatively, an optical or pulse-sensitive tachometer may be used.

7.3 Operating the fuel lift pump hand-priming plunger

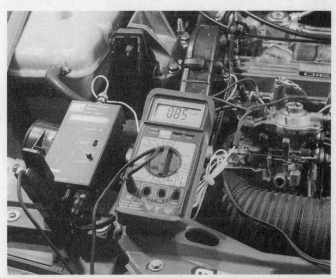

8.1 Using the Sykes-Pickavant timing light adapter to check the idle speed

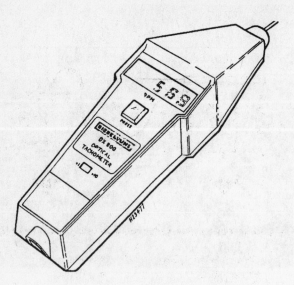

Fig. 3.8 Optical tachometer (Sec 8)

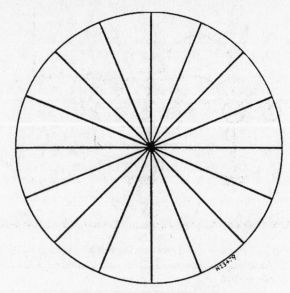

Fig. 3.9 Home-made tachometer disc (Sec 8)

2   The optical tachometer registers the passage of a paint mark or (more usually) a strip of reflective foil placed on the crankshaft pulley. It is not as convenient to use as the electronic or pulse-sensitive types, since it has to be held so that it can "see" the pulley, but it has the advantage that it can be used on any engine, petrol or diesel, with or without a diagnostic socket.

3   The pulse-sensitive tachometer uses a transducer similar to that needed for a timing light. The transducer converts hydraulic or mechanical impulses in an injector pipe into electrical signals, which are displayed on the tachometer as engine speed.

4   Some dynamic timing equipment for diesel engines incorporates a means of displaying engine speed. If this equipment is available, a separate tachometer will not be required.

5   The owner-mechanic who only wishes to check the idle speed of one engine occasionally may well feel that the purchase of a special tachometer is not justified. Assuming that mains electric light is available, the use of a stroboscopic disc is a cheap alternative. The principle will be familiar to anyone who has used such a disc to check the speed of a record-player turntable.

6   A disc must be constructed of stiff paper or card to fit onto the crankshaft pulley (or camshaft pulley, if appropriate - but remember that this rotates at half speed). The disc should be white or light-coloured, and divided using a protractor into regular segments with heavy black lines. The number of segments required will depend on the desired idle speed and the frequency of the alternating current supply. For the 50 Hz supply used in the UK and most of Europe, the figures are as follows:

Speed (rpm)	No of segments	Angle per segment
706	17	21° 11'
750	16	22° 30'
800	15	24°
857	14	25° 43'
923	13	27° 42'

7   Attach the disc to the crankshaft pulley (after removing the right-hand roadwheel and inner wheelarch access panel), and position the vehicle so that the disc can be viewed using only artificial light. A fluo-

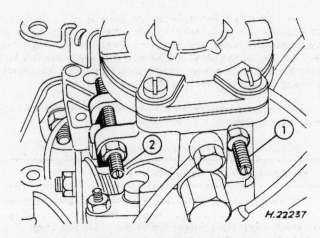

Fig. 3.10 Idle speed adjusting screw (1) and maximum no-load speed screw (2) (Sec 8)

rescent tube is best; failing this, a low-wattage incandescent bulb will give better results than a high-wattage one.

8   The disc is observed with the engine running at idling speed. If the engine speed corresponds to the calculated disc speed, the disc segments will appear to be stationary. If the speed is different, the segments will appear to drift in the direction of engine rotation (too fast) or against it (too slow). The segments will also appear to be stationary at multiples or sub-multiples of the calculated speed - twice or half the speed, and so on - so some common sense must be used.

9   Bring the engine to normal operating temperature, and connect a tachometer (or suitable alternative) to it. The cooling fan must have operated at least once. **Warning:** *Do not run the engine in a confined space without some means of extracting the exhaust fumes.*

10   Disconnect the wiring lead from the fast idle speed solenoid.

11   Allow the engine to idle, and check the speed against that given in the Specifications.

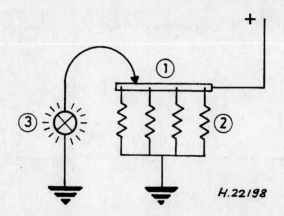

Fig. 3.11 Checking for glow plug supply voltage with a test lamp (Sec 9)

1 *Glow plug supply wire*   3 *Test lamp*
2 *Glow plugs*

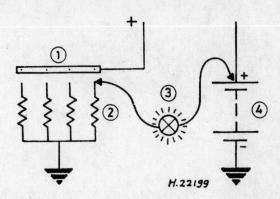

Fig. 3.12 Checking glow plug continuity using a test lamp (Sec 9)

1 *Glow plug supply wire*   3 *Test lamp*
   (disconnected)   4 *Battery*
2 *Glow plugs*

12   If adjustment is necessary, slacken the locknut and turn the idle speed adjusting screw. Tighten the locknut when the adjustment is correct.

13   Check the adjustment of the fast idle solenoid as follows. Connect a 12-volt supply to the solenoid. Accelerate the engine slightly to allow the solenoid plunger to extend, then release the accelerator and check that the fast idle speed is as given in the Specifications. If adjustment is required, screw the plunger adjuster in or out. Disconnect the 12-volt supply, and check that idle speed returns to normal.

14   Stop the engine and reconnect the wiring lead to the fast idle speed solenoid. Disconnect the tachometer.

9   Preheating and cold start system - checking

1   The minimum equipment required is a 12-volt test lamp. More detailed testing will require a multi-meter with the appropriate voltage and current ranges. For a comprehensive test of the glow plugs, they should be taken to a Rover dealer or diesel specialist who will check them in a glow plug tester.

Voltage supply checks with a test lamp or voltmeter

2   Connect the test lamp or voltmeter between the glow plug supply wire and a suitable earth. Do not let the live side connections touch earth. Have an assistant energise the preheating system. The test lamp should light brightly, or the voltmeter should read at least 10 volts.

3   If there is no voltage at all, this suggests a fault such as a blown fuse, a disconnected wire, a defective relay or a defective switch. A blown fuse may only be a pointer to some underlying fault, such as a short-circuit in the wiring or a glow plug which has failed so as to cause a short.

4   If the voltage is low and the battery is OK, this suggests a bad connection somewhere in the wiring, or possibly a faulty relay.

Glow plug checks with a test lamp or multi-meter

5   A simple continuity check can be made by disconnecting the wires from the glow plugs (ignition switched off!), then connecting the test lamp between the battery positive terminal and each glow plug terminal in turn. Alternatively, measure the resistance between each

glow plug terminal and earth. The lamp should light brightly, or the meter read a very low resistance (typically 1 ohm or less).

6   If the lamp does not light or the meter shows a high resistance, the glow plug has failed open-circuit, and must be renewed.

7   The above is only a rough test, and will not detect a glow plug which has failed so as to cause a short-circuit, or one which is no longer heating properly even though its resistance is still more or less correct. More accurate testing requires the use of an ammeter, of range 0 to 25 or 0 to 30 amps. It should incorporate some kind of overload protection, either in the instrument itself, or by means of a fuse in its lead.

8   Connect the ammeter between the battery positive terminal and one of the glow plugs (the glow plugs must still be disconnected from each other). Note the current draw over a period of 20 seconds. Typically, an initial surge of 25 amps or more will fall over 20 seconds to a steady draw of 12 amps. A very high draw shows a short-circuit; zero amps shows an open-circuit.

9   Repeat the current draw check on the other glow plugs, and compare the results. Obvious differences will not be hard to spot. A difference in the rate at which the current falls off is also significant, and may indicate that the glow plug in question is no longer heating at the tip first.

10   The physical condition of the glow plugs is also important. To establish this, they must be removed and inspected for burning or erosion. Damage can be caused by a fault resulting in too long a post-heating time, but it is more often due to an injector fault. If damaged glow plugs are found, the injectors in the cylinders in question should be removed and checked. Take them to a Rover dealer or fuel system specialist, who will have the necessary equipment to test the spray pattern and calibration.

11   As a final check, the glow plugs can be energised while they are out of the engine and inspected to see that they heat evenly, with the tip glowing first, and no local hot or cold spots. Some means of supporting the plug while it is being tested must be devised, and the power supply lead should be fused, or should incorporate some other overload protection. Ideally, a purpose-made glow plug tester with a hot test chamber should be used.

12   Any glow plug which takes much longer than specified for its tip to glow red, or which shows uneven heating, should be renewed.

9.16 Fast idle solenoid

9.18 Automatic advance unit located on the front of the injection pump

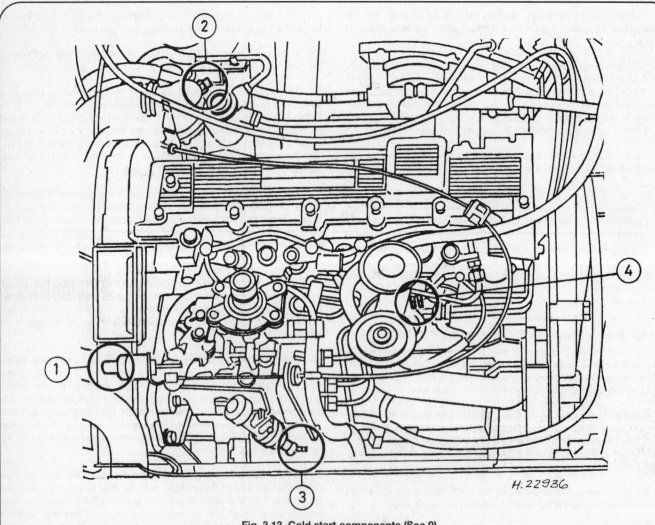

Fig. 3.13 Cold start components (Sec 9)

1   Fast idle solenoid
2   Fast idle solenoid supply
    temperature switch

3   Automatic advance unit
4   Automatic advance unit supply
    temperature switch

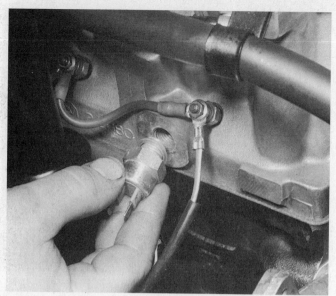

9.19 Removing the temperature switch for the automatic advance unit from the cylinder head

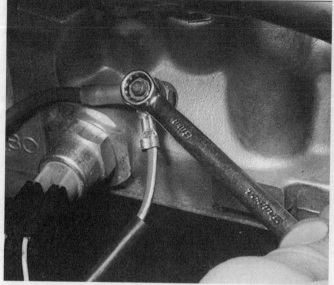

10.2A Unscrew the nut . . .

Control circuitry checks

13 The preheating control unit (and on single-stage injection, the resistor), are located on the left-hand inner wing, behind the battery.

14 The system continues to apply voltage to the glow plugs (via the resistor, when fitted) for up to 90 seconds after a cold start.

15 For those wishing to check the system, reference should be made to the wiring diagrams at the end of this manual. Alternatively, have the system checked by a Rover dealer.

Cold idle and cold start devices

16 With the engine cold (coolant at 20°C) switch on the ignition and depress the accelerator pedal once, then check that the fast idle solenoid has moved the control lever on the injection pump to the fast idle position (photo). If not, connect a 12-volt supply to the solenoid. If there is still no movement, check that there is a 12-volt supply at the temperature switch located on the thermostat housing. If there is voltage at the temperature switch input terminal but not at the output terminal, then the switch is faulty, and should be renewed. If there is no voltage at the switch, check all of the associated wiring.

17 If the engine is warm and the coolant temperature above 30°C, the fast idle solenoid will not be energised.

18 The automatic advance unit located on the front of the injection pump (photo) can only be accurately tested using special equipment. A fault in the unit may be indicated if the engine is difficult to start from cold, or if there is excessive white smoke from the exhaust when it does start. In this case, the unit may not have changed the timing position for a cold start. If the engine is noisy when warm or low on power, the unit may not have returned the timing to normal after the cold start.

19 To check the electrical supply to the automatic advance unit, connect a 12-volt test lamp between the unit and its disconnected wire. With the engine cold (coolant at 20°C) and the ignition switched on, the lamp should remain off; with the engine warm (coolant above 30°C), the lamp should be lit. If either of these conditions is incorrect, check the temperature switch located on the front-facing side of the cylinder head by the oil filler tube. If necessary, disconnect the wiring and unscrew the switch from the head (photo).

10 Glow plugs - removal and refitting

Warning: *If the glow plugs have just been operated in the engine, or if the engine has just been running, they may be very hot.*

Removal

1 Make sure that the ignition is switched off.

2 Unscrew the nut and disconnect the current feed wires from the glow plugs. Note that the main supply wire is also fitted to No 4 glow plug. Recover any terminal nut washers (photos).

3 Brush or blow away any debris from around the glow plugs.

4 Unscrew and remove the glow plugs from the cylinder head, us-

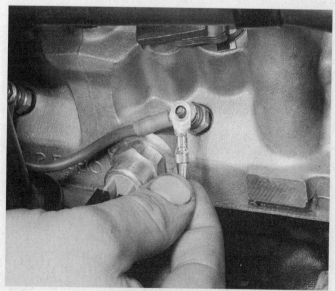

10.2B . . . and disconnect the main supply wire from No 4 glow plug

10.4A Use a deep socket to unscrew the glow plugs

10.4B Removing a glow plug

ing a deep socket (photos).

5   If the glow plugs are not to be refitted immediately, plug or cover the openings in the cylinder head.

Refitting

6   Commence refitting by applying a smear of copper-based anti-seize compound to the threads of each glow plug.

7   If the openings in the cylinder head were plugged while the glow plugs were removed, open up the plug holes and check that the glow plug seats are clean.

8   Insert the glow plugs into their holes, tightening them by hand first.

9   Tighten them to the specified torque. Beware of overtightening, which (as well as stripping the thread) can damage the glow plug by reducing the gap between the element and its surround.

10   Reconnect and secure the current feed wires.

11   Accelerator cable - removal, refitting and adjustment

Removal

1   Pull the locking sleeve from the socket on the injection pump end of the accelerator cable, and release the cable end socket from the pump control lever on the injection pump (photos).

2   Working inside the vehicle, disconnect the end of the cable from the accelerator pedal.

3   Loosen the cable adjustment nuts. Unscrew and remove the end nut, and remove the cable from the support bracket (photo).

4   Release the cable rubber mountings from the support brackets on the camshaft cover, and remove the cable from the engine compartment through the bulkhead (photos).

Refitting and adjustment

5   Insert the cable through the bulkhead, and locate the mounting rubbers in the support brackets.

11.1A Pull off the locking sleeve . . .

11.1B . . . and release the cable end socket

11.3 Removing the cable from the support bracket

11.4A Cable support bracket on the left-hand side of the camshaft cover

6   Insert the end of the cable through the support bracket on the injection pump, and lightly tighten the end nut.

7   Connect the end of the cable to the accelerator pedal.

8   Locate the cable end socket on the injection pump control lever, then lock it by sliding the locking sleeve onto it.

9   With the accelerator pedal fully released, adjust the tension of the cable by means of the two locknuts (photo), until the inner cable side movement midway between the injection pump control lever and the outer cable is between 8.0 and 10.0 mm. Tighten the locknuts on completion.

10   Have an assistant depress the accelerator pedal fully, and check that the control lever contacts the maximum speed screw. Check that, with the accelerator pedal fully released, the control lever is in contact with the idle speed adjusting screw.

11.4B Cable support bracket on the right-hand side of the camshaft cover

11.9 Adjusting the accelerator cable tension at the two locknuts

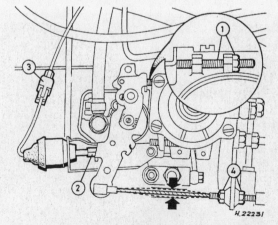

Fig. 3.14 Accelerator cable adjustment (arrowed) and idle speed adjustment (Sec 11)

1   Idle speed adjustment screw and locknut
2   Fast idle plunger adjuster
3   Fast idle solenoid wiring connector
4   Accelerator cable adjustment locknuts

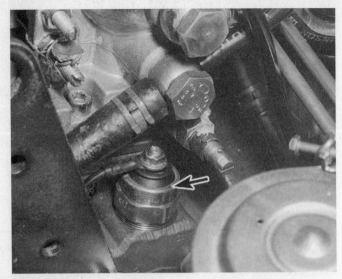

12.4A Stop solenoid (arrowed)

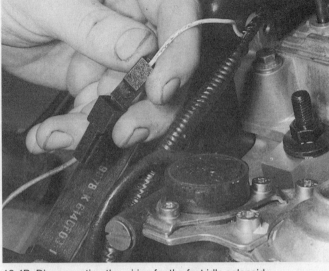

12.4B Disconnecting the wiring for the fast idle solenoid

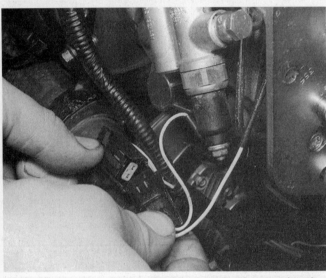

12.4C Disconnecting the wiring for the automatic advance unit and stop solenoid

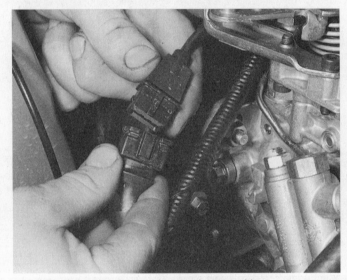

12.5A Disconnecting the throttle potentiometer wiring

12.5B Disconnecting the manifold pressure line from the compensator

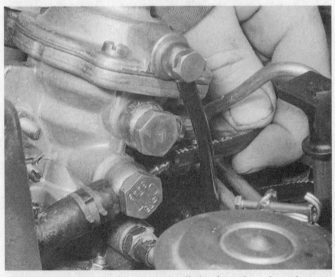

12.7 Disconnecting the injector leak-off pipe from the union adapter

12.8 Disconnecting the fuel leak-off hose at the rear of the injection pump

12.9A Unscrew the high-pressure pipe union nuts . . .

12 Fuel injection pump - removal and refitting

Removal

1   Disconnect the battery earth (negative) lead.

2   Remove the timing belt as described in Chapter 1. If preferred, it is not essential to completely remove the belt, in which case do not drain the cooling system or remove the crankshaft pulley.

3   Disconnect the accelerator cable from the injection pump with reference to Section 11.

4   Disconnect the wiring leads from the stop solenoid, the fast idle solenoid and the automatic advance unit (photos).

5   Disconnect the wiring lead from the throttle potentiometer (where fitted). Where applicable, unscrew the union bolt and disconnect the manifold pressure line from the compensator on the top of the injection pump (photos).

6   Place cloth rags beneath the fuel injection pump, then unscrew the fuel inlet hose union bolt, and recover the sealing washers. Alternatively, loosen the clip and disconnect the fuel inlet hose from the union adapter on the injection pump. Plug the hose, to prevent loss of fuel.

7   Note the routing of the fuel main leak-off pipe to ensure correct refitting (the routing varies between Turbo and non-Turbo models), then disconnect the injector leak-off pipe from the union adapter (photo).

8   Unscrew the fuel leak-off banjo union bolt while holding the adapter stationary. Move the hose to one side, and recover the sealing washers. Alternatively, disconnect the leak-off hose at the rear of the injection pump, and plug the hose (photo).

9   Identify the high-pressure pipes for location, then unscrew the high-pressure pipe union nuts, and remove the pipes from the injection pump and injectors. Always counterhold the delivery valves when loosening the high-pressure pipe unions at the injection pump (photos).

10   Plug or cover the openings in the injection pump, to prevent the ingress of dust and dirt.

12.9B . . . and disconnect the pipes from the injection pump . . .

12.9C . . . and injectors

12.11A Unscrew the locking bolt . . .

12.11B . . . and remove the arrow-shaped spacer from the injection pump

11   If the same injection pump is to be refitted, lock its timing as follows. Unscrew the locking bolt, and remove the arrow-shaped spacer. Make sure that the pump gear timing marks are correctly aligned, then refit and tighten the locking bolt to lock the injection pump shaft (photos).

12   Counterhold the injection pump pulley gear using the tool described in Chapter 1, then unscrew the nut and remove the washer.

13   Unscrew and remove the two timing bolts securing the gear to the injection pump mounting bracket.

14   Using a suitable puller, pull the gear/pulley off the injection pump driveshaft. The Rover tool is described in Chapter 1, and consists of a circular block of metal bolted to the gear, through which a central bolt is screwed. The bolt bears against the driveshaft, and forces the gear off. An alternative puller may be made out of 9 mm thick metal bar to the dimensions shown in Fig. 3.15. Two 8 mm diameter (M8) bolts are then screwed into the holes in the gear, and a 12 mm diameter (M12) bolt in the centre hole pulls the gear off.

15   If necessary, remove the location key from the driveshaft.

16   Mark the injection pump flange and the mounting bracket in relation to each other, as a reference for refitting the pump.

17   If the same injection pump is to be refitted, unscrew and remove the two mounting bolts securing the small rear mounting bracket to the main mounting bracket. The bolts are slightly concealed, but by removing these bolts instead of the rear support plate bolts, the pump timing will be maintained for the refitting procedure (photo).

18   If a different injection pump is being fitted, unscrew the two lower bolts securing the rear support plate to the small bracket. The bolts are located just below the high-pressure delivery valves.

19   Unscrew the nuts securing the pump flange to the mounting bracket, then withdraw the injection pump and remove it from the engine compartment (photos).

20   If a new injection pump is being fitted, unbolt the rear support plate (using an Allen key for the upper bolts), transfer the plate to the new pump, and tighten the bolts securely. Also transfer the stop solenoid to the new pump (photo).

12.11C Injection pump gear timing marks (arrowed)

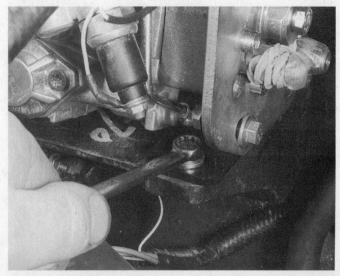

12.17 Unscrew these bolts if the same injection pump is to be refitted

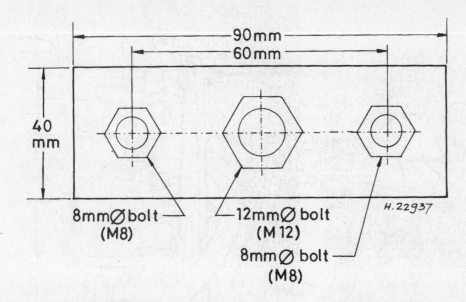

Fig. 3.15 Injection pump gear/pulley removal puller dimensions (Sec 12)

12.19A Unscrew the flange nuts . . .

12.19B . . . and remove the injection pump

12.19C Fuel injection pump removed from the engine

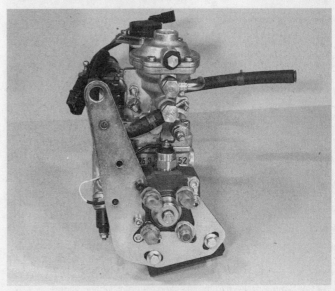

12.20 Showing the rear support plate on the injection pump

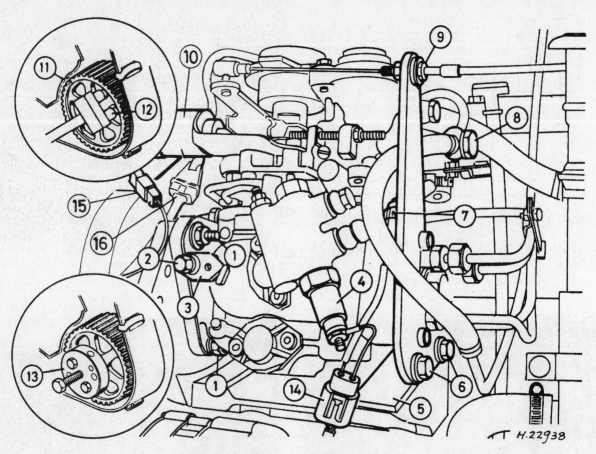

Fig. 3.16 Fuel injection pump removal (Sec 12)

1	Flange nut	7	Stop solenoid	13	Puller
2	Locking bolt	8	Fuel return union	14	Automatic advance/stop solenoid
3	Arrow-shaped spacer	9	Accelerator cable adjuster		connector
4	Automatic advance unit	10	Fast idle solenoid	15	Fast idle connector
5	Support bracket	11	Pump gear/pulley timing marks	16	Throttle potentiometer connector
6	Pump-to-bracket bolts	12	Counterholding tool		plug (where fitted)

12.24 Slots (arrowed) in the injection pump mounting flange

21   If necessary, unbolt the injection pump mounting bracket from the cylinder block, and unbolt the small bracket from the main bracket.

Refitting

22   Start by refitting the main mounting bracket to the cylinder block (if removed), and tighten the bolts.

23   Where applicable, attach the small bracket to the main mounting bracket, and finger-tighten the bolts.

24   Locate the injection pump in the mounting bracket. Where applicable, position it in the mid-range of the travel allowed by the slots, and finger-tighten the nuts at this stage. Insert the rear mounting bolts and finger-tighten as well (photo).

25   Fully tighten the two bolts securing the small bracket to the main bracket.

26   If removed, refit the location key in the injection pump driveshaft groove.

27   Locate the gear/pulley on the injection pump driveshaft with the correct timing marks aligned, and refit the washer and nut. Make sure that the gear/pulley engages correctly with the key, and does not push

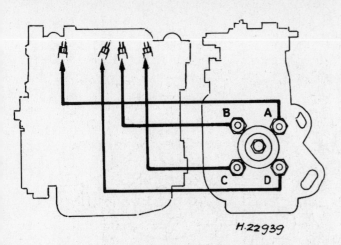

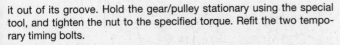

Fig. 3.17 High-pressure pipe connections to the injectors and fuel injection pump (Sec 12)

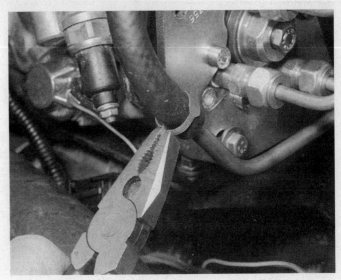

12.33 Tightening the leak-off hose at the rear of the injection pump

it out of its groove. Hold the gear/pulley stationary using the special tool, and tighten the nut to the specified torque. Refit the two temporary timing bolts.

28   Make sure that the camshaft and flywheel timing pins are still in position, then check that the injection pump timing marks are aligned.

29   Unscrew the timing locking screw on the side of the injection pump, refit the arrow-shaped spacer, then tighten the screw to the specified torque.

30   Refit the timing belt and adjust its tension as described in Chapter 1. **Do not** attempt to turn the engine until after the timing pins and injection pump gear holding bolts have been removed.

31   Check and adjust the injection pump timing with reference to Section 13, then fully tighten the pump flange nuts and the two rear support plate bolts. Where the original pump is being refitted, align the previously-made marks as a starting point.

32   Reconnect the high-pressure pipes to the injection pump and injectors. Counterhold the delivery valves, and tighten the high-pressure pipe unions at the injector pump to the specified torque. **Do not** overtighten the unions, as the delivery valves can be distorted. Leave the unions at the injector ends loose at this stage.

33   Refit and tighten the leak-off banjo union bolt and the injector leak-off pipe (make sure that the union bolt with "OUT" stamped on it is used). Renew the aluminium sealing washers if necessary, and make sure that the pipe is routed correctly (the routing in Fig. 3.16 is for Turbo models - on non-Turbo models, the pipe is located on the other side of the support plate). If the hose at the rear of the pump was disconnected on removal, reconnect the hose and fit the clip (photo).

34   Refit the fuel inlet hose or union (as removed). Renew the copper union sealing washers if necessary. Note that the inlet union bolt is identified by having three large holes in it.

35   Reconnect the wiring lead to the throttle potentiometer where fitted.

36   Reconnect the wiring leads to the automatic advance unit, fast idle solenoid and stop solenoid.

37   Refit the accelerator cable to the injection pump, and adjust with reference to Section 11.

38   Reconnect the battery earth (negative) lead.

39   Bleed the fuel system as described in Section 7, and finally tighten the high-pressure pipe unions at the injectors to the specified torque.

13   Fuel injection pump timing - adjustment

Note: *A dial test indicator will be required for this work.*

1   For complete combustion of the diesel fuel and optimum engine performance, a finely-controlled amount of fuel must be supplied by the fuel injection pump to the injector of each cylinder, so that the fuel is injected when the piston reaches a predetermined point before TDC on the compression stroke. If the timing is incorrect, the engine will exhibit various symptoms such as emission of smoke, lack of power, knocking noises, etc. It follows, therefore, that whenever the fuel injection pump has been removed, or if any of the timing components are renewed, the timing should be checked, and if necessary reset.

2   For the home mechanic, the injection timing is checked statically, but some garages may have special equipment for checking the timing dynamically. Having said that, at the time of writing, neither Rover nor Perkins provide dynamic timing values.

3   Start by disconnecting the battery earth (negative) lead.

4   Unscrew the blanking screw from the right-hand end of the camshaft cover, then have an assistant turn the engine slowly clockwise using a socket on the crankshaft pulley bolt, while you look through the hole in the camshaft cover. When the timing hole in the camshaft appears, align it with the cover, and insert a timing pin (or 6.75 mm drill) to lock it. Access to the crankshaft pulley bolt may be better if the front right-hand side of the vehicle is jacked up, and the roadwheel and inner wheelarch cover removed first.

5   Insert another timing pin through the adapter plate into the flywheel. If this pin will not enter, then it will be necessary to remove the timing belt cover and loosen the camshaft gear mounting centre bolt (taper-mounted gear) or the camshaft gear hub mounting bolts (hub-mounted gear), so that the crankshaft may be moved slightly to the TDC position. Tighten the centre bolt or hub bolts, using a suitable tool to counterhold the camshaft gear.

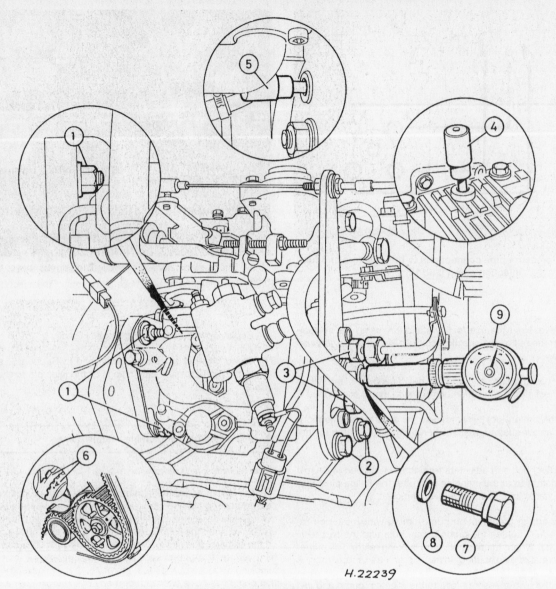

H.22239

Fig. 3.18 Injection pump static timing (Sec 13)

1	Flange nuts	5	Crankshaft timing pin	7	Pump timing access plug
2	Support bracket bolts	6	Pump gear/pulley	8	Washer
3	Delivery valves		timing marks (see text)	9	Dial test indicator
4	Camshaft timing pin				

6   Remove the timing cover, and check that the timing mark on the injection pump gear is aligned with the mark on the timing belt inner cover. Note that there are two timing marks, on opposite sides of the gear - the "A" mark is for non-Turbo models, and the "B" mark is for Turbo models.

7   Wipe clean the rear of the injection pump. Unscrew the blanking screw (photo), and remove the washer from the rear of the injection pump - be prepared for some spillage of fuel. **Do not** allow any dust or foreign matter to enter the injection pump.

8   Fit a dial test indicator (DTI), adapter and probe, so that the probe enters the access hole, and the DTI displays movement of the pump plunger (photos). Temporarily preload the DTI by 2.0 mm.

9   Remove both timing pins, then slowly turn the crankshaft anti-clockwise until the DTI pointer reaches its lowest reading (pump plunger at BDC). Zero the DTI at this point.

10   Slowly turn the crankshaft clockwise until the timing pin can be inserted in the **flywheel** timing hole.

11   Note the plunger movement on the DTI, and compare with the value given in the Specifications. If the movement is not within 0.03 mm (0.0012 in) of the specified value, the timing must be adjusted as follows.

12   Loosen the high-pressure pipe unions at the injectors. Counter-hold the delivery valves, then unscrew the high-pressure pipe unions and disconnect the pipes from them (photo).

13   Loosen the two lower bolts securing the rear support plate to the small bracket. The bolts are located just below the high-pressure delivery valves.

14   Loosen the nuts securing the pump flange to the mounting bracket.

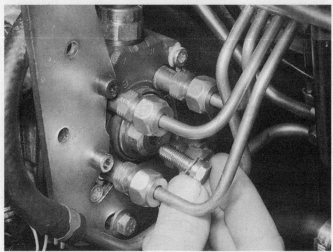

13.7 Removing the blanking screw from the rear of the injection pump

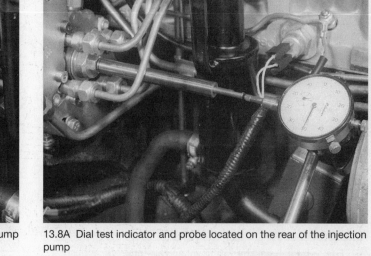

13.8A Dial test indicator and probe located on the rear of the injection pump

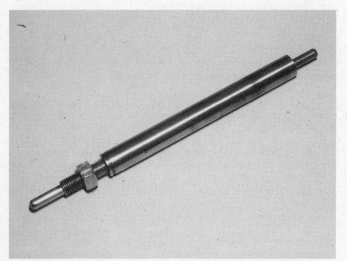

13.8B Home-made probe for fitting to the rear of the injector pump

13.12 Unscrewing the high-pressure pipe union nuts

15   If the plunger movement is too low, move the top of the injection pump body towards the engine (ie clockwise viewed from the left-hand, or flywheel, side of the engine) until the reading is correct. **Note:** *"Left-hand" and "right-hand" are always as seen from the driver's seat.*

16   If the plunger movement is too high, move the top of the injection pump body away from the engine (ie anti-clockwise viewed from the left-hand, or flywheel, side of the engine) until the reading is correct.

17   With the plunger movement correct, tighten the pump flange nuts and the rear support plate bolts.

18   Remove the timing pin from the **flywheel,** and turn the crankshaft a quarter-turn anti-clockwise. Now turn the crankshaft clockwise until the timing pin can be inserted in the **camshaft** timing hole.

19   Check that the plunger movement is the same as given in the Specifications. If not, check the timing belt tension, and recheck the injection pump timing again.

20   Remove the timing pin, and refit the blanking screw to the right-hand end of the camshaft cover.

21   Remove the dial test indicator and adapter, then refit the blanking screw and washer. Tighten the screw securely.

22   Reconnect the high-pressure pipes, and tighten the unions at the injection pump ends. Do not forget to counterhold the delivery valves. Leave the high-pressure pipe unions at the injectors loose at this stage.

23   Reconnect the battery earth (negative) lead.

24   Bleed the fuel system as described in Section 7, and finally tighten the high-pressure pipe unions at the injectors to the specified torque.

---

14   Fuel injection pump stop solenoid - removal and refitting

Removal

1   Unbolt and remove the pump rear support plate to improve access.

2   Make sure that the ignition is switched off, then unscrew the solenoid terminal nut and disconnect the wire.

3   Clean around the solenoid. Unscrew it from the pump, and re-

cover the sealing washer. Operate the hand-priming plunger on the fuel lift pump as the solenoid is removed, to flush away any dirt.

Refitting

4   Refitting is a reversal of the removal procedure.

15 Fuel tank and fuel gauge sender unit - removal and refitting

1   The removal and refitting procedures for the fuel tank are much the same as those described for the petrol-engined variant of the Maestro/Montego model concerned. Reference should be made to the relevant Haynes Owners Workshop Manual.

2   The removal and refitting of the fuel gauge sender unit is also described in the appropriate Manual.

16 Fuel vapour separator - removal and refitting

Note: *This item is not fitted to all models.*

Removal

1   Unscrew the mounting bolt, and lift the EGR modulator valve and bracket from the left-hand side of the engine compartment, leaving all the wiring and vacuum hoses still attached.

2   Identify the hoses for position, then loosen the clips and disconnect them from the fuel vapour separator (photo).

3   Unscrew the mounting bolts and withdraw the unit.

Refitting

4   Refitting is a reversal of the removal procedure.

17 Turbocharger - removal, testing and refitting

Removal

1   Apply the handbrake, then jack up the front of the vehicle and support on axle stands.

2   Remove the right-hand roadwheel and the inner wing access panel.

3   On models fitted with EGR, disconnect the vacuum hose and wiring multi-plug from the EGR valve, and unscrew the nuts securing the exhaust gas recirculation pipe to the exhaust manifold. Recover the gasket.

4   Loosen the clip securing the outlet hose to the turbocharger.

5   Unscrew the bolts securing the outlet elbow to the inlet manifold, then remove the elbow while disconnecting the hose from the turbocharger, and recover the gasket. Plug the turbocharger outlet with clean rag or paper, or tape it over, to prevent the entry of dirt.

6   Loosen the clip and disconnect the inlet hose from the turbocharger. Plug the turbocharger inlet with clean rag or paper, or tape it over.

7   Unscrew the union nut and disconnect the boost pressure pipe from the turbocharger.

16.2 Fuel vapour separator and hoses

8   Partially drain the cooling system with reference to Chapter 2; approximately half of the coolant should be drained.

9   Loosen the clips, and disconnect the hoses from each end of the heater coolant rail attached to the inlet manifold. Unbolt and remove the heater rail.

10   Disconnect the wiring from the coolant temperature sensor located on the thermostat housing.

11   Detach the brake vacuum pump drain pipe clip bracket, then release the clips from the hoses, and remove the drain pipe from the vacuum pump and sump adapter.

12   Unscrew the bolt securing the turbocharger oil feed pipe to the cylinder block. Unscrew the union nut, and disconnect the pipe from the oil pump.

13   Loosen the clips and move the oil drain hose onto the sump adapter.

14   Unscrew and remove the inlet manifold retaining bolts, and withdraw the inlet manifold from the cylinder head.

15   Unscrew the nuts and disconnect the exhaust pipe from the turbocharger elbow flange. Recover the gasket.

16   Unscrew the bolts securing the turbocharger stiffening plate to the elbow and cylinder block.

17   If necessary, the vehicle may be lowered to the ground at this stage, after refitting the roadwheel. This is purely to make working in the engine compartment easier.

18   Unscrew the bolts securing the exhaust manifold to the cylinder head, then remove the manifold together with the turbocharger unit upwards from the engine compartment (photo). Recover the gasket.

19   Unscrew the union nut, and disconnect the inner end of the oil feed pipe from the turbocharger.

20   Unscrew the nuts securing the exhaust manifold to the turbocharger, separate the two components, and recover the gasket (photos).

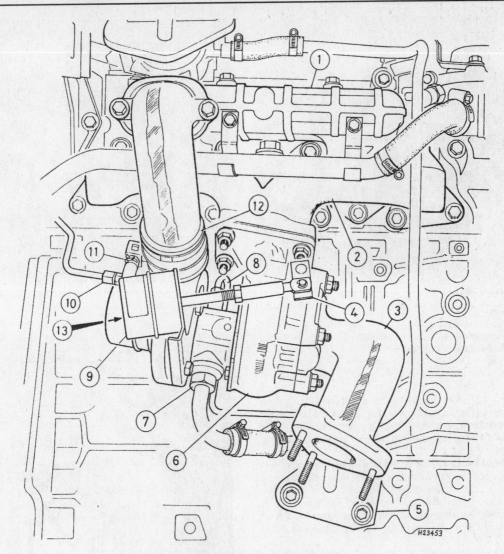

Fig. 3.19 Turbocharger details (Sec 17)

1	Inlet manifold	6	Turbocharger	11	Wastegate actuator hose
2	Exhaust manifold	7	Oil return pipe	12	Air outlet
3	Elbow	8	Oil feed pipe	13	Air inlet
4	Wastegate linkage	9	Wastegate actuator		
5	Elbow stiffening plate	10	Boost pressure pipe		

17.18 Turbocharger and manifold assembly

17.20A Removing the exhaust manifold and gasket from the turbocharger

17.20B Turbocharger assembly

17.21 Nuts securing the elbow to the turbocharger

21   Unscrew the retaining nuts and remove the elbow from the turbocharger (photo). Recover the gasket.

Testing

22   If an unusual high-pitched noise has been noticed when the engine is running with the turbocharger operating, check the air inlet and outlet hoses for possible cracks. Also check the joints between the exhaust downpipe and elbow, and between the elbow and turbocharger.

23   Testing of the wastegate requires the use of special equipment, and therefore this work should be carried out by a Rover dealer.

24   The compressor and turbine may be checked as follows with the turbocharger removed from the vehicle. First, visually examine the turbine and compressor rotors for signs of damage, distortion and discoloration.

25   Check that the shaft turns smoothly while moving it side to side, and make sure that the rotor tips do not rub against the housing.

26   Mount a dial test indicator with its probe touching the end of the turbine, then move the turbine from side to side and check that the endfloat is between 0.01 and 0.10 mm.

27   Insert the probe through the oil drain hole, and zero it on the shaft, then move the shaft radially and check that the clearance is between 0.05 and 0.10 mm.

28   If any of the readings are outside the tolerances, the turbocharger must be renewed, as it is not possible to make repairs. Remove the dial test indicator on completion.

Refitting

29   Before refitting the turbocharger, inject 140 ml (a quarter of a pint) of clean engine oil into the turbo oil inlet (photo). Spin the shaft to distribute the oil over the bearings.

30   Refit the exhaust outlet elbow to the turbocharger, using a new gasket. Tighten the retaining nuts progressively.

31   Refit the turbocharger to the exhaust manifold, using a new gasket. Tighten the retaining nuts progressively and in diagonal sequence.

32   Make sure that the mating faces are clean, then locate a new

17.29 Injecting clean oil into the turbo oil inlet

manifold gasket on the cylinder head with its shiny side facing outwards. Retain it with two of the inlet manifold bolts, inserted by a few threads.

33   Connect the inner end of the oil feed pipe to the turbocharger; tighten the nut, making sure that the pipe is located in its normal position.

34   Locate the turbocharger and exhaust manifold assembly on the rear of the cylinder head, and insert the retaining bolts finger-tight at this stage.

35   If the vehicle is on the ground, jack it up and support on axle stands.

36   Move the oil drain hose onto the sump adapter, and tighten the clips.

37   Locate the oil feed pipe retaining bolt on the cylinder block, then screw the union nut loosely onto the oil pump. Tighten the retaining bolt and union nut.

18.3 Multi-plug (arrowed) on the bottom of the EGR control unit

18.4 Removing the EGR control unit from the bulkhead

38   Refit the stiffening plate to the elbow and cylinder block, but do not fully tighten them at this stage.

39   Refit the exhaust pipe to the turbocharger elbow flange, together with a new gasket, but leave the nuts loose at this stage.

40   Remove the two location bolts, then locate the inlet manifold on the cylinder head, and insert all of the bolts loosely.

41   Tighten the inlet and exhaust manifold retaining bolts to the specified torque, in the sequence shown in Fig. 3.21.

42   Tighten the nuts securing the exhaust pipe to the turbocharger. Note that there must be no stress applied to the turbocharger elbow, otherwise premature failure of the turbocharger may result. Re-position the exhaust pipe if necessary.

43   Tighten the stiffener plate bolts.

44   Refit the brake vacuum pump drain pipe and hoses, and tighten the clips. Refit the bracket.

45   Refit the outlet elbow to the inlet manifold, at the same time connecting the hose to the turbocharger (do not forget to remove the rag or paper used to plug the outlet). Fit a new gasket. Tighten the bolts and the hose clip.

46   Reconnect the boost control pipe, and tighten the union nut.

47   Refit the inlet hose to the turbocharger, and tighten the clip (do not forget to remove the rag or paper used to plug the inlet).

48   Reconnect the wiring to the coolant temperature sensor on the thermostat housing.

49   Refit the heater rail to the inlet manifold, and tighten the bolts. Reconnect the hoses to the rail, and tighten the clips.

50   On models fitted with EGR, refit the exhaust gas recirculation pipe to the exhaust manifold together with a new gasket, and tighten the bolts to the specified torque. Reconnect the wiring multi-plug and vacuum hose.

51   Refit the inner wing access panel and the right-hand roadwheel. Lower the vehicle to the ground.

52   Disconnect the wiring from the stop solenoid on the injection pump, then spin the engine on the starter motor until the low oil pressure warning light goes out. Reconnect the wiring.

53   Refill the cooling system with reference to Chapter 2.

54   Change the engine oil and filter with reference to Chapter 1.

18   EGR control unit - removal and refitting

Removal

1   Disconnect the battery earth (negative) lead.

2   With the left-hand passenger door open, pull the carpet from the bulkhead to reveal the EGR control unit.

3   Carefully disconnect the multi-plug from the bottom of the unit (photo).

4   Unscrew the two crosshead mounting screws, and withdraw the control unit from the bulkhead (photo).

Refitting

5   Refitting is a reversal of the removal procedure.

19   EGR valve - removal, cleaning and refitting

Removal

1   Disconnect the battery earth (negative) lead.

2   Carefully disconnect the multi-plug from the top of the valve.

3   Disconnect the vacuum hose from the top of the valve.

19.4 Removing the recirculation pipe-to-EGR valve bolts

19.6 Removing the EGR valve

4   Unscrew and remove the bolts securing the recirculation pipe to the EGR valve (photo).

5   Using an Allen key, unscrew and remove the bolts securing the EGR valve to the inlet manifold.

6   Withdraw the EGR valve from the inlet manifold and recirculation pipe, and recover the gaskets (photo).

Cleaning

7   Using a small wire brush, clean all carbon from the valve apertures and mating surfaces of the valve, recirculation pipe and inlet manifold. Also clean the outer surfaces of the valve. Take care not to damage the valve diaphragm.

8   Using a screwdriver, depress the valve against its diaphragm, and check the valve seating for deposits of carbon.

9   To check the diaphragm, apply vacuum to the port, and make sure that the valve moves away from, and back onto, its seat correctly.

Refitting

10   Refitting is a reversal of the removal procedure, but use new gaskets and tighten all bolts to the specified torque.

20   EGR modulator valve - removal and refitting

Removal

1   Disconnect the battery earth (negative) lead.

2   Disconnect the multi-plug from the side of the valve (photo).

3   Identify the hose positions, then disconnect them from the modulator valve.

4   Unscrew the mounting screws, and remove the modulator valve from the mounting on the side of the front suspension turret.

Refitting

5   Refitting is a reversal of the removal procedure.

20.2 Disconnecting the multi-plug from the side of the EGR modulator valve

21   Inlet and exhaust manifolds (non-Turbo models) - removal and refitting

Removal

1   Disconnect the battery earth (negative) lead.

2   Loosen the clip and disconnect the inlet air duct from the inlet manifold.

3   Unscrew and remove the bolts securing the coolant rail to the inlet manifold.

4   Loosen (but do not remove) the bolts securing the manifolds to the cylinder head, using the reverse sequence to that shown in Fig. 3.21.

5   Remove the bolts and withdraw the inlet manifold from the cylinder head. Note that the upper bolts have thick washers fitted, whereas the lower bolts do not have any washers.

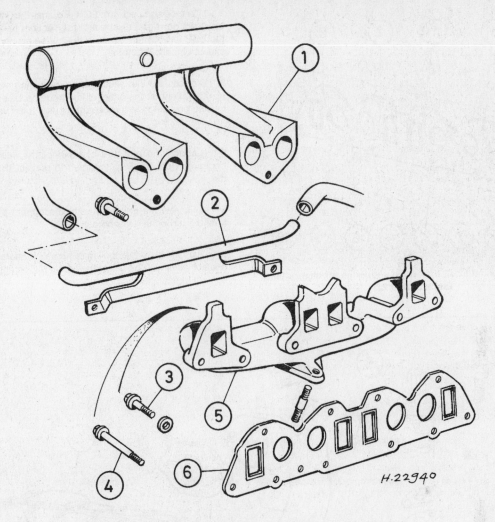

Fig. 3.20 Inlet and exhaust manifolds on non-Turbo models (Sec 21)

1	Inlet manifold	3	Bolt (35 mm long)	5	Exhaust manifold
2	Coolant rail	4	Bolt (55 mm long)	6	Gasket

6   Unscrew and remove the nuts securing the exhaust pipe flange to the exhaust manifold, and separate the exhaust pipe. Recover the gasket.

7   Remove the bolts and withdraw the exhaust manifold from the cylinder head. Recover the gasket.

Refitting

8   Clean the mating surfaces of the manifolds and cylinder head.

9   Insert two bolts through the exhaust manifold, and locate the manifold gasket on them, making sure that the shiny side is towards the manifold; the shiny side should be marked "THIS SIDE OUT".

10   Using a new gasket, locate the exhaust manifold on the exhaust pipe and lightly tighten the nuts.

11   Offer the exhaust manifold and gasket onto the cylinder head, and lightly tighten the two bolts.

12   Refit the coolant rail, and insert the remaining bolts. Lightly tighten the bolts.

13   Locate the inlet manifold on the cylinder head, then insert the bolts and lightly tighten them. Fit the thick washers to the upper bolts.

14   Progressively tighten the manifold bolts to the specified torque, in the sequence shown in Fig. 3.21.

15   Tighten the exhaust pipe flange nuts.

16   Tighten the coolant rail bolts.

17   Refit the inlet air duct to the inlet manifold, and tighten the clip.

18   Reconnect the battery earth (negative) lead.

22 Inlet and exhaust manifolds (Turbo models) - removal and refitting

Removal

1   Apply the handbrake, then jack up the front of the vehicle and support on axle stands. Remove the right-hand roadwheel and the access panel from inside the wheelarch.

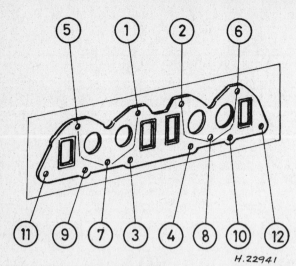

Fig. 3.21 Manifold bolt tightening sequence for all models (Secs 21 and 22)

2   On models fitted with EGR (Exhaust Gas Recirculation - September 1992 onwards) disconnect the vacuum hose and multi-plug from the EGR valve, then unscrew the bolts securing the EGR pipe to the exhaust manifold (photos).

3   Loosen the clip securing the turbocharger outlet hose to the elbow, then unbolt the outlet elbow from the inlet manifold. Recover the gasket, and plug the turbocharger outlet to prevent the ingress of dust and dirt (photo).

4   Loosen the clip and disconnect the inlet hose from the turbocharger (photo). Plug the inlet, to prevent the ingress of dust and dirt.

5   Unscrew the union nut, and disconnect the boost control pipe from the turbocharger (photos).

6   Partially drain the cooling system with reference to Chapter 2. The coolant level must be below the heater rail, so approximately half of the coolant capacity should be drained.

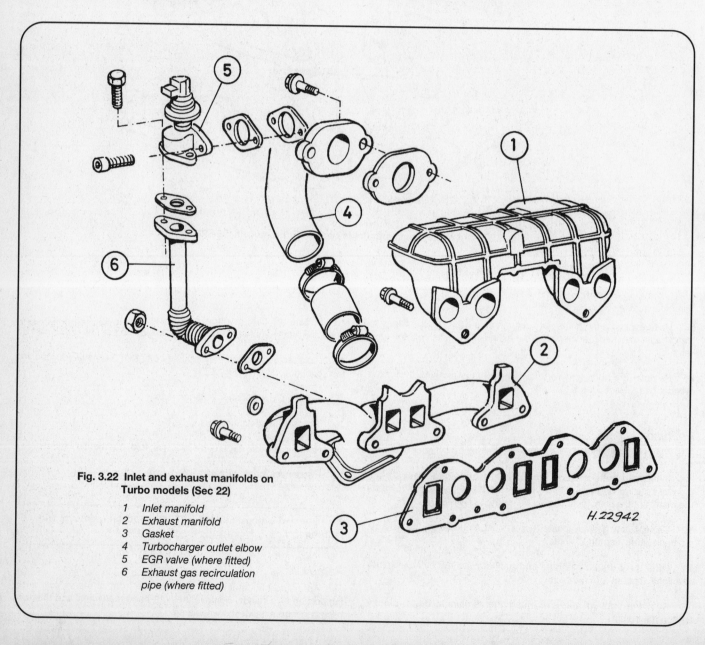

Fig. 3.22 Inlet and exhaust manifolds on Turbo models (Sec 22)

1   Inlet manifold
2   Exhaust manifold
3   Gasket
4   Turbocharger outlet elbow
5   EGR valve (where fitted)
6   Exhaust gas recirculation pipe (where fitted)

22.2A Disconnecting the vacuum hose . . .

22.2B . . . and multi-plug from the EGR valve

22.3 Removing the turbocharger outlet elbow and gasket from the inlet manifold

22.4 Disconnecting the inlet hose from the turbocharger

22.5A Unscrew the union nut . . .

22.5B . . . and disconnect the boost control pipe (arrowed) from the turbocharger

22.7A Disconnecting the coolant hose from the left-hand end of the heater rail

22.7B Hose connection to the right-hand end of the heater rail - also shown is a heater rail mounting bolt (arrowed)

22.10 Brake vacuum pump drain pipe hose (arrowed) on the crankcase adapter

22.11 Unbolting the turbocharger oil feed pipe bracket (arrowed) from the cylinder block

22.12 Turbocharger oil drain pipe hose (arrowed)

22.14A Unscrew the mounting bolts . . .

22.14B . . . and remove the inlet manifold

22.15A Unscrewing the exhaust pipe-to-turbocharger mounting nuts

7   Loosen the clips and disconnect the hoses from each end of the heater rail, then unbolt the rail from the inlet manifold (photos).

8   Disconnect the wiring from the coolant temperature sensor on the thermostat housing.

9   Disconnect the brake vacuum pump drain pipe support from the bracket on the thermostat cover.

10   Loosen the clips securing the hoses to each end of the brake vacuum pump drain pipe, and remove the pipe (photo).

11   Unscrew the bolt securing the turbocharger oil feed pipe bracket to the cylinder block, then unscrew the union nut and disconnect the pipe from the oil pump (photo).

12   Loosen the turbocharger oil drain pipe hose clips, and slide the hose onto the adapter on the sump (photo).

13   Loosen (but do not remove) the bolts securing the inlet and ex-

haust manifolds to the cylinder head, in the reverse sequence to that shown in Fig. 3.21.

14   Remove the bolts and withdraw the inlet manifold (photos).

15   Unscrew the nuts and disconnect the exhaust pipe from the turbocharger elbow. Recover the gasket (photos).

16   Unbolt the turbocharger stiffening plate from the cylinder block and elbow (photo).

17   Remove the bolts and withdraw the exhaust manifold, together with the turbocharger and elbow. Recover the gasket.

Refitting

18   Clean the mating surfaces of the manifolds and cylinder head.

19   Locate a new gasket on the cylinder head, with its shiny side facing outwards, and retain in position using two bolts inserted in the inlet

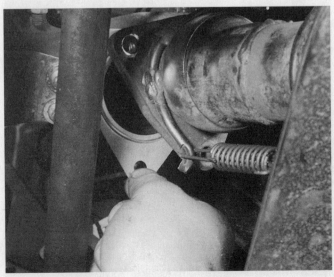

22.15B Removing the exhaust pipe flange gasket

22.16 Removing the turbocharger stiffening plate

22.19A Manifold gasket held in position with inlet manifold bolts

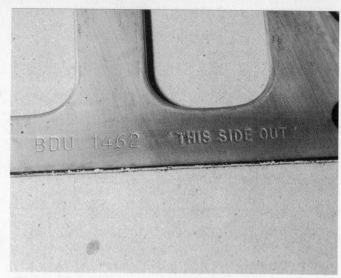

22.19B Orientation marking on the manifold gasket

manifold bolt holes. The shiny side of the gasket should be marked "THIS SIDE OUT" (photos).

20   Refit the exhaust manifold together with the turbocharger and elbow, and lightly tighten the mounting bolts (photos).

21   Slide the turbocharger oil drain pipe hose centrally onto the pipe and adapter, and tighten the two clips.

22   Connect the turbocharger oil feed pipe to the oil pump, and loosely tighten the union nut. Insert and tighten the bolt securing the pipe to the cylinder block, then tighten the union nut.

23   Refit the turbocharger stiffening plate, and insert the bolts loosely.

24   Refit the exhaust pipe to the turbocharger elbow flange together with a new gasket, and lightly tighten the nuts.

25   Remove the two bolts, then refit the inlet manifold and insert the bolts loosely.

26   Tighten the inlet and exhaust manifold bolts progressively to the specified torque, in the sequence shown in Fig. 3.21.

27   Tighten the stiffening plate bolts and turbocharger elbow flange nuts. Make sure that the exhaust pipe is aligned correctly, and that no stress is applied to the elbow.

28   Refit the brake vacuum pump drain pipe, and tighten the hose clips. Reconnect the pipe to the support on the thermostat cover.

29   Refit the boost control pipe, and tighten the union nut.

30   Refit the inlet hose to the turbocharger, and tighten the clip.

31   Refit the turbocharger outlet elbow together with a new gasket, and tighten the bolts and hose clip.

32   Reconnect the wiring to the coolant temperature sensor on the thermostat housing.

22.20A Exhaust manifold central mounting bolt (arrowed)

22.20B Inserting an outer exhaust manifold mounting bolt

33   Refit the heater rail, and tighten the bolts. Reconnect the hoses, and tighten the clips.

34   On models fitted with EGR (September 1992 onwards) refit the exhaust gas recirculation pipe to the exhaust manifold together with a new gasket, and tighten the bolts (photo). Reconnect the multi-plug and vacuum hose to the EGR valve.

35   Refit the access panel and roadwheel, then lower the vehicle to the ground.

36   Refill the cooling system with reference to Chapter 2.

23 Exhaust system - inspection, removal and refitting

1   The exhaust system should be examined for leaks, damage and security at regular intervals (see *"Routine maintenance"*). To do this, apply the handbrake and allow the engine to idle. Lie down on each side of the vehicle in turn, and check the full length of the exhaust system for leaks while an assistant briefly places a wad of cloth over the end of the tailpipe. If a leak is evident, stop the engine and use a proprietary repair kit to seal it. Holts Flexiwrap and Holts Gun Gum exhaust repair systems can be used for effective repairs to exhaust pipes and silencer boxes, including ends and bends. Holts Flexiwrap is an MOT-approved permanent exhaust repair. If the leak is excessive, or damage is evident, renew the section. Note that Holts Firegum is suitable for the assembly of all exhaust system joints. Check the rubber mountings for deterioration, and renew them if necessary.

2   To remove the exhaust system, jack up the front and/or rear of the vehicle, and support it securely on axle stands. Alternatively, drive the front or rear wheels up on ramps.

3   The exhaust system is in three sections. To remove the rear section, unscrew the nuts of the U-clamp securing the rear section to the intermediate section. Release the rear rubber mounting block, and using a twisting action, withdraw the rear section from the intermediate section. If the joint is stubborn, liberally apply penetrating oil and leave it to soak. Tap the joint with a hammer and it should now be possible to twist it free. If necessary, carefully heat the joint with a blowlamp to assist removal, *but shield the fuel tank, fuel lines and underbody adequately from heat.* Pass the rear silencer over the rear axle, and remove the exhaust section from the rear.

4   To remove the intermediate section, first remove the rear section. The intermediate section can now be removed using the procedure described above.

22.34 Locating a new EGR recirculation pipe gasket on the exhaust manifold

5   To remove the front section, first remove the rear and intermediate sections. Where applicable, unscrew the bolts securing the anti-roll bar clamps to the front crossmember, lever down the anti-roll bar as far as possible, and wedge it in this position using blocks of wood. Unscrew the nuts securing the downpipe flange to the exhaust manifold (or turbocharger elbow), separate the joint and recover the gasket. Lower the front section, and remove it from under the vehicle. Remove the tension springs.

6   Refitting is a reversal of the removal procedure. Position the joints so that there is adequate clearance between all parts of the system and the underbody, and ensure that there is equal load on all rubber mounting blocks. Always use a new gasket on the downpipe flange. When fitting the front pipe, position it at least 20 mm (0.75 in) above the front subframe. On Turbo models, do not stress the turbocharger outlet elbow, otherwise premature failure of the turbocharger may result; align the downpipe first before tightening the bolts. When connecting the rear exhaust section to the front section, apply exhaust jointing compound to the pipe ends first. The anti-roll bar long mounting bolts should be fitted in the rear holes; tighten all bolts securely, or to the specified torque, where applicable.

24 Fault diagnosis - fuel system

Symptom	Reason(s)
Engine turns but will not start (cold)	Incorrect use of preheating system Preheating system fault Fuel waxing (in very cold weather) Cold start advance mechanism defective
Engine turns but will not start (hot or cold)	Low cranking speed Poor compression No fuel in tank Air in fuel system Fuel feed restriction Fuel contaminated Engine stop solenoid defective Major mechanical failure Injection pump internal fault
Low cranking speed	Inadequate battery capacity Incorrect grade of oil High resistance in starter motor circuit Starter motor internal fault
Engine is difficult to start	Incorrect starting procedure Battery or starter motor fault Preheating system fault Air in fuel system Fuel feed restriction Fuel lift pump defective Poor compression Valve clearances incorrect Valves sticking Blockage in exhaust system Valve timing incorrect Injector(s) faulty Injection pump timing incorrect Injection pump internal fault
Engine starts but stops again	Very low fuel level in tank Air in fuel system Idle adjustment incorrect Fast idle unit fault Fuel feed restriction Fuel return restriction Air cleaner dirty Blockage in induction system Blockage in exhaust system Injector(s) faulty
Engine will not stop when switched off	Stop solenoid defective
Misfiring/rough idle	Air cleaner dirty Blockage in induction system Air in fuel system Fuel feed restriction Valve clearances incorrect Fuel lift pump defective Valve(s) sticking Valve spring(s) weak or broken Poor compression Overheating Injector pipe(s) wrongly connected or wrong type Valve timing incorrect Injector(s) faulty or wrong type Injection pump timing incorrect Injection pump faulty or wrong type

Lack of power

Accelerator linkage not moving through full travel (cable slack or pedal obstructed)
Air cleaner dirty
Blockage in induction system
Air in fuel system
Fuel feed restriction
Fuel lift pump defective
Valve timing incorrect
Injection pump timing incorrect
Blockage in exhaust system
Turbo boost pressure inadequate (where applicable)
Valve clearances incorrect
Poor compression
Injector(s) faulty or wrong type
Injection pump faulty or wrong type

Fuel consumption excessive

External leakage
Fuel passing into sump
Air cleaner dirty
Blockage in induction system
Valve clearances incorrect
Valve(s) sticking
Valve spring(s) weak
Poor compression
Valve timing incorrect
Injection pump timing incorrect
Injector(s) faulty or wrong type
Injection pump faulty or wrong type

Engine knocks

Air in fuel system
Fuel grade incorrect or quality poor
Injector(s) faulty or wrong type
Valve spring(s) weak or broken
Valve(s) sticking
Valve clearances incorrect
Valve timing incorrect
Injection pump timing incorrect
Piston protrusion excessive/head gasket thickness inadequate (after repair)
Valve recess incorrect (after repair)
Piston rings broken or worn
Pistons and/or bores worn
Crankshaft bearings worn or damaged
Small-end bearings worn
Camshaft worn

Black smoke in exhaust

Air cleaner dirty
Blockage in induction system
Valve clearances incorrect
Poor compression
Turbo boost pressure inadequate (where applicable)
Blockage in exhaust system
Valve timing incorrect
Injector(s) faulty or wrong type
Injection pump timing incorrect
Injection pump faulty or wrong type

Blue or white smoke in exhaust

Incorrect-grade or poor-quality engine oil
Glow plug(s) defective, or controller faulty (smoke at start-up only)
Air cleaner dirty
Blockage in induction system
Valve timing incorrect
Injection pump timing incorrect
Injector(s) defective
Engine running too cool
Oil entering via valve stems
Poor compression
Head gasket blown
Piston rings broken or worn
Pistons and/or bores worn

Oil consumption excessive

External leakage (standing or running)
New engine not yet run-in
Incorrect-grade or poor-quality engine oil
Oil level too high
Crankcase ventilation system obstructed
Oil leakage from vacuum pump
Oil cooler leaking into coolant
Air cleaner dirty
Blockage in induction system
Cylinder bores glazed
Piston rings broken or worn
Pistons and/or bores worn
Valve stems or guides worn
Valve stem oil seals worn

Overheating

Coolant leakage
Engine oil level too high
Electric cooling fan malfunctioning
Water pump drivebelt slack or broken
Water pump defective
Radiator clogged externally
Radiator clogged internally
Hoses blocked or collapsed
Pressure cap defective or incorrect rating
Thermostat defective or incorrect
Head gasket blown
Cylinder head cracked or warped
Valve timing incorrect
Injection pump timing incorrect
Injector(s) faulty or wrong type
Injection pump faulty or wrong type
Imminent seizure (piston pick-up)

Crankcase pressure excessive (oil being blown out)

Blockage in crankcase ventilation system
Leakage in vacuum pump
Piston rings broken or sticking
Pistons or bores worn
Head gasket blown

Erratic running

Operating temperature incorrect
Air cleaner dirty
Blockage in induction system
Air in fuel system
Injector pipe(s) wrongly connected or wrong type
Fuel feed restriction
Fuel return restriction
Fuel lift pump defective
Valve clearances incorrect
Valve(s) sticking
Valve spring(s) broken or weak
Valve timing incorrect
Poor compression
Injector(s) faulty or wrong type
Injection pump mountings loose
Injection pump timing incorrect
Injection pump faulty

Vibration

Engine mountings loose or worn
Injector pipe(s) wrongly connected or wrong type
Valve(s) sticking
Flywheel loose
Poor (uneven) compression

Low oil pressure

Oil level low
Oil grade or quality incorrect
Oil filter clogged
Overheating
Oil contaminated
Gauge or warning light sender inaccurate

Low oil pressure (continued)

Oil pump pick-up strainer clogged
Oil pump suction pipe loose or cracked
Oil pressure relief valve defective or stuck open
Oil pump worn
Crankshaft bearings worn

High oil pressure

Oil grade or quality incorrect
Gauge inaccurate
Oil pressure relief valve stuck shut

Injector pipe(s) break or split repeatedly

Missing or wrongly-located clamps
Wrong type or length of pipe
Faulty injector
Faulty delivery valve

Notes

Chapter 4 Clutch

Contents

Specifications

Type .... Single dry plate, operated by self-adjusting cable

Clutch disc diameter .... 215.0 mm

Torque wrench setting

	Nm	lbf ft
Clutch cover to flywheel	23	17

1   General description

The clutch fitted to all diesel-engined models is the same as the clutch fitted to petrol-engined Montego models with the Honda gearbox (1989-on 1.6 litre Montego, and all 2.0 litre Montego models). Maestro petrol-engined models (fitted with the VW gearbox) have a different-type clutch.

The clutch is of conventional diaphragm spring type, operated mechanically by a self-adjusting cable. The clutch components comprise a steel cover assembly, clutch disc or driven plate, release bearing and release mechanism. The cover assembly, which is bolted and dowelled to the rear face of the flywheel, contains the pressure plate and diaphragm spring.

The clutch disc is free to slide along the gearbox input shaft splines, and is held in position between the flywheel and pressure plate by the pressure of the diaphragm spring.

Friction material is riveted to the clutch disc, which has a spring-cushioned hub to absorb transmission shocks and to help ensure a smooth take-up of the drive.

Depressing the clutch pedal moves the clutch release lever on the gearbox by means of the clutch cable. This movement is transmitted to the release bearing, which moves inwards against the fingers of the diaphragm spring. The spring is sandwiched between two annular rings, which act as fulcrum points. As the release bearing pushes the spring fingers in, the outer circumference pivots out, so moving the pressure plate away from the flywheel and releasing its grip on the clutch disc.

When the pedal is released, the diaphragm spring forces the pressure plate into contact with the friction linings of the clutch disc. The disc is now firmly sandwiched between the pressure plate and the flywheel, thus transmitting engine power to the gearbox.

Adjustment of the clutch to compensate for wear of the clutch disc friction linings is automatically taken up by the self-adjusting mechanism incorporated in the cable.

3.3 Releasing the inner cable from the clutch operating lever

3.4 Removing the clutch cable assembly from the gearbox mounting bracket

2   Routine maintenance

Carry out the following procedure at the intervals given in the *"Routine maintenance"* Section at the start of this manual.

Check the cable self-adjusting mechanism

1   Using moderate hand pressure, push the clutch lever on the bell-housing downwards (in the opposite direction to its normal travel) through its full stroke.

2   When released, the lever should return to its original position.

3   Press the adjuster body into its abutment on the engine bulkhead with one hand, and with the other, pull the outer cable away from the bulkhead until resistance is felt (hold the outer cable at a point just behind the spring).

4   Release both parts of the cable.

5   This procedure should ensure the self-adjusting mechanism is correctly set and working properly. If the adjuster fails to operate correctly, refer to Section 3.

3   Clutch cable - removal and refitting

Removal

1   Working in the engine compartment, release the clutch outer cable from its retaining clips and cable ties.

2   Using pliers, withdraw the retaining clip from the cable at the end of the self-adjusting spring.

3   Release the inner cable from the clutch operating lever by sliding out the retaining clip and cable seating plate located on the underside of the lever. On later models, it is only necessary to pull out the end fitting, and slide the inner cable through the slot in the lever (photo).

4   Withdraw the inner cable end from the operating lever rubber pad, release the rubber retainer, and withdraw the cable assembly from the gearbox mounting bracket (photo).

5   From inside the vehicle, unhook the cable end from the clutch pedal, and withdraw the cable into the engine compartment. Remove the cable assembly from the vehicle.

Refitting

6   To refit the cable, feed the hooked end through the engine compartment bulkhead, and connect it to the pedal. Ensure that the outer cable is located correctly in the bulkhead tube.

7   Route the cable through the engine compartment, locating it in its retaining clips and cable ties.

8   Feed the cable through the mounting bracket until the guide sleeve is seated squarely in the bracket.

9   Feed the inner cable through the rubber pad of the operating lever, and slide on the cable seating plate and retaining clip. On later models, slide the inner cable onto the lever.

10   Refit the retaining clip to the cable at the end of the self-adjusting spring. Press down on the clutch operating lever, and at the same time pull up on the cable to operate the self-adjusting mechanism.

4   Clutch assembly - removal, inspection and refitting

Removal

1   Remove the gearbox with reference to Chapter 5, but leave it positioned to the left-hand side of the engine compartment.

2   In a diagonal sequence, and half a turn at a time, slacken the bolts securing the clutch cover assembly to the flywheel (photo).

3   When all of the bolts have been slackened, remove them and then ease the cover assembly off the locating dowels. Collect the clutch disc, which will drop out when the cover assembly is removed (photo).

4   With the clutch assembly removed, clean off all traces of asbestos dust, using a dry cloth. This is best done outside, or in a well-ventilated area - *asbestos dust is harmful, and must not be inhaled.*

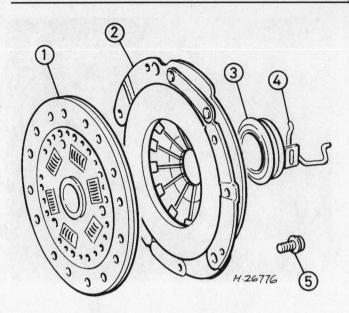

Fig.4.1 Clutch components (Sec 4)

1 Clutch disc
2 Clutch cover
3 Release bearing

4 Retaining clip
5 Clutch cover bolt

4.2 Unscrewing the clutch cover bolts

Inspection

5   Examine the linings of the clutch disc for wear and loose rivets, and the disc for rim distortion, cracks, broken torsion springs and worn splines. The surface of the friction linings may be highly-glazed in appearance, but, as long as the friction material pattern can be clearly seen, this is satisfactory. If there is any sign of oil contamination, indicated by a continuous, or patchy, shiny black discolouration, the disc must be renewed, and the source of the contamination traced and rectified. This will be either a leaking crankshaft oil seal or gearbox mainshaft oil seal - or both. Renewal procedures are given in Chapter 1 and Chapter 5, Section 9 respectively. The disc must also be renewed if the lining thickness has worn down to, or just above, the level of the rivet heads.

6   Check the machined faces of the flywheel and pressure plate. If either is grooved, or heavily-scored, renewal is necessary. The pres-

sure plate must also be renewed if any cracks are apparent, or if the diaphragm spring is damaged or its pressure suspect.

7   With the gearbox removed, it is advisable to check the condition of the release bearing, as described in the following Section.

Refitting

8   To refit the clutch assembly, place the clutch disc in position, with the raised portion of the spring hub facing away from the flywheel. The words "FLYWHEEL SIDE" will also usually be found on the other side of the disc that faces the flywheel (photo).

9   Hold the disc in place, and refit the cover assembly loosely on the dowels. Refit the retaining bolts, and tighten them finger-tight so that the clutch disc is gripped, but can still be moved.

10   The clutch disc must now be centralised, so that when the engine and gearbox are mated, the gearbox input shaft splines will pass through the splines in the centre of the hub.

11   Centralisation can be carried out quite easily, by inserting a round bar or long screwdriver through the hole in the centre of the clutch

4.3 Removing the clutch cover and disc from the flywheel

4.8 "FLYWHEEL SIDE" marking on the disc

4.11 Checking the clutch disc centralisation with a socket and steel rule

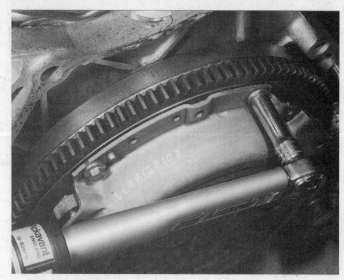

4.12 Tightening the clutch cover bolts

disc, so that the end of the bar rests in the hole in the centre of the crankshaft. Moving the bar sideways or up and down will move the clutch disc in whichever direction is necessary to achieve centralisation. It is possible to view the edge of the clutch disc through the cut-outs in the cover, and to align this with the shoulder on the flywheel; centralisation is correct when the disc is aligned all the way round the flywheel. If the engine has been removed from the vehicle, centralisation will be easier. With the bar removed, view the clutch disc hub in relation to the hole in the end of the crankshaft and the circle created by the ends of the diaphragm spring fingers. When the hub appears exactly in the centre, all is correct. A close-fitting socket may be located in the flywheel hole, and vernier calipers or a steel rule used to measure the distance between the ends of the fingers and the socket (photo). Alternatively, if a clutch-aligning tool can be obtained (these are readily-available from good motor accessory shops) this will eliminate all the guesswork, and obviates the need for visual alignment.

12   Tighten the cover retaining bolts gradually, in a diagonal sequence, to the specified torque wrench setting (photo).

13   The gearbox can now be refitted, with reference to Chapter 5.

5   Clutch release bearing - removal, inspection and refitting

Removal

1   Remove the gearbox with reference to Chapter 5.

2   Release the retaining spring clip (where fitted) from the bearing and fork, then slide the bearing off the gearbox input shaft (photos).

3   If it is required to remove the operating lever, unscrew the fork retaining bolt, then slide the lever out of the gearbox housing (photo). Recover the fork and seal.

Inspection

4   Check the bearing for smoothness of operation, and renew it if there is any roughness or harshness as the bearing is spun.

5   Check and if necessary renew the operating lever bush in the gearbox housing.

5.2A Release the spring clip . . .

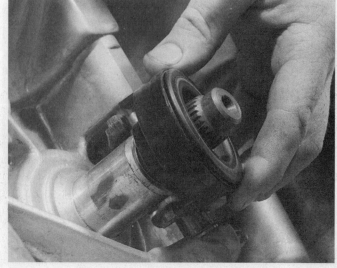

5.2B . . . and slide the bearing off the gearbox input shaft

Refitting

6   Refitting is a reversal of the removal procedure, but before tightening the fork retaining bolt onto the operating lever, make sure that the location hole is correctly aligned. Ensure that the retaining spring clip is located correctly (where applicable) when refitting the release bearing.

5.3 Fork retaining bolt and release bearing

6   Fault diagnosis - clutch

Symptom	Reason(s)
Judder when taking up drive	Loose or worn engine/gearbox mountings
	Clutch disc linings contaminated with oil, or worn
	Clutch cable sticking or defective
	Clutch disc hub sticking on input shaft splines
Clutch fails to disengage	Clutch cable sticking or defective
	Excessive free play in the cable or release mechanism
	Clutch disc linings contaminated with oil
	Clutch disc hub sticking on input shaft splines
Clutch slips	Clutch cable sticking or defective
	Clutch release mechanism sticking or partially-seized
	Faulty pressure plate or diaphragm assembly
	Clutch disc linings worn, or contaminated with oil
Noise when depressing clutch pedal	Worn release bearing
	Defective release mechanism
	Faulty pressure plate or diaphragm assembly
Noise when releasing clutch pedal	Faulty pressure plate assembly
	Broken clutch disc torsion springs
	Gearbox internal wear

Notes

Chapter 5 Gearbox

Contents

Specifications

Type .... Five forward speeds (all synchromesh) and reverse. Final drive integral with main gearbox

Lubrication

Oil type/specification. .... Multigrade engine oil, viscosity 10W/40, or equivalent multigrade engine oil having a viscosity rating compatible with temperatures in the vehicle operating area - see manufacturer's handbook (Duckhams QXR or 10W/40 Motor Oil). A 15W/40 oil (such as Duckhams Diesel) may be used for topping-up

Capacity .... 2.0 litres

Gearbox code numbers	M4 AR, M5 AR, M7 AR, M5 AO, T4 AO, S6 AR, S6 AO

Gear ratios

All types except T4 AO, S6 AR and S6 AO:

1st	3.166 : 1
2nd	1.842 : 1
3rd	1.222 : 1
4th	0.848 : 1
5th	0.648 : 1
Reverse	3.000 : 1

T4 AO:

1st	3.250 : 1
2nd	1.894 : 1
3rd	1.222 : 1
4th	0.906 : 1
5th	0.714 : 1
Reverse	3.000 : 1

S6 AR and S6 AO:

1st	3.250 : 1
2nd	1.895 : 1
3rd	1.222 : 1
4th	0.848 : 1
5th	0.648 : 1
Reverse	3.000 : 1

Final drive ratios

M4 AR, T4 AO	4.200 : 1
M5 AR, M5 AO	4.062 : 1
M7 AR, M7 AO	3.647 : 1
S6 AR, S6 AO	3.938 : 1

Gearbox overhaul data

Mainshaft endfloat	0.014 to 0.021 mm
Endfloat adjustment	Selective shims
Countershaft endfloat	0.03 to 0.08 mm
Endfloat adjustment	Selective distance collars and thrustwashers
Minimum baulk ring-to-gear clearance	0.40 mm
Maximum reverse idler gear-to-shaft clearance	0.014 mm
Maximum selector fork-to-synchro sleeve clearance	1.0 mm
Maximum reverse gear fork-to-gear clearance	0.7 mm
End cover seal minimum diameter	50.1 mm
Differential endfloat	0.15 mm
Endfloat adjustment	Selective circlips

Torque wrench settings

	Nm	lbf ft
Bellhousing to engine adapter plate	90	66
Gearbox steady rod bolt	8	6
Gear lever to gearchange rod	25	18
Remote control housing to underbody	25	18
Oil filler plug	45	33
Oil drain plug	40	30
Countershaft access plug	70	52
Reversing lamp switch	25	18
Reverse idler shaft retaining bolt	67	49
Gearcase-to-bellhousing bolts	27	20
Speedometer pinion retaining bolt	11	8
Clutch release fork-to-operating lever bolt	29	21
Countershaft retaining nut	110	81
Reverse gear fork bracket bolts	14	10
Gearchange holder and interlock retaining bolts:		
M8 bolt	29	21
M6 bolts	13	9
Gearchange shaft detent plug	22	16

2.2 Unscrewing the gearbox filler plug

2.4 Topping-up the gearbox oil level

1 General description

The gearbox is a Honda design, and was originally manufactured by Honda for Rover; from approximately September 1987 onwards, Rover have built the gearbox in the UK. The gearbox has five forward gears and one reverse, with synchromesh gear engagement on all forward gears.

The mainshaft and countershaft carry the constant-mesh gear cluster assemblies, and are supported on ball- and roller-bearings. The short input end of the mainshaft eliminates the need for additional support from a crankshaft spigot bearing. The synchromesh gear engagement is by spring rings, which act against baulk rings under the movement of the synchroniser sleeves. Gear selection is by means of a floor-mounted lever, connected by a remote control housing and gearchange rod to the gearchange shaft in the gearbox. Gearchange shaft movement is transmitted to the selector forks via the gearchange holder and interlock assembly.

The final drive (differential) unit is integral with the main gearbox, and is located between the bellhousing and gearcase. The gearbox and final drive components both share the same lubricating oil.

2 Routine maintenance

Carry out the following procedures at the intervals given in the *"Routine maintenance"* Section at the start of this manual.

Check gearbox oil level

1   The filler plug is located on the left-hand side of the gearcase, and can be reached from above, through the engine compartment, after removal of the air cleaner assembly. Alternatively, the vehicle may be supported on axle stands and the plug reached from underneath (or from under the wheelarch, after removing the roadwheel and plastic wheelarch cover).

2   Wipe the area around the filler plug with a rag, then unscrew and remove the plug using a socket or spanner (photo). Recover the sealing washer.

3   Check that the oil level is up to the bottom of the filler plug orifice.

4   Top-up if necessary using the specified oil, to bring the level up to the filler plug orifice (photo).

5   Check the sealing washer, and renew it if necessary.

6   Refit and tighten the filler plug together with its sealing washer, and wipe away any excess oil.

7   Carefully inspect the gearbox joint faces and oil seals for signs of damage, deterioration or oil leakage.

8   Lower the vehicle to the ground (where applicable).

Renew the gearbox oil

9   To drain the old oil, position a suitable container beneath the drain plug, located on the gearbox filler plug side, below the driveshaft inner joint. A square key is required to remove and refit the drain plug, but the 3/8 in square drive end of a socket bar will suffice (photos).

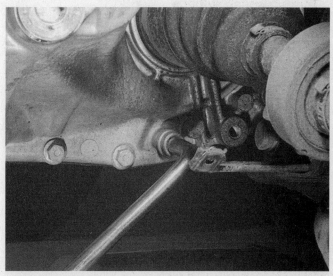

2.9A Use a 3/8 in square key to unscrew the gearbox drain plug

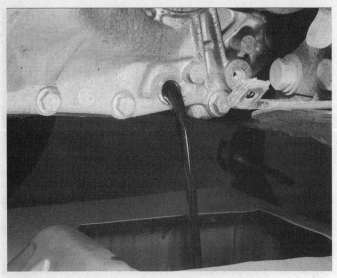

2.9B   Draining the gearbox oil into a plastic container

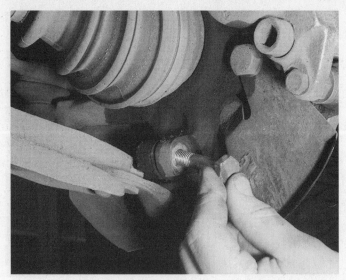

3.7A   Removing the bolt securing the lower suspension arm to the swivel hub assembly

10   When the oil is fully drained, refit and tighten the drain plug to the specified torque wrench setting.

11   Refill the gearbox with the specified quantity and grade of oil through the filler hole.

12   Check that the oil level is up to the bottom of the filler plug orifice, then refit and tighten the filler plug to the specified torque.

---

3   Gearbox - removal and refitting

Note: *The gearbox may be removed in one of two ways - either the engine and gearbox can be removed from the vehicle as described in Chapter 1 and the gearbox then separated from the engine, or the gearbox can be removed separately, leaving the engine in position in the vehicle, as described in this Section.*

Removal

1   Mark the position of the bonnet hinges, and where necessary disconnect the windscreen washer hose. Unscrew the bolts and remove the bonnet.

2   Remove the battery and battery tray.

3   Remove the radiator with reference to Chapter 2.

4   Apply the handbrake, then jack up the front of the vehicle and support on axle stands.

5   Remove the left-hand front roadwheel. Unscrew the screws and remove the plastic cover from under the left-hand wheelarch.

6   Position a suitable container beneath the gearbox, then unscrew the drain plug and drain the oil with reference to Section 2.

7   Unscrew and remove the bolt securing the lower suspension arm

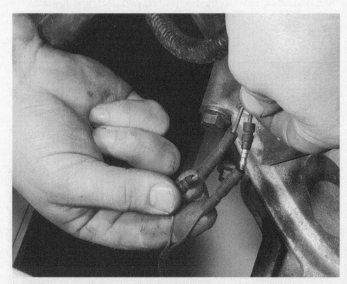

3.7B   Disconnecting the lower suspension arm from the swivel hub assembly

3.15   Disconnecting the wiring for the reversing light switch

3.17 Removing the gearbox mounting bolt near the starter motor position

3.18 Unclipping the engine wiring harness from the front of the adapter plate

to the swivel hub assembly, noting which way round it is fitted. Lever the lower suspension arm down from the swivel hub assembly (photos).

8   Unbolt the brake caliper from the swivel hub, and tie it to the front suspension coil, taking care not to strain the flexible hydraulic hose.

9   Unscrew and remove the nut securing the tie-rod outer balljoint to the swivel hub steering arm. Release the balljoint from the steering arm using a balljoint separator tool.

10   Unscrew and remove the upper bolts securing the suspension strut to the swivel hub assembly.

11   Using a suitable flat bar or large screwdriver, lever between the inner constant velocity joint and differential housing to release the joint from the differential sun gear.

12   Withdraw the inner joint fully from the differential, then remove the driveshaft and swivel hub assembly from under the wheelarch.

13   On models with power steering, remove the power steering drive-belt cover with reference to Chapter 8.

14   Remove the air cleaner assembly with reference to Chapter 3.

15   Disconnect the wiring for the reversing light switch on the front of the gearbox (photo).

16   Remove the starter motor with reference to Chapter 9.

17   Unscrew and remove the bolt securing the gearbox to the engine adapter plate near the starter motor position, noting that a wiring harness support clip is attached to the bolt (photo).

18   Release the engine wiring harness clip from the front of the adapter plate (photo).

19   Unscrew the mounting bolt and remove the speedometer drive pinion assembly from the rear of the gearbox (photos).

20   Unbolt the earth lead from the gearbox, noting that the bolt also

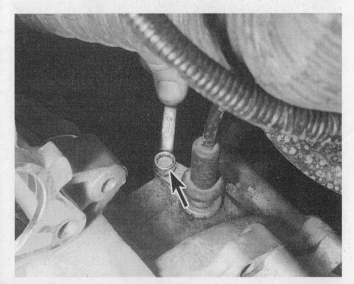

3.19A Unscrew the mounting bolt (arrowed) . . .

3.19B . . . and remove the speedometer drive pinion assembly

3.20 Earth lead and breather bracket location on the gearbox (arrowed)

3.22A Remove the spring clip . . .

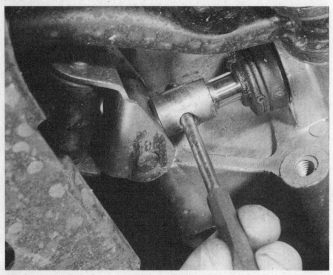

3.22B . . . drive out the roll pin . . .

3.22C . . . and slide the gearchange rod off the shaft

3.23 Removing the gearbox steady rod and washer

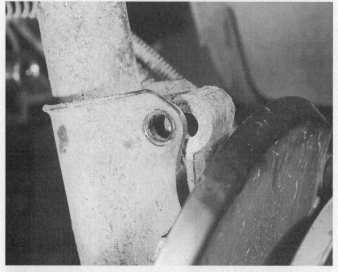

3.25 Tilting the right-hand swivel hub assembly outwards when disconnecting the driveshaft from the gearbox

3.26 Supporting the weight of the engine with a lifting bar across the engine compartment

3.27 Removing the bolts from the left-hand engine/gearbox mounting

secures the breather bracket (photo).

21 Disconnect the clutch cable with reference to Chapter 4.

22 Remove the spring clip to expose the gearchange rod-to-gearchange shaft retaining roll pin. Using a suitable punch, drive out the roll pin, and slide the gearchange rod rearwards, off the shaft (photos).

23 Remove the engine rear mounting with reference to Chapter 1. Also unbolt the gearbox steady rod from the gearbox, and recover the washer (photo).

24 Unscrew and remove the upper bolt securing the right-hand suspension strut to the swivel hub assembly, and loosen (but do not remove) the lower bolt.

25 Using a suitable flat bar or large screwdriver, lever between the inner constant velocity joint and differential housing to release the joint from the differential sun gear. At the same time, tilt the right-hand swivel hub assembly outwards slightly (photo).

26 Support the weight of the engine with a trolley jack and piece of wood, or using a hoist or lifting bar across the engine compartment. One of the rear cylinder head bolt extensions can be used to attach the lifting eye (photo).

27 Unscrew and remove the bolts securing the left-hand engine/gearbox mounting to the gearbox. Unbolt the mounting from the body bracket (photo).

28 Lower the engine as necessary, so that the gearbox is aligned with the opening between the subframe and body.

29 Support the weight of the gearbox with a trolley jack, then unscrew and remove the remaining mounting bolts (photo).

30 Make a final check that everything securing the gearbox to the engine has been disconnected and moved well clear.

31 With the help of an assistant, ease the gearbox bellhousing off the locating dowels, and move it over the subframe as far as possible to the left of the engine compartment (photo).

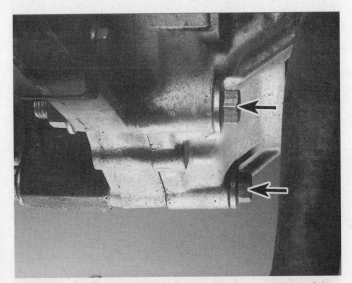

3.29 Gearbox-to-engine mounting bolts (arrowed) on the front of the gearbox

3.31 Gearbox disconnected from the engine and moved to the left-hand side of the engine compartment

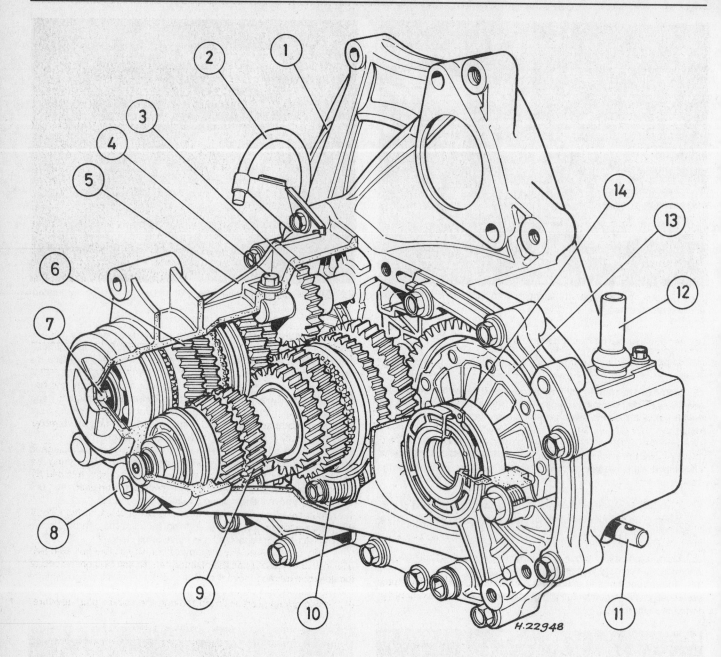

Fig. 5.1 Cutaway view of the gearbox (Sec 5)

1	Bellhousing	6	Mainshaft assembly
2	Gearbox breather and bracket	7	Oil guide plate
3	Reverse idler gear	8	Countershaft access plug
4	Reverse idler shaft retaining bolt	9	Countershaft assembly
5	Gearcase	10	Gearchange holder and interlock assembly

11	Gearchange shaft
12	Speedometer pinion
13	Final drive differential
14	Differential endfloat circlip shim

32   Remove the clutch assembly with reference to Chapter 4.

33   Turn the gearbox as necessary, and lift it out of the engine compartment. There is little room to spare, and care is needed to prevent damage to surrounding components.

Refitting

34   Refitting is a reversal of the removal procedure, but note the following additional points.

(a) *Tighten all retaining nuts and bolts to the specified torque (where applicable).*
(b) *Refit the clutch cable with reference to Chapter 4.*
(c) *Refer to Chapter 6 when refitting the driveshafts.*
(d) *Refit the starter motor with reference to Chapter 9.*
(e) *Refit the air cleaner with reference to Chapter 3.*
(f) *Refit the radiator with reference to Chapter 2.*
(g) *Fill the gearbox with the specified grade and quantity of oil, as described in Section 2.*

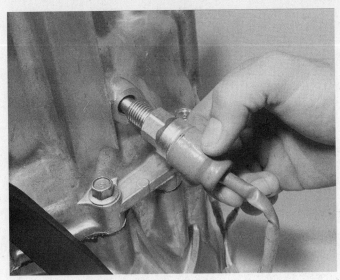

5.1 Unscrewing the reversing light switch

5.4 Reverse idler shaft retaining bolt

4 Gearbox overhaul - general

Dismantling, overhaul and reassembly of the gearbox is reasonably straightforward, and can be carried out without recourse to the manufacturer's special tools. It should be noted however that any repair or overhaul work on the final drive differential must be limited to the renewal of the carrier support bearings. Owing to the complicated nature of this unit and the costs involved, the advice of a Rover dealer should be sought if further repair is necessary.

Before starting any work on the gearbox, clean the exterior of the casings using paraffin. Dry the unit with a lint-free rag. Make sure that an uncluttered working area is available, with some small containers and trays handy to store the various parts. Label everything as it is removed.

Before starting reassembly, all the components must be spotlessly-clean, and should be lubricated with the recommended grade of oil during reassembly.

5 Gearbox - dismantling

1   Stand the gearbox on its bellhousing face on the bench, and begin dismantling by removing the reversing light switch (photo).

2   Undo the retaining bolt and plate, and lift out the speedometer pinion assembly (if this was not done during gearbox removal).

3   Undo all the gearcase-to-bellhousing retaining bolts, noting the location of the breather pipe and bracket, which are also retained by one of the case bolts. Remove the breather pipe and bracket.

4   Undo the reverse idler shaft retaining bolt located on the side of the gearcase (photo).

5   Using a large Allen key, hexagonal bar, or suitable bolt with two nuts locked together, undo the countershaft access plug on the end of the gearcase (photo).

6   Using circlip pliers inserted through the access plug aperture,

5.5 Countershaft access plug (arrowed)

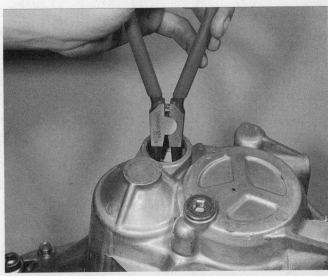

5.6A Release the countershaft bearing retaining circlip . . .

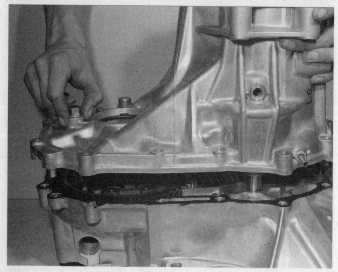

5.6B . . . then withdraw the gearcase from the bellhousing and gear clusters

5.10 Lift the mainshaft and countershaft, then remove the selector forks and shafts

spread the countershaft retaining circlip, at the same time lifting upwards on the gearcase. Tap the case with a soft mallet if necessary. When the circlip is clear of its groove, lift the case up and off the bellhousing and gear clusters (photos).

7   Undo the two retaining bolts, and remove the reverse gear fork and bracket.

8   Lift out the reverse gear idler shaft with reverse gear.

9   Undo the three bolts, and remove the gearchange holder and interlock assembly. Note that the holder locates in a slot in the 1st/2nd selector shaft.

10   With the help of an assistant, lift up the mainshaft and countershaft as an assembly by approximately 0.5 in (12.0 mm), and withdraw

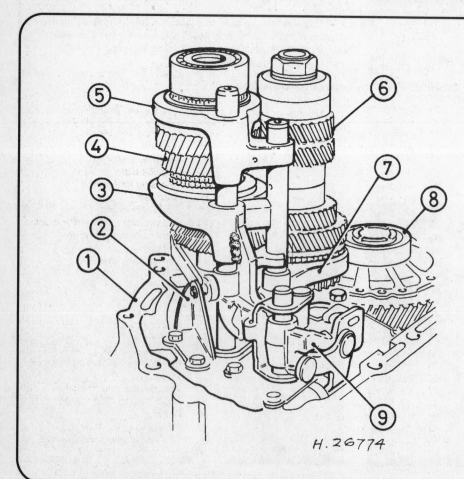

Fig. 5.2 Geartrain and gear selector components (Sec 5)

1   Bellhousing
2   Reverse gear fork and bracket
3   3rd/4th gear selector fork
4   Mainshaft assembly
5   5th gear selector fork
6   Countershaft assembly
7   1st/2nd gear selector fork
8   Final drive differential
9   Gearchange holder and interlock assembly

H. 26774

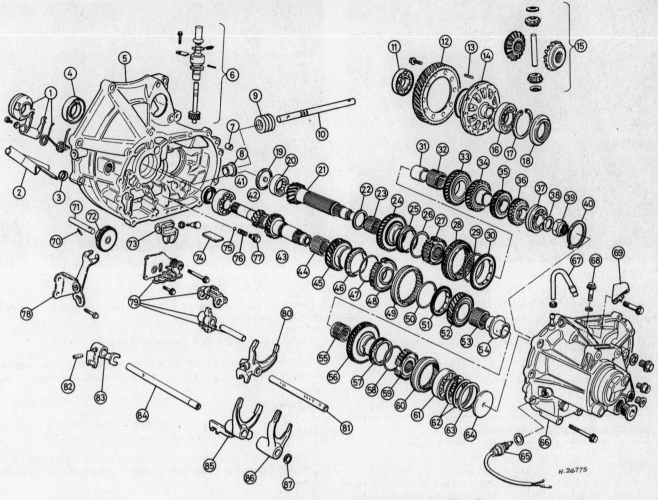

Fig. 5.3 Exploded view of the gearbox components (Sec 5)

1 Clutch release bearing, fork and retaining spring wire
2 Clutch operating lever
3 Clutch operating lever oil seal
4 Differential oil seal
5 Bellhousing
6 Speedometer pinion assembly
7 Locating dowel
8 Gearchange shaft oil seal
9 Rubber boot
10 Gearchange shaft
11 Final drive support bearing
12 Final drivegear
13 Roll pin
14 Final drive casing
15 Differential sun and planet gear components
16 Final drive support bearing
17 Differential endfloat circlip shim
18 Differential oil seal
19 Oil guide plate
20 Countershaft roller bearing
21 Countershaft
22 Thrustwasher
23 Needle roller bearing
24 1st gear
25 Baulk ring
26 Spring ring
27 1st/2nd synchro hub
28 1st/2nd synchro sleeve

29 Spring ring
30 Baulk ring
31 Distance collar
32 Needle roller bearing
33 2nd gear
34 3rd gear
35 4th gear
36 5th gear
37 Countershaft ball-bearing
38 Tongued washer
39 Retaining nut
40 Circlip
41 Mainshaft oil seal
42 Mainshaft ball-bearing
43 Mainshaft
44 Needle roller bearing
45 3rd gear
46 Baulk ring
47 Spring ring
48 3rd/4th synchro hub
49 3rd/4th synchro sleeve
50 Spring ring
51 Baulk ring
52 4th gear
53 Needle roller bearing
54 Distance collar
55 Needle roller bearing
56 5th gear
57 Baulk ring
58 Spring ring

59 5th gear synchro hub
60 5th gear synchro sleeve
61 Mainshaft ball-bearing
62 Selective circlips
63 Belleville washer
64 Oil guide plate
65 Reversing light switch
66 Gearcase
67 Gearbox breather
68 Reverse idler shaft retaining bolt
69 Gearbox breather bracket
70 Roll pin
71 Reverse idler shaft
72 Reverse idler gear
73 Gearchange arm
74 Magnet
75 Detent ball
76 Detent spring
77 Detent plug
78 Reverse gear fork and bracket
79 Gearchange holder and interlock assembly
80 1st/2nd gear selector fork
81 1st/2nd gear selector shaft
82 Roll pin
83 5th/reverse gear selector
84 5th/reverse gear selector shaft
85 3rd/4th gear selector fork
86 5th gear selector fork
87 Circlip

5.11 Withdraw the mainshaft and countershaft together from the bellhousing

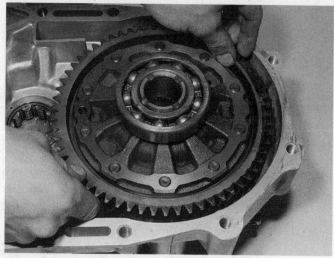

5.12 Remove the differential from the bellhousing

the selector shafts and forks from the bellhousing and gear clusters (photo).

11   Lift the mainshaft and countershaft out of their respective bearings in the bellhousing (photo).

12   Finally, remove the differential from the bellhousing (photo).

---

6   Mainshaft - dismantling and reassembly

Dismantling

1   Remove the mainshaft bearing, using a two- or three-legged puller if necessary, unless the bearing remained in the gearcase during removal.

2   Withdraw the 5th gear synchroniser hub and sleeve assembly from the mainshaft, using a two- or three-legged puller if it is tight. Recover the 5th gear baulk ring from the cone face of 5th gear, and place it, together with the spring ring, on the synchroniser unit.

3   Slide off 5th gear, followed by the 5th gear needle roller bearing.

4   Withdraw the distance collar, followed by 4th gear and the needle roller bearing.

5   Remove the 3rd/4th synchro hub and sleeve assembly, complete with baulk rings and spring rings.

6   Remove 3rd gear and its needle roller bearing.

7   Carry out a careful inspection of the mainshaft components as described in Section 10, and obtain any new parts as necessary.

Reassembly

8   During reassembly, lightly lubricate all the parts with the specified grade of oil as the work proceeds.

9   Slide the 3rd gear needle roller bearing onto the mainshaft, followed by 3rd gear with its flat face towards the other gears on the shaft (photos).

10   Place the 3rd gear baulk ring and spring ring on the cone face of 3rd gear, then fit the 3rd/4th synchro hub and sleeve assembly. Ensure that the lugs on the baulk ring engage with the slots in the synchro hub (photos).

11   Locate the 4th gear spring ring and baulk ring in the synchro unit, then slide on 4th gear with its needle roller bearing (photos).

12   Fit the distance collar with its shoulder towards 4th gear (photo).

13   Place the 5th gear needle roller bearing over the collar, then slide 5th gear onto the bearing (photos).

6.9A Slide the 3rd gear needle roller bearing onto the mainshaft . . .

6.9B . . . followed by 3rd gear

6.10A Place the baulk ring and spring ring on 3rd gear . . .

6.10B . . . then fit the 3rd/4th synchro hub and sleeve assembly

6.11A Locate the spring ring and baulk ring on the synchro unit . . .

6.11B . . . then fit 4th gear with its needle roller bearing

6.12 Fit the distance collar with its shoulder towards 4th gear

6.13A Position the 5th gear needle roller bearing over the collar . . .

6.13B . . . then slide on 5th gear

6.14 Fit the 5th gear synchro unit, complete with spring ring and baulk ring

14   Locate the 5th gear baulk ring and spring ring in the 5th gear synchro unit, then fit this assembly to the mainshaft (photo).

15   If the mainshaft (or any of its components), the gearcase or bellhousing have been renewed, then the mainshaft endfloat must be checked, and if necessary adjusted, as follows. To do this, it will be necessary to remove the mainshaft ball-bearing in the gearcase, remove the selective circlips, Belleville washer and oil guide, then refit the bearing.

16   Position the assembled mainshaft in the bellhousing, fit the gearcase and temporarily secure it with several evenly-spaced bolts. Tighten the bolts securely.

17   Support the bellhousing face of the gearbox on blocks, so as to provide access to the protruding mainshaft.

18   Place a straightedge across the bellhousing face, in line with the mainshaft, then accurately measure and record the distance from straightedge to mainshaft.

19   Turn the gearbox over so that the bellhousing is uppermost, and gently tap the mainshaft back into the gearcase using a soft-faced mallet. Take a second measurement of the mainshaft-to-straightedge distance.

20   Subtract the first measurement from the second measurement, and identify this as dimension "A".

21   Measure the thickness of the Belleville washer, and add an allowance of 0.006 in (0.17 mm), which is the nominal mainshaft endfloat. Identify this as dimension "B".

22   Subtract dimension "B" from dimension "A", and the value obtained is the thickness of selected circlip(s) required to give the specified mainshaft endfloat.

23   Remove the gearcase and the mainshaft. Remove the bearing from the gearcase, refit the oil guide, Belleville washer and circlips of the required thickness, then refit the bearing.

7   Countershaft - dismantling and reassembly

Dismantling

1   Support the pinion gear on the countershaft in a vice between two blocks of wood. Tighten the vice just sufficiently to prevent the countershaft turning as the nut is undone.

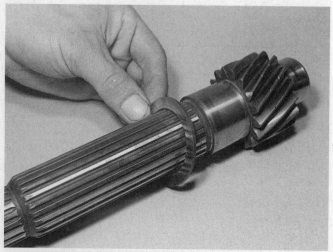

7.11A Fit the thrustwasher to the countershaft . . .

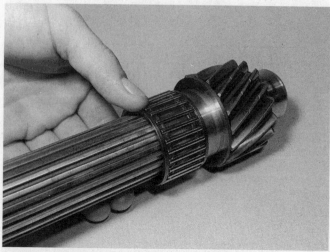

7.11B . . . followed by the needle roller bearing . . .

7.11C . . . and 1st gear

7.12A Fit the baulk ring and spring ring to 1st gear . . .

2   Using a small punch, release the staking on the countershaft nut, then undo and remove the nut. Note that the nut has a *left-hand thread*, and must be turned *clockwise* to unscrew it. Discard the nut once removed - a new nut should be obtained for reassembly.

3   Remove the tongued washer, then draw off the countershaft bearing using a two- or three-legged puller.

4   Slide 5th, 4th, 3rd and 2nd gears off the countershaft, noting their fitted directions.

5   Remove the 2nd gear baulk ring and spring ring.

6   Slide off the 2nd gear needle roller bearing, followed by the distance collar. Use two screwdrivers to lever off the collar if it is tight.

7   Remove the 1st/2nd synchro hub and sleeve assembly, followed by the 1st gear baulk ring and spring ring.

8   Slide off 1st gear, followed by the needle roller bearing and thrustwasher.

9   Carry out a careful inspection of the countershaft components as described in Section 10, and obtain any new parts as necessary.

Reassembly

10   During reassembly, lightly lubricate all the parts with the specified grade of oil as the work proceeds.

11   Fit the thrustwasher to the countershaft, followed by the needle roller bearing and 1st gear (photos).

12   Fit the baulk ring and spring ring to the cone face of 1st gear, then slide on the 1st/2nd synchro unit. The synchro unit must be fitted with the selector fork groove in the synchro sleeve away from 1st gear. As the unit is fitted, ensure that the lugs on the baulk ring engage with the slots in the synchro hub (photos).

13   Warm the distance collar in boiling water, then slide it onto the countershaft, with the oil hole offset towards 1st gear (photo).

7.12B . . . then slide on the 1st/2nd synchro unit

7.13 Fit the distance collar with its oil hole (arrowed) offset towards 1st gear

7.14 Locate the 2nd gear needle roller bearing over the distance collar

7.15A Fit the baulk ring and spring ring . . .

7.15B . . . followed by 2nd gear

7.16 Fit 3rd gear with its boss away from 2nd gear

7.17 Fit 4th gear with its boss towards 3rd gear

7.18A Fit 5th gear . . .

7.18B . . . followed by the countershaft bearing . . .

7.18C . . . then drive the bearing fully onto the shaft

14   Fit the 2nd gear needle roller bearing to the distance collar (photo).

15   Locate the 2nd gear baulk ring and spring ring on the synchro unit, then slide 2nd gear into place over the needle roller bearing (photos).

16   Fit 3rd gear to the countershaft, with its longer boss away from 2nd gear (photo).

17   Fit 4th gear, with its boss towards the 3rd gear boss (photo).

18   Fit 5th gear with its flat face towards 4th gear, then tap the countershaft bearing into position using a hammer and suitable tube (photos).

19   Fit the tongued washer, followed by a new countershaft nut (photos). Hold the pinion between blocks of wood in the vice as before, and tighten the nut to the specified torque.

20   Using feeler gauges, measure the clearance between the rear face of the pinion and 1st gear, and between the 2nd and 3rd gear

7.19A Engage the tongued washer with the countershaft groove . . .

7.19B . . . and screw a new nut onto the shaft

7.20A Check the clearance between the pinion and 1st gear . . .

7.20B . . . and between 2nd and 3rd gear

8.6 Fit a new differential oil seal with its open side facing inwards

faces (photos). Compare the measurements with the countershaft endfloat dimension given in the Specifications. If the recorded endfloat is outside the tolerance range, dismantle the countershaft again and fit an alternative thrustwasher or distance collar.

21   With the countershaft assembled and the endfloat correctly set, recheck the torque of the countershaft nut, then stake its edge into the countershaft groove using a small punch.

8   Gearcase - inspection and overhaul

1   Check the gearcase for cracks or damage to its bellhousing mating face. Renew the case if damaged.

2   Check the condition of the mainshaft bearing in the gearcase, and ensure that it spins smoothly, with no trace of roughness or harshness. The bearing must be removed if it is worn, if the gearcase is to be renewed, or if it is necessary to gain access to the mainshaft endfloat selective circlips located behind it.

3   Removal of the bearing entails the use of a slide hammer, with an

adaptor consisting of an internally-expanding flange or legs, to locate behind the inner race. A Rover special tool is available for this purpose, but it may be possible to make up a suitable alternative with readily-available tools. Whichever option is chosen, it is quite likely that the oil guide plate will be damaged or broken in the process. If so, a new one must be obtained.

4   If any of the mainshaft components are being renewed during the course of overhaul, do not refit the bearing, circlips, Belleville washer or oil guide plate until after the mainshaft endfloat has been checked and adjusted.

5   When the bearing is fitted this can be done by tapping it squarely into place using a hammer and tube of suitable diameter in contact with the bearing outer race.

6   If there is any sign of leakage, the differential oil seal in the gearcase should be renewed. Drive or hook out the old seal, and install the new one with its open side facing inwards (ie towards the differential) (photo). Tap the seal squarely into place using a suitable tube, or the old seal. Smear a little grease around the sealing lip, to aid refitting of the driveshaft. **Note:** If the differential or differential bearings have been renewed or disturbed from their original position, do not fit the oil

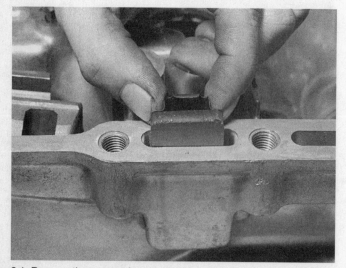

9.1 Remove the magnet from the bellhousing

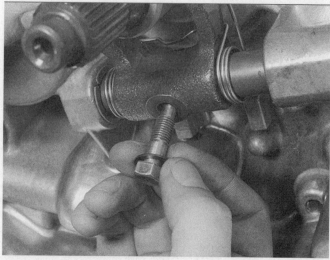

9.3 Undo and remove the clutch release fork peg-bolt

9.5A Undo the gearchange shaft detent plug . . .

seal until the gearbox has been completely reassembled. The differential bearing clearances are checked through the oil seal aperture, and this cannot be done with the seal in place.

9 Bellhousing - inspection and overhaul

1   With the mainshaft and countershaft removed, lift out the magnet from its location in the bellhousing edge (photo).

2   Remove the clutch release bearing as described in Chapter 4.

3   Undo the retaining peg-bolt securing the release fork to the clutch operating lever (photo).

4   Withdraw the lever from the fork, then lift out the fork, noting the fitted position of the release bearing retaining spring wire.

5   Undo the gearchange shaft detent plug, and lift out the detent spring and ball (photos).

6   Undo the bolt securing the gearchange arm to the shaft, and slide the arm off the shaft (photos).

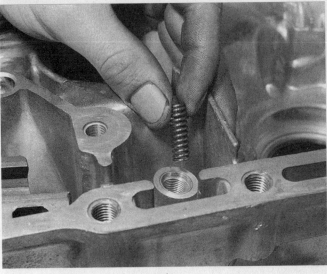

9.5B . . . then lift out the detent spring . . .

9.5C . . . and detent ball

9.6A Undo the gearchange arm retaining bolt (arrowed) . . .

9.6B . . . slide off the arm and remove the shaft

9.10 Mainshaft ball-bearing (A), countershaft roller bearing (B), oil guide plate (C), and bearing oil holes (D)

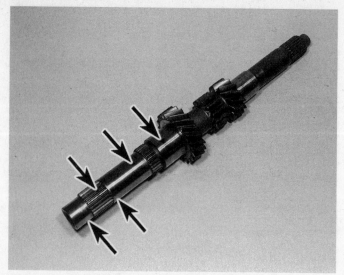

10.3A Gearbox mainshaft showing oil holes (arrowed) . . .

7   Withdraw the gearchange shaft from the bellhousing, and recover the rubber boot.

8   Examine the bellhousing for cracks or damage to its gearcase mating face. Renew the case if damaged.

9   Check the condition of the ball- and roller bearings in the bell-housing, ensuring that they spin smoothly, with no trace of roughness or harshness.

10   Renewal of the bearings entails the use of a slide hammer, with an adaptor consisting of an internally-expanding flange or legs, to locate through the centre of the bearing. A Rover special tool is available for the purpose, but it may be possible to make up a suitable substitute with readily-available tools. Another alternative would be to take the bellhousing along to your dealer, and have him renew the bearings for you. Whichever option is chosen, it is quite likely that the oil guide plate behind the countershaft roller bearing will be damaged or broken in the process (assuming this bearing is to be renewed) and if so, a new guide plate must be obtained (photo).

11   Refit the bearings by tapping them squarely into place using a hammer and tube of suitable diameter. Ensure that the oil hole in the countershaft bearing faces the gearbox interior.

12   Carefully inspect all the oil seals in the bellhousing, and renew any that show signs of leakage. The old oil seals can be driven out with a tube or punch, and the new seals tapped squarely into place using a block of wood or the old seal. Ensure that in all cases, the open side of the seal faces inwards. In the case of the mainshaft oil seal, it will be necessary to remove the mainshaft bearing to enable a new seal to be fitted.

13   Inspect the gearchange shaft for distortion or wear across the detent grooves, and check the gearchange arm for wear of the forks. Renew these components if wear is evident.

14   With the new bearings and seals in position and any other new parts obtained as necessary, refit the gearchange shaft and rubber boot with the detent grooves facing outwards (ie towards the gear clusters).

15   Slide on the gearchange arm so that its forked side is facing away from the bellhousing starter motor aperture. Refit the retaining bolt and washer, and tighten to the specified torque.

16   Refit the detent ball, followed by the spring and detent plug bolt. Tighten the bolt to the specified torque.

17   Slide the clutch operating lever into the bellhousing, and engage the release fork. Ensure that the joined end of the bearing retaining spring wire is positioned behind the release fork arms. Refit and tighten the retaining bolt.

18   Refit the magnet with its forked end down, then refit the clutch release bearing as described in Chapter 4.

10   Mainshaft and countershaft components and synchro units - inspection and overhaul

1   With the mainshaft and countershaft dismantled, examine the shafts and gears for signs of pitting, scoring, wear ridges or chipped teeth. Check the fit of the gears on the mainshaft and countershaft splines, and ensure that there is no lateral free play.

2   Check the smoothness of the bearings, and check for any signs of scoring on the needle roller bearing tracks and distance collars.

3   Check the mainshaft and countershaft for straightness, check for damaged threads or splines, and ensure that the lubrication holes are clear (photos).

4   Mark one side of each synchro hub and sleeve before separating the two parts, so that they may be refitted in the same position.

5   Withdraw the hub from the sleeve, and examine the internal gear teeth for wear or ridges. Ensure that the hub and sleeve are a snug sliding fit, with the minimum of lateral movement.

6   Check the fit of the selector forks in their respective synchro sleeve grooves. If the clearance exceeds the figure given in the Specifications, check for wear ridges, to give an indication of whether it is the fork or the sleeve groove that has worn. As a general rule, the selector fork usually wears first, but not always. If in doubt, compare with new parts.

7   Place each baulk ring on the cone face of its respective gear, and measure the distance between the baulk ring and the gear face. If the clearance is less than specified, renew the baulk ring. Renew them

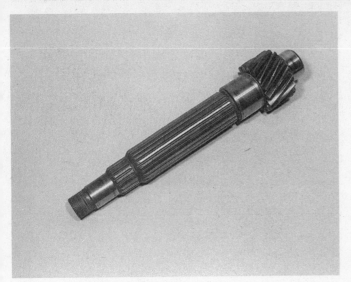

10.3B . . . and gearbox countershaft

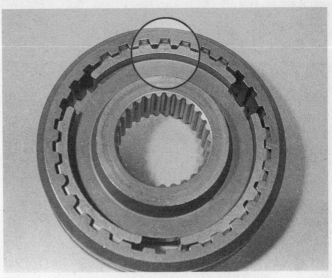

10.8 Oversized teeth in the synchro sleeve engaged with corresponding grooves in the hub

also if there is excessive wear or rounding of the dog teeth around their periphery, if they are cracked, or if they are in any way damaged. If the gearbox is in reasonable condition and is to be rebuilt, it is advisable to renew all the baulk rings as a matter of course. The improvement in the synchromesh action when changing gear will justify the expense.

8   When reassembling the synchro units, make sure that the two oversize teeth in the synchro sleeve engage with the two oversize grooves in the hub (photo).

9   If any of the gears on the mainshaft are to be renewed, then the corresponding gear on the countershaft must also be renewed, and *vice-versa*. This applies to the countershaft and differential final drivegear as well.

11   Selector forks, shafts and gearchange mechanism - inspection and overhaul

1   Visually inspect the selector forks for obvious signs of wear ridges, cracks or deformation.

2   Slide the selector forks off the shafts, noting their fitted position, and check the detent action as the fork is removed. Note that the detent balls and springs are located in the selector forks, and cannot be removed. If the detent action is weak, or if there is evidence of a broken spring or damaged ball, the fork must be renewed.

3   Check the fit of the selector forks in their respective synchro sleeves, if not already done. If the clearance exceeds the figure given in the Specifications, check for wear ridges, to give an indication of whether it is the fork or the sleeve groove that is worn. If in doubt, compare them with new parts and renew any that are worn.

4   Examine the selector shafts for wear ridges around the detent grooves, and for any obvious signs of distortion. Renew any suspect shafts.

5   Examine the gearchange holder and interlock assembly for any visible signs of wear or damage. It is advisable not to dismantle the mechanism, unless it is obviously worn and is in need of renewal. If this is the case, it can be separated into three main units and the worn part can be renewed.

6   Having obtained any new parts as required, reassemble the selector forks back onto the shafts, and reassemble the gearchange holder and interlock components if these were dismantled for renewal.

12   Final drive differential - inspection and overhaul

1   As mentioned earlier, the only parts which can be renewed as a practical proposition are the two main support bearings on the final drive casing. The differential unit should be examined for any signs of wear or damage, but if any is found, it is recommended that you seek the advice of your dealer. Differential parts are supplied in sets, ie final drivegear and matching countershaft; sun gears and matching planet gears etc, and consequently are extremely expensive. The cost of individual parts may even equal the price of a complete exchange gearbox.

2   Check that the bearings spin freely, with no sign of harshness or roughness. If renewal is necessary, remove the bearings by levering them off the differential, using two screwdrivers or use a small puller.

3   Fit the new bearings by tapping them into place using a hammer and tube in contact with the bearing inner race.

13   Gearbox - reassembly

1   Position the differential in its location in the bellhousing, and tap it down gently using a soft-faced mallet, to ensure that the bearing is fully seated.

2   Fit the gearcase to the bellhousing, and secure it temporarily with several bolts tightened to the specified torque.

3   Using feeler gauges inserted through the oil seal aperture in the gearcase, measure the clearance between the bearing and the circliptype shim in the bearing recess. If the clearance is not equal to the differential endfloat dimension given in the Specifications, slacken the case retaining bolts, extract the circlip through the oil seal aperture, and substitute a thicker or thinner circlip as required from the range available. Repeat this procedure until the correct endfloat is obtained, then remove the gearcase. Gearbox reassembly can now proceed as follows.

13.7 Lift up the mainshaft and countershaft to allow fitment of the selector forks and shafts

13.8 Fit the gearchange holder and interlock assembly . . .

13.9 . . . and secure with the three retaining bolts (arrowed)

13.10 Fit the reverse idler shaft and gear

13.11 Engage the reverse gear fork with reverse gear and with the 5th/reverse selector peg (arrowed)

4   Insert the magnet into its location in the edge of the bellhousing, forked end first.

5   Refit the gearchange shaft and arm as described in Section 9, if this has not already been done.

6   With the bearings in place in the bellhousing, hold the assembled mainshaft and countershaft together, and insert them into their locations.

7   With the help of an assistant, lift up the mainshaft and countershaft assemblies together by approximately 0.5 in (12.0 mm). Engage the selector forks with their respective synchro sleeves, and locate the selector shafts in the bellhousing (photo). Return the mainshaft and countershaft to their original positions, ensuring that the selector shafts engage fully with their holes in the bellhousing.

8   Refit the gearchange holder and interlock assembly, noting that the holder locates in a slot in the 1st/2nd selector shaft (photo).

9   Refit the three gearchange holder and interlock retaining bolts, and tighten them to their specified torques (photo).

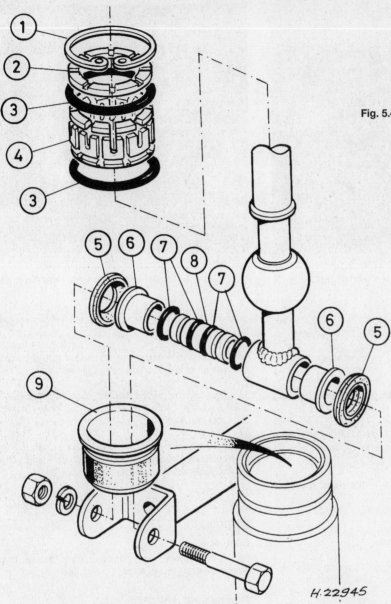

**Fig. 5.4 Exploded view of the gear lever
(Sec 14)**

1 Circlip
2 Retaining ring
3 O-ring
4 Gear lever seat
5 Sealing washers
6 Bushes
7 O-rings
8 Spacer
9 Dust cover

H.22945

10   Refit the reverse gear idler shaft with reverse gear, noting that the long boss on the gear must face the bellhousing, and the hole in the top of the shaft faces away from the gear clusters (photo).

11   Engage the reverse gear fork over the reverse gear teeth and over the peg on the 5th/reverse selector. Secure the reverse gear fork bracket with the two retaining bolts, tightened to the specified torque (photo).

12   Apply a continuous bead of RTV sealant to the gearcase mating face. Lower the gearcase over the gear clusters, and engage the shafts and bearings in their locations. Using circlip pliers inserted through the countershaft access plug aperture, spread the circlip, and tap the gearcase fully into position using a soft-faced mallet. Release the circlip, ensuring that it enters the groove on the countershaft bearing.

13   Refit the gearcase-to-bellhousing retaining bolts and breather bracket, then tighten the bolts progressively to the specified torque.

14   Refit the reverse idler shaft retaining bolt, and tighten it to the specified torque.

15   Apply RTV sealant to the threads of the countershaft access plug, refit the plug and tighten it to the specified torque.

16   Refit the speedometer drive pinion, if this was not removed when removing the gearbox from the vehicle, and the reversing light switch.

17   Finally refit the final drive differential oil seal to the gearcase, if not already done.

18   Check the operation of the gearchange mechanism, ensuring that all gears can be engaged, then refit the gearbox to the vehicle as described in Section 3.

14   Gear lever and remote control housing - removal and refitting

Removal

Gear lever

1   Jack up the front of the vehicle and support it on axle stands.

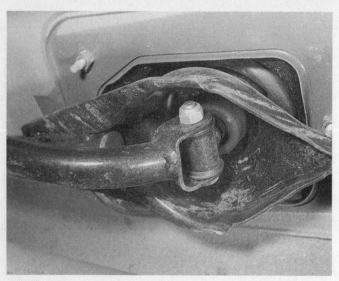

14.2 Gear lever-to-gearchange remote control rod retaining bolt

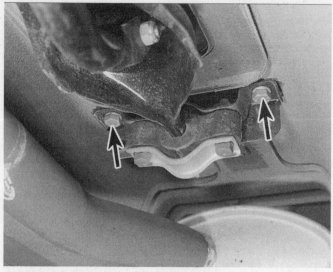

14.12 Remote control housing bracket retaining bolts (arrowed)

2   From under the vehicle, undo the nut and withdraw the bolt securing the gear lever to the gearchange remote control rod (photo).

3   From inside the vehicle, unscrew the gear lever knob, then remove the gaiter and rubber boot.

4   Remove the retaining circlip, and withdraw the gear lever from the remote control housing.

5   Release the sealing washers and extract the bushes, then slide out the spacer located at the base of the gear lever, complete with O-ring seals. Examine the components for wear.

6   Inspect the O-rings and gear lever seat in the remote control housing for signs of wear or damage.

Remote control housing

7   Remove the gear lever as described above.

8   From under the front of the vehicle, remove the spring clip to expose the gearchange rod-to-gearbox gearchange shaft retaining roll pin.

9   Using a suitable punch, drive out the roll pin and slide the

gearchange rod rearwards off the shaft. Remove the rod from under the vehicle.

10   Undo and remove the small bolt in the centre of the gearbox steady rod, at the gearbox end of the remote control housing.

11   Remove the dished washer, slide off the steady rod, and remove the flat washer. Note that the lip on the inner washer faces the steady rod rubber bush.

12   At the remote control housing end, undo the two bolts securing the mounting bracket to the vehicle floor, and withdraw the remote control assembly from under the vehicle (photo).

Refitting

Gear lever

13   Renew any worn or damaged parts, then reassemble and refit the gear lever using the reverse sequence to removal.

Remote control housing

14   Refitting is the reverse sequence of removal.

15 Fault diagnosis - gearbox

Symptom	Reason(s)
Gearbox noisy in neutral	Mainshaft bearings worn
Gearbox noisy only when moving (in all gears)	Countershaft bearings worn Differential bearings worn Differential final drivegear or countershaft pinion chipped or worn
Gearbox noisy in only one gear	Worn, damaged or chipped gear teeth Worn needle roller bearings
Gearbox jumps out of gear	Worn synchro hubs or synchro sleeves Weak or broken selector shaft detent spring Weak or broken gearchange shaft detent spring Worn shaft detent grooves Worn selector forks
Ineffective synchromesh	Worn baulk rings or synchro hubs
Difficulty in engaging gears	Clutch fault Ineffective synchromesh Worn gear lever bushes and linkage Gear linkage retaining clips broken

Notes

Chapter 6 Driveshafts

Contents

Specifications

Type .... Unequal-length solid-steel, splined to inner and outer
constant velocity joints

Lubrication

Lubricant type:
    Constant velocity joint.. Duckhams Q5795 grease, or equivalent
    Hub bearing water shield .... Duckhams LBM 10, or equivalent
Quantity:
    Outer constant velocity joint .... 90 cc
    Inner constant velocity joint .... 190 to 205 cc

Torque wrench settings

	Nm	lbf ft
Driveshaft retaining nut*	203	150
Roadwheel nuts:		
Except Van models	72	53
Van models	80	59
Swivel hub-to-strut nuts	90	66
Tie-rod outer balljoint to steering arm	45	33

*Refer to Section 3

3.3 Remove the driveshaft retaining nut and recover the thrustwasher (castellated nut shown)

3.5A Unscrew the nut ...

1   General description

Drive is transmitted from the differential to the front wheels by means of two unequal-length, solid-steel driveshafts.

Both driveshafts are fitted with constant velocity joints at each end. The outer joints are of the Rzeppa ball-and-cage type, and are splined to accept the driveshaft and wheel hub drive flange. The inner joints are of the sliding tripode type, allowing lateral movement of the driveshaft, to cater for suspension travel. The inner joints are splined, to accept the driveshafts and differential sun gears.

To eliminate driveshaft-induced harmonic vibrations and resonance, a rubber-mounted steel damper is attached to the longer right-hand driveshaft.

Driveshaft repair procedures are limited, as only the inner and outer rubber boots and outer constant velocity joints are available separately. The driveshafts and inner joints are supplied as complete assemblies.

2   Routine maintenance

Carry out the following procedures at the intervals given in the *"Routine maintenance"* Section at the start of this manual.

Check the driveshaft joints and rubber boots
1   At the intervals given in *"Routine maintenance"* at the beginning of this manual, carry out a thorough inspection of the driveshafts and joints as follows.

2   Jack up the front of the vehicle, and support it securely on axle stands.

3   Slowly rotate the roadwheel, and inspect the condition of the outer joint rubber boots. Check for signs of cracking, splits, or deterioration of the rubber, which may allow the grease to escape and lead to water

and grit entry into the joint. Also check the security and condition of the retaining clips. Repeat these checks on the inner constant velocity joints. If any damage or deterioration is found, the boots should be renewed as described in Section 5.

4   Continue rotating the roadwheel, and check for any distortion or damage to the driveshaft. Check for any free play in the joints by first holding the driveshaft and attempting to rotate the wheel. Repeat this check by holding the inner joint and attempting to rotate the driveshaft. Any appreciable movement indicates wear in the joints, wear in the driveshaft splines, or a loose driveshaft retaining nut.

5   Road test the vehicle, and listen for a metallic clicking from the front as the vehicle is driven slowly in a circle with the steering on full lock. If a clicking noise is heard, this indicates wear in the outer constant velocity joint, caused by excessive clearance between the balls in the joint and the recesses in which they operate. Remove and inspect the joint, as described in Section 4.

6   If a vibration consistent with road speed is felt through the vehicle when accelerating, there is a possibility of wear in the inner constant velocity joint. If so, renewal of the driveshaft complete with inner joint will be necessary.

3   Driveshaft - removal and refitting

Removal
1   While the vehicle is standing on its wheels, firmly apply the handbrake and put the transmission in gear.

2   Remove the wheel trim and extract the driveshaft retaining nut split pin (where fitted). Where the retaining nut is of the staked type, tap up the staking to release it from the driveshaft joint groove. Using a suitable socket and bar, loosen (but do not remove) the driveshaft nut.

3   Slacken the wheel nuts, jack up the front of the vehicle and support it on axle stands. Remove the roadwheel and return the gear lever to neutral. Remove the driveshaft nut and washer (where fitted)

3.5B ... and use a balljoint separator tool ...

3.5C ... to release the tie-rod from the steering arm

3.6 Suspension strut-to-swivel hub retaining nuts

3.7 Remove the outer constant velocity joint from the hub

(photo). It is recommended that the nut should be discarded, and a new one obtained.

4   Place a suitable container beneath the gearbox drain plug (see Chapter 5), unscrew the plug and allow the oil to drain. Refit the plug after draining.

5   Unscrew and remove the nut securing the tie-rod outer balljoint to the swivel hub steering arm. Release the balljoint from the steering arm using a balljoint separator tool (photos).

6   Unscrew and remove the nuts and washers, then withdraw the two bolts securing the suspension strut to the swivel hub (photo).

7   Pull the upper part of the swivel hub outwards as far as possible, without placing undue strain on the flexible brake hose. Push the drive-shaft inwards, and manoeuvre the outer constant velocity joint from the hub (photo).

8   Using a suitable flat bar or large screwdriver, lever between the in-ner constant velocity joint and differential housing to release the joint from the differential sun gear (photo).

3.8 Releasing an inner constant velocity joint from the differential sun gear with a screwdriver

9   Withdraw the inner joint fully from the differential, then remove the driveshaft assembly from under the wheel arch. Recover the plastic bearing water shield from the end of the outer constant velocity joint (photo).

Refitting

10   To refit the driveshaft, place it in position under the vehicle, and enter the inner joint splines into the differential sun gear. Push the driveshaft firmly inwards to engage the internal spring ring on the sun gear with the groove in the inner joint splines.

11   Position the bearing water shield on the flange of the outer joint, and fill the water shield groove with the specified grease.

12   Pull the swivel hub out at the top, and enter the outer constant velocity joint into the hub. Refit the driveshaft retaining nut (together with its thrustwasher, where applicable), and use the nut to draw the joint fully into place.

13   Refit the swivel hub to the suspension strut, and secure with the two bolts, washers and nuts tightened to the specified torque.

14   Refit the steering tie-rod outer balljoint to the swivel hub arm. Screw on the nut and tighten it to the specified torque.

15   Refit the roadwheel then lower the vehicle to the ground.

16   With the vehicle standing on its wheels, tighten the wheel nuts, and then the driveshaft retaining nut, to their specified torques.

17   Where a castellated nut is fitted, if the split pin hole in the constant velocity joint is aligned with one of the castellations in the nut, fit a new split pin and secure by bending over its ends. If the split pin hole does not align with one of the castellations in the nut, continue tightening

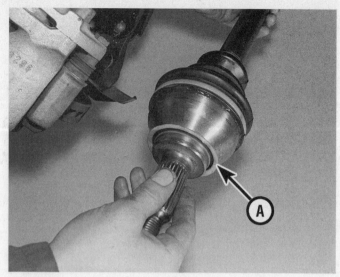

3.9 Withdraw the driveshaft assembly, and recover the bearing water shield (A)

until it does, but only up to a maximum torque of 215 Nm (158 lbf ft). If the hole is still not aligned, remove the nut and thrustwasher, and fit a new thrustwasher of different thickness from the range listed below. Using the new thrustwasher, repeat the tightening procedure until the split pin can be inserted.

Silver	6.1 mm
Green	6.2 mm
Dark grey	6.3 mm

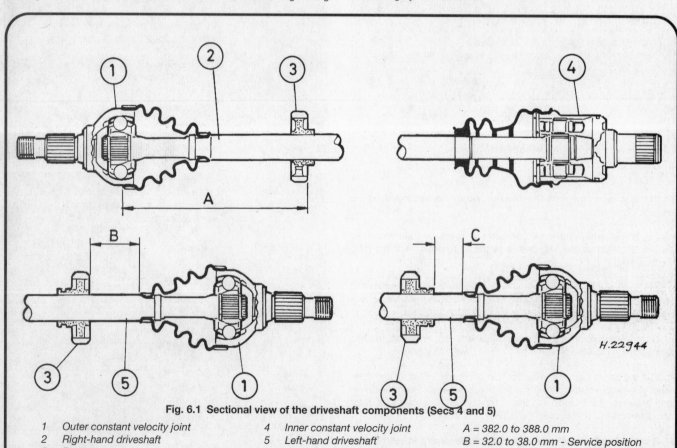

Fig. 6.1 Sectional view of the driveshaft components (Secs 4 and 5)

1   Outer constant velocity joint
2   Right-hand driveshaft
3   Damper
4   Inner constant velocity joint
5   Left-hand driveshaft

A = 382.0 to 388.0 mm
B = 32.0 to 38.0 mm - Service position
C = 17.0 to 23.0 mm - Production position

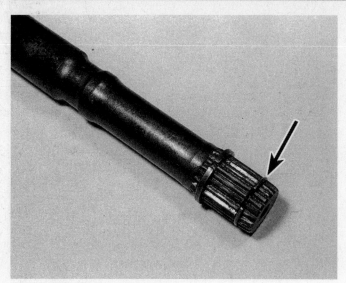

4.8 Constant velocity joint retaining circlip (arrowed) fitted to driveshaft groove

4.10 Fitting the outer constant velocity joint to the driveshaft

18 Where a staked nut is fitted, tap the flange of the new nut into the driveshaft joint groove using a punch.

19 Refit the wheel trim.

20 Refill the gearbox using the specified grade of oil, with reference to Chapter 5.

4 Outer constant velocity joint - removal, inspection and refitting

1 Remove the driveshaft from the vehicle as described in the previous Section.

2 With the driveshaft on the bench, release the two rubber boot retaining clips and fold back the boot to expose the outer joint.

3 Firmly grasp the driveshaft, or support it in a vice. Using a hide or plastic mallet, sharply strike the outer edge of the joint and drive it off the shaft. The outer joint is retained on the driveshaft by an internal circular-section circlip, and striking the joint in the manner described forces the circlip to contract into a groove, so allowing the joint to slide off.

4 With the constant velocity joint removed from the driveshaft, thoroughly clean the joint using paraffin, or a suitable solvent, and dry it, preferably using compressed air. Carry out a careful visual inspection of the joint, paying particular attention to the following areas.

5 Move the inner splined driving member from side to side to expose each ball in turn at the top of its track. Examine the balls for cracks, flat spots or signs of surface pitting.

6 Inspect the ball tracks on the inner and outer members. If the tracks have widened, the balls will no longer be a tight fit. At the same time, check the ball cage windows for wear or for cracking between the balls. Wear in the balls, ball tracks and ball cage windows will lead to the characteristic clicking noise on full lock described in Section 2.

7 If any of the above checks indicate wear in the joint, it will be necessary to renew it complete, as the internal parts are not available separately. If the joint is in a satisfactory condition, obtain a repair kit consisting of a new rubber boot, retaining clips, and the correct quantity of grease.

8 The help of an assistant will be necessary whilst refitting the joint to the driveshaft. Ensure that the circlip is undamaged and correctly located in its groove in the driveshaft (photo). Position the new rubber boot over the shaft, and locate its end in the shaft groove.

9 Place the retaining clip over the rubber boot, and wrap it round until the slot in the clip end can be engaged with the tag. Make sure the clip is as tight as possible, using pliers or a screwdriver if necessary. Fully tighten the clip by squeezing the raised portion with pincers or pliers.

10 Fold back the rubber boot, and position the constant velocity joint over the splines on the driveshaft until it abuts the circlip (photo).

11 Using two small screwdrivers placed either side of the circlip, compress the clip and at the same time have your assistant firmly strike the end of the joint with a hide or plastic mallet.

12 The joint should slide over the compressed circlip and into position on the shaft. It will probably take several attempts until you achieve success. If the joint does not spring into place the moment it is struck, remove it, reposition the circlip and try again. Do not force the joint, otherwise the circlip will be damaged.

13 With the joint in position against the retaining collar, pack it thoroughly with the specified quantity of the grease supplied in the repair kit. Work the grease well into the ball tracks while twisting the joint, and fill the rubber boot with any excess.

14 Ease the rubber boot over the joint, and secure it with the retaining clip, as described in paragraph 9.

15 The driveshaft can now be refitted to the vehicle, as described in Section 3.

5 Constant velocity joint rubber boots - renewal

1 Remove the driveshaft from the vehicle as described in Section 3.

Outer joint rubber boot
2 Remove the outer constant velocity joint from the driveshaft as described in Section 4. Renewal of the rubber boot is also covered in Section 4, as it is an integral part of the outer joint removal and refitting procedure.

5.10A Fit the inner joint rubber boot ...

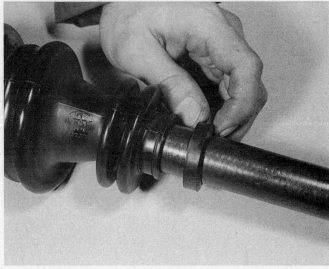

5.10B ... and secure its small end with the rubber retaining ring

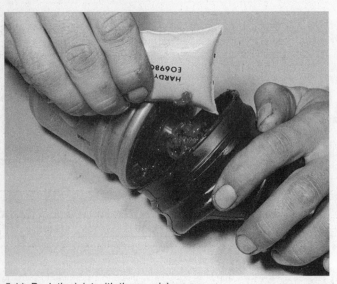

5.11 Pack the joint with the special grease

5.13 Use a screwdriver to stretch the retaining clip slot over the tag

Inner joint rubber boot

3   Remove the outer constant velocity joint and rubber boot as described in Section 4.

4   If working on the right-hand driveshaft (or a left-hand driveshaft where a damper has been fitted to stop whine or vibration), mark the position of the damper on the shaft, then release the retaining clip and slide off the damper.

5   Release the rubber retaining ring on the small end of the inner joint boot, and slide the ring off the driveshaft.

6   Release the retaining clip, slip the boot off the inner joint and withdraw it from the driveshaft.

7   Clean out as much of the grease in the inner constant velocity joint as possible, using a wooden spatula and old rags. As the joint cannot be dismantled, it is advisable not to clean it using paraffin or solvents.

8   Examine the bearing tracks in the joint outer member for signs of

scoring, wear ridges or evidence of lack of lubrication. Also examine the three bearing caps in the same way, and check for evidence of excessive play between the roller bearing caps and their tracks in the outer member.

9   If any of the above checks indicate wear in the joint, it will be necessary to renew the driveshaft and inner joint as an assembly; they are not available separately. If the joint is in a satisfactory condition, obtain a repair kit consisting of the new rubber boot, retaining clips and the specified grease.

10   Slide the new rubber boot onto the driveshaft, followed by the rubber retaining ring. Position the small end of the boot in the driveshaft groove, then slip the rubber ring over it to secure it in place (photos).

11   Fold back the boot, and pack the constant velocity joint with the specified quantity of the grease supplied in the kit (photo). Work the grease well into the joint while moving it from side to side. Fill the boot with any excess.

5.14 Tighten the clip fully by squeezing the raised portion

5.16 Secure the damper in place with the retaining clip

12 Position the large end of the boot over the joint outer member so that it locates squarely in the groove.

13 Position the retaining clip over the boot and engage one of the slots in the clip end over the small tag. Make sure the clip is as tight as possible and, if necessary, use a screwdriver to ease the slot over the tag (photo).

14 Fully tighten the clip by squeezing the raised portion with pincers or pliers (photo).

15 Refit the damper to the driveshaft (where applicable) and position it against the marks made on the shaft during removal. If a new driveshaft has been fitted, or if the marks have been lost, use the setting dimension given in Fig. 6.1.

16 Secure the damper in position with the retaining clip, as described in paragraphs 13 and 14 (photo).

17 Refit the outer constant velocity joint and rubber boot as described in Section 4, then refit the driveshaft as described in Section 3.

6   Fault diagnosis - driveshafts

Symptom	Reason(s)
Vibration and/or noise on turns	Worn constant velocity outer joint(s)
Vibration when accelerating	Worn constant velocity innerjoint(s) Bent or distorted driveshaft
Noise on taking up drive	Worn driveshaft or constant velocity joint splines Loose driveshaft retaining nut Worn constant velocity joints

Notes

Chapter 7 Braking system

Contents

Specifications

System type ....

Diagonally-split dual circuit, hydraulic with front discs and rear drums. Pressure-regulating valve in rear hydraulic circuit. Cable-operated handbrake on rear wheels. Servo assistance from vacuum pump operated from eccentric on camshaft

Vacuum pump
Type ....
Minimum vacuum at idle speed ....

Clayton DeWandre/REGA 1560
22 inHg (560 mmHg)

Torque wrench setting

	Nm	lbf ft
Vacuum pump mounting bolts	22	16

1 General description

The braking system is identical to the equivalent petrol-engined model, with the following exception.

Because there is no throttle butterfly in the air inlet passage on diesel engines, it is not possible to use the inlet manifold as a source of vacuum for the vacuum servo unit. A plunger-type brake vacuum pump (exhauster) operated by an eccentric on the camshaft is fitted, and supplies vacuum to the servo unit at all times when the engine is running.

All servicing and repair procedures for the various components in the braking system are described in the appropriate model-specific manual for petrol engine vehicles.

2 Routine maintenance

The maintenance procedures for the braking system are as described for the equivalent petrol engine model, and there is no specific check for the brake servo vacuum pump. However, if excessive foot-brake pedal pressure is necessary during the road test, a fault may be indicated in the vacuum servo unit and/or vacuum pump.

3 Vacuum pump - testing, removal and refitting

Testing

1 A vacuum gauge which registers a minimum of 22 inHg (560 mmHg) will be required to test the vacuum pump accurately.

3.2 Disconnecting the vacuum hose from the left-hand (servo) outlet on the vacuum pump

3.7 Loosening the clip on the vacuum pump oil drain hose

2   Disconnect the vacuum hose from the left-hand nozzle on the vacuum pump (ie the nozzle leading to the brake vacuum servo unit) (photo).

3   Connect the vacuum gauge to the vacuum pump nozzle, then start the engine and run it at idle speed. The vacuum reading should be at least the amount given in the Specifications. If not, the pump should be renewed. Note that it is not possible to dismantle the pump.

4   If a vacuum gauge is not available, a quick check can be made of the pump as follows (note that the vacuum hose must be connected to the pump). First disperse all the vacuum from the brake vacuum servo unit by repeatedly depressing the footbrake pedal.

5   Hold the footbrake pedal down, then start the engine and allow it to idle. The pedal should be felt to move slightly downwards towards the floor as the vacuum builds up in the servo unit. This proves that both the servo unit and the vacuum pump are functioning correctly - if the pedal does not move towards the floor, there may be a fault in the servo unit or vacuum pump, or both.

Removal

6   Unscrew the blanking screw from the right-hand end of the camshaft cover housing, then turn the crankshaft in a clockwise direction (using a socket on the crankshaft pulley bolt) until the camshaft timing hole is in alignment. In this position, No 1 piston is at TDC - refer to Chapter 1 for further details if necessary. With the camshaft in this position, the vacuum pump plunger will be on the back of the eccentric, and there will be less pressure from the pump spring. If this precaution is not taken, the pump mounting bolt threads may be damaged as they are unscrewed. Refit and tighten the blanking screw.

7   Position some rags beneath the vacuum pump oil drain nozzle (right-hand side of the pump), then loosen the clip and disconnect the hose (photo).

8   If not already done, disconnect the vacuum hose from the left-hand nozzle on the pump.

9   Progressively unscrew the pump mounting bolts, noting that two short bolts are located on the rear of the camshaft cover housing, and

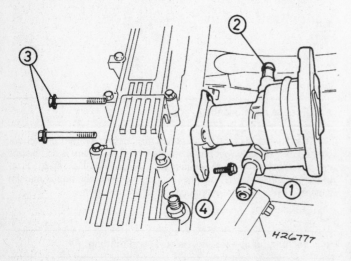

Fig. 7.1 Brake servo vacuum pump (Sec 3)

1	*Vacuum nozzle*	*3*	*Long mounting bolt*
2	*Oil drain nozzle*	*4*	*Short mounting bolt*

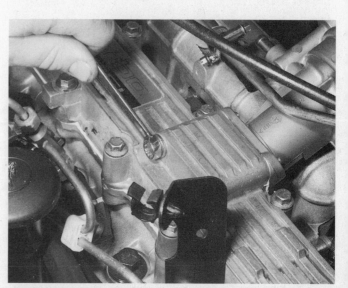

3.9A Progressively unscrew the pump mounting bolts ...

3.9B ... then hold the vacuum pump against the spring pressure, and withdraw the bolts

3.13 Locating the vacuum pump on the camshaft cover housing

two long bolts are located on the front of the housing. When they are completely loosened, hold the vacuum pump against the spring pressure, and withdraw the bolts (photos).

10 Remove the vacuum pump from the camshaft cover housing. During production, a rubber ring seal is fitted; discard this seal if found.

Refitting

11 Clean the mating faces of the vacuum pump and camshaft cover housing. Make sure that all traces of sealant are removed from the pump flange.

12 Apply a 3 mm bead of RTV sealant to the vacuum pump flange.

13 Locate the pump on the camshaft cover housing (photo), and insert the mounting bolts loosely.

14 Progressively tighten the mounting bolts to the specified torque.

15 Reconnect the vacuum hose to the left-hand nozzle.

16 Reconnect the oil drain hose to the right-hand nozzle, and tighten the clip.

17 Check that the pump operates correctly as described earlier.

Notes

Chapter 8 Suspension and steering

Contents

Specifications

Front suspension

Type...	Independent, by MacPherson struts with coil springs and integral telescopic shock absorber. Anti-roll bar on all models

Coil spring free length:
Maestro Hatchback..	428 mm
Maestro Van...	298 mm
Montego Saloon...	450 mm
Montego Estate...	428 mm

Trim height (measured from the centre of the front hub to the edge
of the wheel arch):
Maestro Hatchback..	363 to 389 mm
Maestro Van...	373 to 399 mm
Montego Saloon and Estate...	376 to 402 mm

Rear suspension

Coil spring free length:
Maestro Hatchback (except Turbo)......................................	343 mm
Maestro Hatchback (Turbo)..	351 mm
Montego Saloon and Estate...	369 mm

Trim height (measured from the centre of the rear hub to the edge
of the wheel arch):
Maestro Hatchback..	371 to 397 mm
Maestro Van...	388 to 414 mm
Montego Saloon...	370 to 396 mm
Montego Estate...	380 to 406 mm

Power steering

Type	Power steering gear with spool-type valve and pump
Drivebelt deflection (midway between the pump and camshaft pulleys)..	7.0 to 12.0 mm (nominal value - see text)
Fluid type	Dexron IID type ATF (Duckhams Uni-Matic or D-Matic)

Roadwheels

Wheel size:

Maestro Hatchback..	5-1/2 J x 14
Maestro Van..	5J x 13 or 5-1/2 J x 14
Montego Saloon and Estate...	5-1/2 J x 14

Tyres

Tyre sizes...	165 SR 13, 165 R 13, 175/70 R 14, 175/82 TR 14, or 185/65 TR 14	
Tyre pressures (cold) - bars (lbf/in²):	**Front**	**Rear**
165 SR 13:		
Maestro 500 Van..	2.0 (28)	2.8 (40)
Maestro 700 Van..	2.0 (28)	3.2 (46)
165 R 13:		
Maestro 700 Van..	2.0 (28)	3.2 (46)
175/70 R 14:		
Maestro Hatchback...	2.1 (30)	2.1 (30)
175/82 TR 14:		
Maestro 500 Van..	1.8 (26)	2.8 (40)
Maestro 700 Van..	1.8 (26)	3.2 (46)
185/65 TR 14:		
Montego Saloon (up to 4 passengers and luggage)....................	1.8 (26)	2.0 (28)
Montego Saloon (over 4 passengers and luggage)....................	2.0 (28)	2.0 (28)
Montego Estate (up to 4 passengers and luggage)....................	2.0 (28)	2.2 (31)
Montego Estate (over 4 passengers and luggage)....................	2.2 (31)	2.6 (38)
195/65 VR 15:		
Montego Estate (up to 4 passengers and luggage)....................	2.0 (28)	2.2 (31)
Montego Estate (over 4 passengers and luggage)....................	2.2 (31)	2.6 (38)

Torque wrench settings

	Nm	lbf ft
Union banjo bolt.	30	22
Pipe-to-hose union nut...	29	21
Hose union nut to steering gear	29	21
Drivebelt camshaft pulley to camshaft..	9	7
Power steering pump pulley nut...	50	37

1 General description

Power-assisted steering is fitted to certain models. It comprises a power steering gear, pump with fluid reservoir, and a fluid cooler. Fluid from the reservoir passes to the pump, and is supplied under pressure to the steering gear. A spool valve in the steering gear directs the pressurised fluid to the appropriate end of a piston in the steering gear to provide assistance. After the amount of assistance has been provided according to the movement of the steering wheel, the excess fluid is returned to the reservoir via cooler pipes.

Unlike petrol versions, the power steering pump is located on the gearbox adapter plate at the front of the cylinder block, and is driven by a drivebelt from a pulley on the left-hand end of the camshaft. The drivebelt is of the multi-ribbed type.

2 Routine maintenance

Carry out the following procedures at the intervals given in the *"Routine maintenance"* Section at the start of this manual.

Check power steering fluid level

1 The fluid level in the steering pump reservoir should be checked when the system is cold, and with the engine stopped.

2 Wipe clean the filler cap and the filler neck of the pump reservoir. Unscrew the cap, wipe the dipstick with a clean rag, then refit the cap fully. Unscrew the cap once more, and note the fluid level on the dipstick, which should be between the "MAX" and "MIN" marks (photo).

2.2 Removing the filler cap/dipstick from the power steering pump fluid reservoir

2.5A Unscrewing the bolts securing the drivebelt outer cover to the rear cover ...

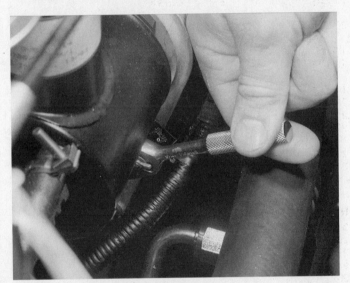

2.5B ... and gearbox adapter plate

2.5C Removing the spacer from the air cleaner bracket bolt

3   If topping-up is necessary, add the specified type and grade of fluid through the filler neck to bring the level up to the "MAX" mark on the dipstick. Take care not to overfill the system. Refit the cap after checking or topping-up the fluid.

4   If frequent topping-up is necessary, this indicates a leak some-where in the system. Check the hoses and connections as described later in this Section.

Check condition and tension of power steering pump drivebelt

5   Unscrew and remove the mounting bolts, and remove the drivebelt outer cover. The outer cover is attached to the rear cover by two bolts at the top, by a third bolt to the gearbox adapter plate, and another bolt to the air cleaner bracket. Recover the spacer from the air cleaner bracket bolt (photos).

6   Examine the full length of the drivebelt for signs of fraying, cracking or damage. Renew the drivebelt if necessary.

2.5D Removing the drivebelt outer cover

2.7 Checking the tension of the power steering pump drivebelt

2.8 Nut (arrowed) securing the tensioner pulley to the tensioner plate

7   Check that the deflection of the drivebelt on its upper run midway between the pump and camshaft pulleys is as given in the Specifications. Ideally, a Rover tension gauge should be used to apply the correct load, but moderate pressure with finger or thumb will normally be sufficient to make the check (photo). If the Rover tension gauge is being used, check that the tension is as follows.

Used belt	5 gauge units
New belt	6 gauge units

8   If adjustment is necessary, loosen the nut securing the tensioner pulley to the tensioner plate by 1 to 2 turns, then turn the tensioner bolt clockwise to increase the tension or anti-clockwise to decrease the tension. Tighten the pulley nut when the tension is correct (photo).

9   If a new drivebelt has been fitted, refer to Section 4, paragraph 9 for the special additional procedure required.

10   Refit the outer cover and tighten the mounting bolts.

Check condition of power steering hydraulic hoses and connections

11   Carefully inspect all pipes, hoses and unions of the power steering circuit for signs of fluid leakage. Check the rubber gaiters on the steering gear for any sign of wetness or obvious signs of fluid inside them, which would indicate failed seals within the steering gear.

12   Check that all union connections and banjo bolts are secure and tightened correctly.

13   Renew any hose, pipe or union as necessary.

---

3   Power steering system - bleeding

1   The power steering system is self-bleeding, but the following procedure should be carried out if the hydraulic circuit has been disconnected for repairs. The procedure is particularly important if both the hydraulic pump and the steering gear have been renewed.

2   Check that all hose and pipe connections are tight.

3   With the vehicle on level ground, fill the fluid reservoir to the "MAX" level mark on the dipstick. Do not overfill the reservoir.

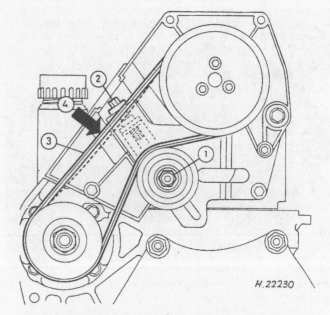

Fig. 8.1 Steering pump drivebelt tensioning details (Sec 2)

1 Tensioner pulley securing nut	3 Drivebelt
2 Tensioner bolt	4 Tension checking point

4   Position the steering with the front wheels pointing straight-ahead. Check and if necessary top-up the fluid level.

5   Start the engine and allow it to idle.

6   Turn the steering to full lock in one direction, then return it to the straight-ahead position.

7   Check and if necessary top-up the fluid level.

8   Turn the steering fully on the opposite lock, then return it to the straight-ahead position.

9   Check and if necessary top-up the fluid level.

10   Turn the steering several times from lock to lock to purge the

4.5 Drivebelt location on the pump pulley

5.2 Power steering drivebelt camshaft pulley and mounting bolts

remaining air from the hydraulic system, then return the steering to the straight-ahead position.

11   Check and if necessary top-up the fluid level.

4   Power steering drivebelt - removal and refitting

Removal

1   Unscrew and remove the mounting bolts, and remove the drivebelt outer cover. The outer cover is attached to the rear cover by two bolts at the top, by a third bolt to the gearbox adapter plate, and another bolt to the air cleaner bracket. Recover the spacer from the air cleaner bracket bolt.

2   If the drivebelt is to be refitted, mark its direction of rotation with chalk, to ensure that it is refitted the same way round.

3   Loosen (but do not remove) the nut securing the tensioner pulley to the tensioner plate.

4   Unscrew the tensioner bolt to release the tension of the belt.

5   Slip the drivebelt from the camshaft and pump pulleys, and remove it from the engine compartment (photo).

Refitting

6   Locate the drivebelt on the camshaft and pump pulleys, with its back surface over the tensioner pulley. If the old drivebelt is being refitted, make sure that the direction markings are facing the right way.

7   With the tensioner pulley nut still loose, tighten the tensioner bolt until the tension is as described in Section 2.

8   Tighten the tensioner pulley nut securely.

9   If a new drivebelt has been fitted, run the engine at 2000 rpm for 10 minutes, then stop the engine and loosen the tensioner pulley securing nut. Tighten the tensioner bolt one complete turn clockwise, then tighten the pulley nut securely.

10   Refit the drivebelt outer cover and tighten the mounting bolts.

5   Power steering drivebelt camshaft pulley - removal and refitting

Removal

1   Remove the drivebelt as described in Section 4.

2   Unscrew the three pulley retaining bolts (photo), and withdraw the drivebelt pulley from the end of the camshaft.

3   Recover the spacer.

Refitting

4   Clean the end of the camshaft, and the mating faces of the spacer and pulley.

5   Locate the spacer on the end of the camshaft, followed by the pulley, and insert the retaining bolts.

6   Tighten the retaining bolts to the specified torque.

7   Refit and tension the drivebelt with reference to Sections 4 and 2.

6   Power steering pump - removal and refitting

Removal

1   Remove the drivebelt as described in Section 4.

2   The pulley must now be held stationary in order to unscrew the retaining nut. Rover technicians use a long-handled tool which engages the cut-outs in the pulley (see Fig. 8.2), and a similar tool may be made out of steel plate with bolts to engage the cut-outs.

3   With the pulley held stationary, unscrew and remove the retaining nut.

4   Slide the pulley off the power steering pump driveshaft, and recover the Woodruff key from the groove.

5   Position a suitable container beneath the power steering pump, to collect the hydraulic fluid when the pipes are disconnected.

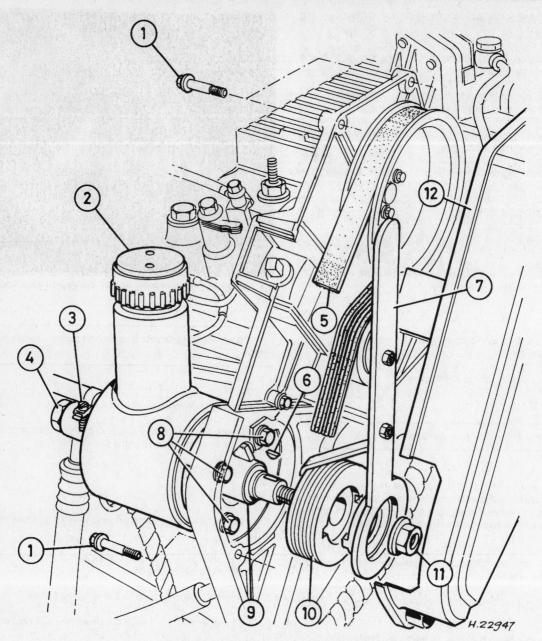

Fig. 8.2 Power steering pump removal (Sec 6)

1	Outer cover mounting bolts	6	Woodruff key	9	Power steering pump
2	Fluid reservoir filler cap	7	Special Rover tool for holding the	10	Pump pulley
3	Return hose clip		pump pulley stationary	11	Pump pulley securing nut
4	High-pressure union banjo bolt	8	Pump mounting bolts	12	Outer cover
5	Drivebelt				

6   Unscrew the banjo bolt and disconnect the high-pressure pipe from the pump. Recover the sealing washers. Tape over the union and pump outlet, to prevent dust and dirt entering the hydraulic system.

7   Loosen the clip and disconnect the low-pressure return hose from the pump (photo). Allow the fluid to drain into the container. Plug the hose, and tape over the pump inlet.

8   Unscrew and remove the pump mounting bolts, and withdraw the power steering pump from the gearbox adapter plate. Take care not to drip hydraulic fluid onto the bodywork.

Refitting

9   If a modified-type power steering pump with larger bearings is being fitted, then the hole in the gearbox adapter plate must be enlarged to accommodate the new pump. To do this, remove the battery and battery tray, and disconnect the air cleaner inlet hose. The mounting hole can now be enlarged using a suitable file. Refit the tray, battery and hose on completion.

10   Locate the pump on the gearbox adapter plate, and insert the mounting bolts. Tighten the bolts securely in a diagonal sequence.

11 Reconnect the low-pressure hose to the pump, and tighten the clip.

12 Using new sealing washers, reconnect the high-pressure pipe and tighten the banjo bolt to the specified torque.

13 Locate the Woodruff key in the groove, then slide on the pulley and fit the nut loosely.

14 Hold the pulley stationary using the method described earlier, and tighten the nut to the specified torque.

15 Fill the fluid reservoir with hydraulic fluid to the "MAX" mark on the dipstick.

16 Turn the pump pulley anti-clockwise by hand several times, to prime the system.

17 Refit and tension the drivebelt with reference to Sections 4 and 2.

18 Bleed the hydraulic system as described in Section 3.

6.7 Low-pressure return hose connection to the power steering pump

Notes

Chapter 9 Electrical system

Contents

Specifications

System type .... 12-volt, negative earth

Battery
Type .... Maintenance-free, "sealed for life"
Cold start performance .... 680 amps/135 minutes reserve capacity

Alternator
Type .... Lucas A127/65
Output at 14 volts and 6000 rpm .... 65 amps
Rotor winding resistance at 20°C .... 3.2 ohms ± 5 %
Stator winding resistance at 20°C .... 0.15 ohms ± 5 %
Brush length:
  New .... 20.0 mm
  Minimum... 10.0 mm

Starter motor

Type	NipponDenso/R 2.0 kW
Brush length (minimum)	10.0 mm
Commutator:	
Minimum diameter	34.0 mm
Maximum run-out	0.05 mm
Solenoid pull-in voltage and current.............................	8.0 volts at 50 amps maximum

Fuses

Circuit	Fuse number	Rating (amps)
Maestro:		
Stop/start relay..	A3	5
Stop/reverse lights, glow plug relay, cold start advance	C5	10
Montego:		
Stop/start relay, glow plug relay, cold start advance, idle control.....	1	10

Torque wrench settings

	Nm	lbf ft
Starter motor mounting bolts	80	60
Starter motor through-bolts	10	7
Starter motor drive end screws	10	7
Alternator adjusting link	22	16
Alternator mounting/pivot bolt...	27	20

1 General description

The electrical system is of the 12-volt negative-earth type, and consists of a 12-volt battery, alternator, starter motor and related electrical accessories, components and wiring. The battery is of the maintenance-free, "sealed for life" type, and is charged by an alternator which is belt-driven from the crankshaft pulley. The starter motor is of the pre-engaged type, incorporating an integral solenoid.

On starting, the solenoid moves the drive pinion into engagement with the flywheel ring gear before the starter motor is energised. Once the engine has started, a one-way clutch prevents the motor armature being driven by the engine until the pinion disengages from the flywheel. Due to the high compression ratio of the diesel engine, the starter motor is fitted with two reduction gears, and the one-way clutch is incorporated in one of these gears.

2 Routine maintenance

Carry out the following procedures at the intervals given in the "Routine maintenance" Section at the start of this manual.

Check the alternator drivebelt condition and tension

Refer to Chapter 2, Section 2.

3 Alternator - removal and refitting

Removal

1 Disconnect the battery earth (negative) lead.

2 Apply the handbrake, then jack up the front of the vehicle and support on axle stands.

3 Release the clip and disconnect the multi-plug from the rear of the alternator.

4 Loosen the alternator pivot bolt and adjustment link bolt. Swivel the alternator towards the engine, and slip the drivebelt off the crankshaft, water pump and alternator pulleys.

5 Unscrew the adjustment link bolt completely.

6 Unscrew and remove the alternator mounting bracket bolts, and withdraw the alternator and bracket assembly from the cylinder block.

7 With the alternator on the bench, unscrew and remove the pivot bolt, and separate the alternator from the mounting bracket. Recover the spacer washer.

Refitting

8 Refit the alternator to the mounting bracket, making sure that the spacer washer is correctly in position between the mounting bracket and the alternator drive end bracket. Insert the pivot bolt, and loosely tighten the nut.

9 Refit the alternator and bracket assembly to the cylinder block, then insert the mounting bolts and tighten them to the specified torque.

10 Swivel up the alternator, align the adjustment hole with the link, then insert the adjustment bolt and loosely tighten it.

11 Refit and adjust the alternator drivebelt with reference to Chapter 2.

12 Reconnect the multi-plug to the rear of the alternator, and refit the clip.

13 Lower the vehicle to the ground.

14 Reconnect the battery earth (negative) lead.

4.4A Air cleaner mounting bracket bolts (arrowed) on Turbo models

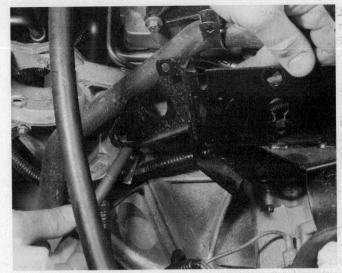

4.4B Removing the air cleaner mounting bracket on Turbo models

4 Starter motor - removal and refitting

Removal

1   Disconnect the battery earth (negative) lead.

2   Remove the air cleaner and inlet air duct, as described in Chapter 3.

3   On non-Turbo models, unbolt the heater support clips from the mounting bracket.

4   Unscrew and remove the bolts securing the air cleaner mounting bracket to the gearbox and cylinder head. Note that the starter motor upper mounting bolt and one of the gearbox mounting bolts also secure the air cleaner mounting bracket. Withdraw the air cleaner mounting bracket (photos).

5   Disconnect the starter motor solenoid trigger wire, then unscrew the nut and disconnect the main supply cables (photo).

6   Unscrew the remaining starter motor mounting bolt, and withdraw the unit from the engine compartment (photo).

Refitting

7   Locate the starter motor in the gearbox aperture, then secure with the lower bolt - loosely tightened at this stage.

8   Reconnect the main supply cable, and tighten the nut.

9   Reconnect the solenoid trigger wire.

10 Refit the air cleaner mounting bracket, and tighten the bolts. Also tighten the starter motor mounting bolts to the specified torque.

11 Refit the heater hose clips to the air cleaner mounting bracket, and tighten the bolts.

12 Refit the air cleaner and inlet air duct with reference to Chapter 3.

13 Reconnect the battery earth (negative) lead.

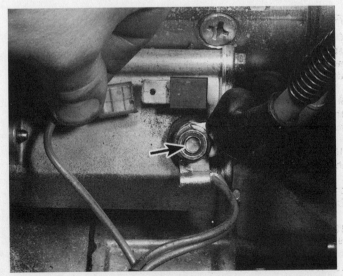

4.5 Disconnecting the starter motor solenoid trigger wire - also shown is the main supply cable terminal (arrowed)

4.6 Withdrawing the starter motor

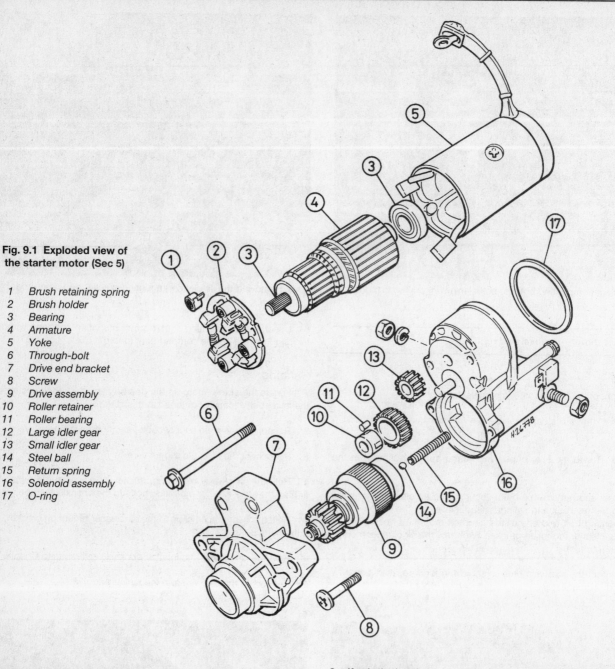

Fig. 9.1 Exploded view of the starter motor (Sec 5)

1   Brush retaining spring
2   Brush holder
3   Bearing
4   Armature
5   Yoke
6   Through-bolt
7   Drive end bracket
8   Screw
9   Drive assembly
10 Roller retainer
11 Roller bearing
12 Large idler gear
13 Small idler gear
14 Steel ball
15 Return spring
16 Solenoid assembly
17 O-ring

---

5   Starter motor - overhaul

Dismantling

1   Unscrew the nut and disconnect the motor supply cable from the solenoid terminal.

2   Using a scriber or dab of paint, mark the yoke in relation to the solenoid and drive end bracket assembly.

3   Unscrew and remove the two through-bolts, then detach the yoke and armature assembly from the solenoid and drive end bracket assembly (photos).

4   Lift the retaining springs, and withdraw the field brushes one at a time from the brush holder (photo).

5   Note the position of the brush holder in relation to the yoke, then slide it off the armature together with the earth brushes.

6   If only the brushes are to be removed, continue from paragraph 11.

7   Carefully tap the open end of the yoke on the bench, in order to free the armature from the end bearing. Withdraw the armature from the yoke (photo).

8   Unscrew the crosshead screws securing the drive end bracket to the solenoid. The screws are very tight, and may require an impact screwdriver to free them.

9   Separate the drive end bracket from the solenoid, and remove the idler gears and roller bearing.

10 Withdraw the drive assembly from the solenoid housing, and recover the steel ball and the return spring.

11 Measure the length of the brushes, and compare with the minimum dimension given in the Specifications (photos).

12 If the field brushes are worn below the minimum length, it will be

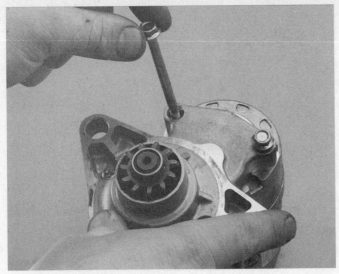

5.3A Remove the through-bolts ...

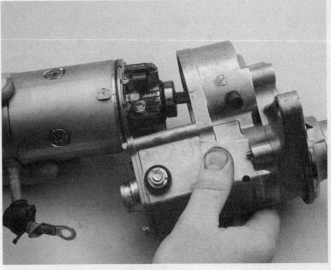

5.3B ... and separate the yoke and armature assembly from the solenoid and drive end bracket assembly

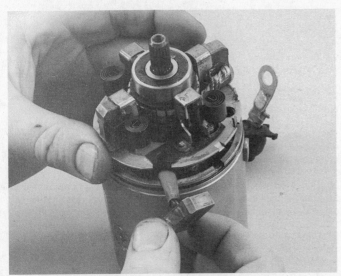

5.4 Withdrawing the field brushes from the brush holder

5.7 Removing the armature from the yoke

5.11A Measuring the length of the field brushes ...

5.11B ... and the earth brushes

necessary to renew the yoke assembly. If the earth brushes are worn excessively, then it will be necessary to renew the brush holder complete. This only applies to parts available from Rover dealers - it is conceivable that separate brushes may be obtainable from other sources, in which case they should be soldered into position.

Inspection

13 Check that all of the brushes move freely in their holders, and if necessary clean them with fine glasspaper. Clean away dust and particles with a fuel-moistened cloth. Check the condition of all the return springs.

14 Examine the drive assembly for signs of excessive wear and damage. Make sure that the pinion turns in one direction only, independent of the clutch body, and that the clutch slides freely on the shaft.

15 Check for continuity of the field windings using an ohmmeter between each field brush and the supply cable. If there is no continuity, an open-circuit will be indicated.

16 Check that there is no continuity between the brushes and the yoke body. If continuity exists, this indicates a short-circuit.

17 Check the run-out of the commutator by placing the armature in "V" blocks, with a dial test indicator probe on the commutator. Zero the dial test indicator, then slowly rotate the armature and note the run-out. If it is outside the specified limits, renew the armature.

18 Using the ohmmeter, check for continuity between each of the armature segments. No reading indicates faulty armature windings.

19 Using vernier calipers, measure the diameter of the commutator, and compare with the dimensions given in the Specifications. Renew the armature if the dimension is under the minimum amount.

20 Check the armature bearings for excessive wear by turning them by hand. If there is any sign of roughness or seizing, renew the bearings by pulling them off the armature with a puller. Drive the new bearings fully on the armature.

21 If new brushes have been fitted, wrap a piece of fine sandpaper around the commutator, with the abrasive side facing outwards. Locate the brush holder over the commutator, and insert the brushes. With the retaining springs on the brushes, rotate the armature several times to shape the ends of the brushes. Remove the brush holder and remove the sandpaper. Clean away all dust, and wipe the commutator with a fuel-moistened cloth.

22 Clean all components ready for reassembly.

Reassembly

23 Locate a new sealing O-ring on the yoke.

24 Locate the armature in the yoke, small bearing first, and tap the end of the armature with a soft-headed mallet until the bearing is fully seated.

25 Pull out the retaining springs, and locate the earth brushes in their holders in the brush holder. Retain the brushes in their retracted position by carefully positioning the edge of the springs against the sides of the brushes.

26 Locate the brush holder over the end of the armature in its previously-noted position, then locate the field brush leads in the baseplate. Position the brush holder fully against the yoke, making sure that the peg engages the slot.

5.27 Brush holder located on the commutator ready for reassembly to the drive end bracket assembly

27 Position the retaining springs on the earth brushes, then insert the field brushes and retain them with their springs (photo).

28 Lightly grease the return spring, steel ball, drive assembly, outer armature bearing, idler gear roller and idler retainer.

29 Locate the return spring on its peg inside the solenoid assembly, and locate the steel ball in the recess in the drive assembly. Locate the drive assembly onto the spring, and push it fully home.

30 Refit the large idler gear without the roller bearing components to the spindle, then locate the rollers in the retainer, and refit to the spindle with the open face towards the solenoid.

31 Engage the small gear with the large gear, making sure that it is aligned with the armature shaft hole so that the armature can be assembled easily later.

32 Assemble the drive end bracket to the solenoid assembly. Insert and tighten the crosshead screws to the specified torque.

33 Refit the yoke and armature assembly to the solenoid and drive end bracket assembly, making sure that the slots in the solenoid body are engaged with the pegs on the brush holder. Also make sure that the previously-made marks are correctly aligned.

34 Insert the through-bolts and tighten them to the specified torque.

35 Reconnect the motor supply cable to the solenoid terminal, and tighten the nut.

36 The starter motor may be tested before refitting to the vehicle, as follows. Mount the starter motor in a suitable sturdy vice, with protected jaws. Connect a jump lead between the earth (negative) terminal of a 12-volt battery and the starter motor body, and connect another jump lead between the live (positive) terminal of the battery and the main solenoid terminal. Connect a further wire lead between the positive terminal and the solenoid trigger terminal, at which time the starter should spin. Hold the motor securely during the test, and make sure that the live jump lead is not allowed to contact the starter motor body at any time.

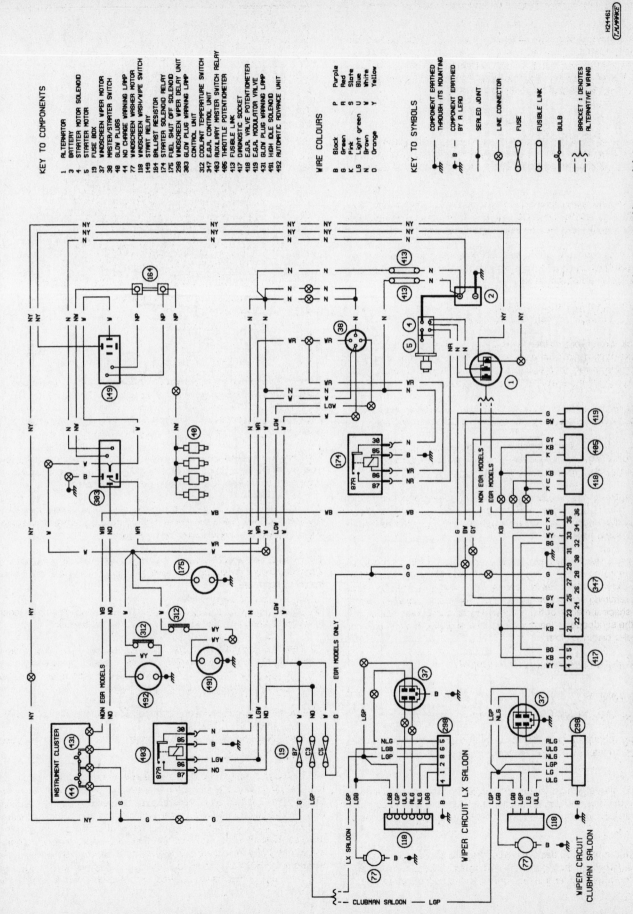

Fig. 9.2 Wiring diagram for windscreen wash/wipe, starting, charging and general engine wiring - except Van models

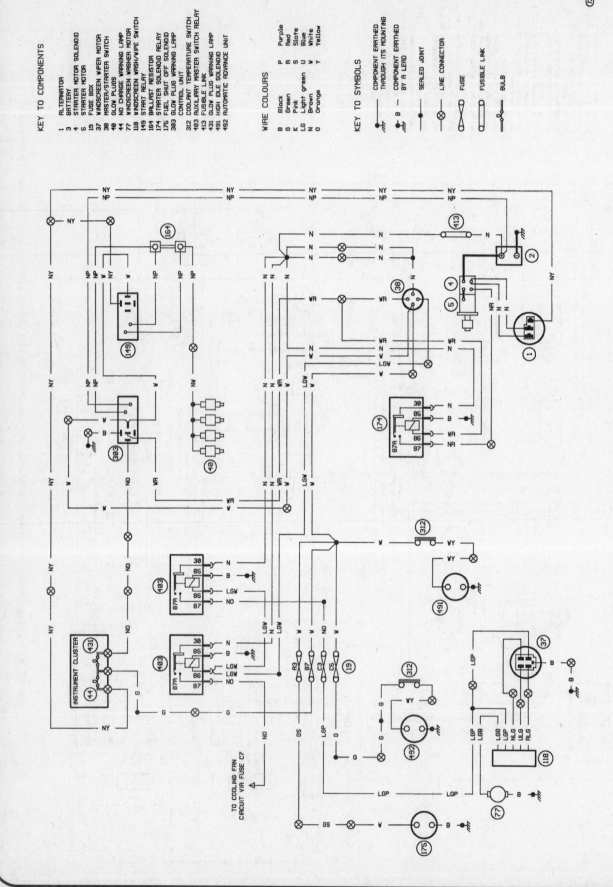

KEY TO COMPONENTS

1 ALTERNATOR
3 BATTERY
4 STARTER MOTOR SOLENOID
5 STARTER MOTOR
19 FUSE BOX
37 WINDSCREEN WIPER MOTOR
38 MASTER/STARTER SWITCH
40 GLOW PLUGS
44 NO CHARGE WARNING LAMP
77 WINDSCREEN WASHER MOTOR
118 WINDSCREEN WASH/WIPE SWITCH
149 START RELAY
164 BALLAST RESISTOR
174 STARTER SOLENOID RELAY
175 FUEL SHUT OFF SOLENOID
303 GLOW PLUG WARNING LAMP
CONTROL UNIT
312 COOLANT TEMPERATURE SWITCH
103 AUXILIARY MASTER SWITCH RELAY
113 FUSIBLE LINK
431 GLOW PLUG WARNING LAMP
491 HIGH IDLE SOLENOID
492 AUTOMATIC ADVANCE UNIT

WIRE COLOURS

B Black   P Purple
G Green   R Red
K Pink   S Slate
LG Light green U Blue
N Brown   W White
O Orange   Y Yellow

KEY TO SYMBOLS

COMPONENT EARTHED THROUGH ITS MOUNTING
COMPONENT EARTHED BY A LEAD
SEALED JOINT
LINE CONNECTOR
FUSE
FUSIBLE LINK
BULB

Fig. 9.3 Wiring diagram for windscreen wash/wipe, starting, charging and general engine wiring - Van models

Index

Haynes Manuals – The Complete List

Title	Book No.
ALFA ROMEO	
Alfa Romeo Alfasud/Sprint (74 - 88)	0292
Alfa Romeo Alfetta (73 - 87)	0531
AUDI	
Audi 80 (72 - Feb 79)	0207
Audi 80, 90 (79 - Oct 86) & Coupe (81 - Nov 88)	0605
Audi 80, 90 (Oct 86 - 90) & Coupe (Nov 88 - 90)	1491
Audi 100 (69 - Sept 76)	0162
Audi 100 (Oct 76 - Oct 82)	0428
Audi 100 (Oct 82 - 90) & 200 (Feb 84 - Oct 89)	0907
AUSTIN	
Austin Allegro 1100, 1300, 1.0, 1.1 & 1.3 (73 - 82)	0164
Austin Ambassador (82 - 84)	0871
Austin/MG Maestro 1.3 & 1.6 (petrol)(83 - 95)	0922
Austin Maxi (69 - 81)	0052
Austin/MG Metro (80 - May 90)	0718
Austin Montego 1.3 & 1.6 (84 - 94)	1066
Austin/MG Montego 2.0 (petrol)(84 - 95)	1067
Mini (59 - 69)	0527
Mini (69 - 95)	0646
Austin/Rover Diesel Engine 2.0 litre (86 - 93)	1857
BEDFORD	
Bedford CF (petrol)(69 - 87)	0163
Bedford HA Van (64 - 83)	0607
Bedford Rascal (86 - Oct 94)	3015
BL	
BL Princess & BLMC 18-22 (75 - 82)	0286
BMW	
BMW 316, 320 & 320i (4-cyl)(75 - Feb 83)	0276
BMW 320, 320i, 323i & 325i (6-cyl) (Oct 77 - Sept 87)	0815
BMW 520i & 525e (Oct 81 - June 88)	1560
BMW 525, 528 & 528i (73 - Sept 81)	0632
BMW 1500, 1502, 1600, 1602, 2000 & 2002 (59 - 77)	0240
BMW 3 Series (sohc, petrol)(83 - 91)	1948
BMW 3 Series (91 on)	3210
BMW 5 Series (sohc, petrol)(81 - 93)	1948
CITROEN	
Citröen 2CV, Ami & Dyane (67 - 90)	0196
Citröen AX (petrol & diesel)(87 - 94)	3014
Citröen BX (83 - 94)	0908
Citröen CX (75 - 88)	0528
Citröen GS & GSA (71 - 85)	0290
Citröen Visa (79 - 88)	0620
Citröen Xantia (petrol & diesel)(93 - Oct 95)	3082
Citröen ZX (diesel)(91 - 93)	1922
Citröen ZX (petrol)(91 - 94)	1881
Citröen Diesel Engines 1.7 & 1.9 litres (84 - 94)	1379
COLT	
Colt 1200, 1250 & 1400 (79 - May 84)	0600
Colt Galant (74 - 78) & Celeste (76 - 81)	0236
Colt Lancer (74 - 77)	0419
DAIMLER	
Daimler Sovereign (68 - Oct 86)	0242
Daimler Double Six (72 - 88)	0478
DATSUN (see also Nissan)	
Datsun 120Y (73 - Aug 78)	0228
Datsun 1300, 1400 & 1600 (69 - Aug 72)	0123
Datsun Cherry (71 - 76)	0195

Title	Book No.
Datsun Cherry (79 - Sept 82)	0679
Datsun Pick-up (75 - 78)	0277
Datsun Sunny (Aug 78 - May 82)	0525
Datsun Violet (78 - 82)	0430
FIAT	
Fiat 124 (66 - 75)	0080
Fiat 126 (73 - 87)	0305
Fiat 127 (71 - 83)	0193
Fiat 500 (57 - 73)	0090
Fiat 850 (64 - 81)	0038
Fiat Panda (81 - 95)	0793
Fiat Punto	3251
Fiat Regata (84 - 88)	1167
Fiat Strada (79 - 88)	0479
Fiat Tipo (88 - 91)	1625
Fiat Uno (83 - 92)	0923
Fiat X1/9 (74 - 89)	0273
FORD	
Ford Capri II & III 1.6 & 2.0 (74 - 87)	0283
Ford Capri II & III 2.8 & 3.0 (74 - 87)	1309
Ford Cortina Mk III 1300 & 1600 (70 - 76)	0070
Ford Cortina Mk III 1600 & 2000 (70 - 76)	0295
Ford Cortina Mk IV & V 1.6 & 2.0 (76 - 83)	0343
Ford Cortina Mk IV & V 2.3 V6 (77 - 83)	0426
Ford Escort (75 - Aug 80)	0280
Ford Escort Mk II Mexico, RS 1600 & RS 2000 (75 - 80)	0735
Ford Escort fwd (Sept 80 - Sept 90)	0686
Ford Escort (Sept 90 - Feb 95)	1737
Ford Fiesta (inc. XR2)(76 - Aug 83)	0334
Ford Fiesta (inc. XR2)(Aug 83 - Feb 89)	1030
Ford Fiesta (Feb 89 - 93)	1595
Ford Granada (Sept 77 - Feb 85)	0481
Ford Granada (Mar 85 - 94)	1245
Ford Mondeo (93 - 96)	1923
Ford Orion (83 - Sept 90)	1009
Ford Orion (Sept 90 - Feb 95)	1737
Ford Sierra 1.3, 1.6, 1.8 & 2.0 (82 - 93)	0903
Ford Sierra 2.3, 2.8 & 2.9 (82 - 91)	0904
Ford Scorpio (Mar 85 - 94)	1245
Ford Transit Mk 1 (diesel)(65 - Feb 78)	0418
Ford Transit Mk 1 (petrol)(65 - Feb 78)	0377
Ford Transit Mk 2 (petrol)(78 - Jan 86)	0719
Ford Transit Mk 3 (petrol)(Feb 86 - 89)	1468
Ford Transit (diesel)(Feb 86 - 95)	3019
Ford Diesel Engines 1.6 & 1.8 litre (fwd)(84 - 95)	1172
Ford Diesel Engines 2.1, 2.3 & 2.5 litres (77 - 90)	1606
Ford Vehicle Carburettors	1783
FREIGHT ROVER	
Sherpa (74 - 87)	0463
HILLMAN	
Hillman Avenger (70 - 82)	0037
Hillman Minx & Husky (56 - 66)	0009
HONDA	
Honda Accord (76 - Feb 84)	0351
Honda Accord (Feb 84 - Oct 85)	1177
Honda Civic 1200 (73 - 79)	0160
Honda Civic (Feb 84 - Oct 87)	1226
Honda Civic (Nov 91 - 96)	3199
JAGUAR	
Jaguar E Type (61 - 72)	0140

Title	Book No.
Jaguar MkI & II, 240 & 340 (55 - 69)	0098
Jaguar XJ6, XJ & Sovereign (68 - Oct 86)	0242
Jaguar XJ12, XJS & Sovereign (72 - 88)	0478
JEEP	
Jeep Cherokee (93 - 96)	1943
LADA	
Lada 1200, 1300, 1500 & 1600 (74 - 91)	0413
Lada Samara (87 - 91)	1610
LANCIA	
Lancia Beta (73 - 80)	0533
LAND ROVER	
Land Rover Series II, IIA & III (petrol)(58 - 85)	0314
Land Rover Series IIA & III (diesel)(58 - 85)	0529
Land Rover 90, 110 & Defender (diesel)(83 - 95)	3017
Land Rover Discovery (diesel)(89 - 95)	3016
MAZDA	
Mazda 323 rwd (77 - Apr 86)	0370
Mazda 323 fwd (Mar 81 - Oct 89)	1608
Mazda 626 fwd (May 83 - Sept 87)	0929
Mazda B-1600, B-1800 & B-2000 Pick-up (72 - 88)	0267
Mazda RX-7 (79 - 85)	0460
MERCEDES-BENZ	
Mercedes-Benz 190 & 190E (83 - 87)	0928
Mercedes-Benz 200, 240, 300 (diesel) (Oct 76 - 85)	1114
Mercedes-Benz 250 & 280 (68 - 72)	0346
Mercedes-Benz 250 & 280 (123 Series) (Oct 76 - 84)	0677
MG	
MG Maestro 1.3 & 1.6 (83 - 95)	0922
MG Metro (80 - May 90)	0718
MG Montego 2.0 (84 - 95)	1067
MG Midget & AH Sprite (58 - 80)	0265
MGB (62 - 80)	0111
MITSUBISHI	
Mitsubishi Shogun & L200 Pick-Ups (83 - 94)	1944
Mitsubishi 1200, 1250 & 1400 (79 - May 84)	0600
MORRIS	
Morris Ital 1.3 (80 - 84)	0705
Morris Marina 1700 (78 - 80)	0526
Morris Marina 1.8 (71 - 78)	0074
Morris Minor 1000 (56 - 71)	0024
NISSAN (See also Datsun)	
Nissan Bluebird 160B & 180B (rwd) (May 80 - May 84)	0957
Nissan Bluebird fwd (May 84 - Mar 86)	1223
Nissan Bluebird T12 & T72 (Mar 86 - 90)	1473
Nissan Cherry N12 (Sept 82 - 86)	1031
Nissan Micra K10 (83 - Jan 93)	0931
Nissan Primera (90 - 95)	1851
Nissan Stanza (82 - 86)	0824
Nissan Sunny B11 (May 82 - Oct 86)	0895
Nissan Sunny (Oct 86 - Mar 91)	1378
Nissan Sunny (Apr 91 - 95)	3219
OPEL	
Opel Ascona (81 - 88)	3215
Opel Ascona & Manta B Series (Sept 75 - 88)	0316
Opel Astra (91 - 96)	3156
Opel Corsa (83 - 93)	3160

Title	Book No.
Opel Corsa (93 - 94)	3159
Opel Kadett (Nov 73 - Nov 79)	0395
Opel Kadett (Nov 79 - Oct 84)	0634
Opel Kadett (84 - 91)	3196
Opel Omega (86 - 93)	3157
Opel Record E Series (Feb 78 to Oct 86)	0543
Opel Vectra (88 - 94)	3158
PEUGEOT	
Peugeot 106 (petrol & diesel)(91 - 94)	1882
Peugeot 205 (83 - 95)	0932
Peugeot 305 (78 - 89)	0538
Peugeot 306 (petrol & diesel)(93 - 95)	3073
Peugeot 309 (86 - 93)	1266
Peugeot 405 (88 - 96)	1559
Peugeot 405 (diesel)(88 - 96)	3198
Peugeot 504 (68 - 82)	0161
Peugeot 504 (diesel)(74 - 82)	0663
Peugeot 505 (79 - 89)	0762
Peugeot Diesel Engines 1.7 & 1.9 litres (82 - 94)	0950
Peugeot Diesel Engines 2.0, 2.1, 2.3 & 2.5 litres (74 - 90)	1607
PORSCHE	
Porsche 911 (65 - 85)	0264
Porsche 924 & 924 Turbo (76 - 85)	0397
RANGE ROVER	
Range Rover V8 (70 - Oct 92)	0606
RELIANT	
Reliant Robin & Kitten (73 - 83)	0436
RENAULT	
Renault 4 (61 - 86)	0072
Renault 5 (72 - Feb 85)	0141
Renault 5 (Feb 85 - 96)	1219
Renault 6 (68 - 79)	0092
Renault 9 & 11 (82 - 89)	0822
Renault 12 (70 - 80)	0097
Renault 14 (77 - 83)	0362
Renault 15 & 17 (72 - 79)	0763
Renault 16 (65 - 79)	0081
Renault 18 (79 - 86)	0598
Renault 19 (petrol)(89 - 94)	1646
Renault 19 (diesel)(89 - 95)	1946
Renault 21 (86 - 94)	1397
Renault 25 (84 - 92)	1228
Renault Clio (petrol)(91 - 93)	1853
Renault Clio (diesel)(91 - 95)	3031
Renault Espace	3197
Renault Fuego (80 - 86)	0764
ROVER	
Rover 111 & 114 (95 - 96)	1711
Rover 213 & 216 (84 - 89)	1116
Rover 214 & 414 (Oct 89 - 92)	1689
Rover 216 & 416 (Oct 89 - 92)	1830
Rover 820, 825 & 827 (petrol)(86 - 95)	1380
Rover 2000, 2300 & 2600 (77 - 87)	0468
Rover 3500 (76 - 87)	0365
Rover Metro (May 90 - 94)	1711
Rover Diesel Engine 2.0 litre (86 - 93)	1857
SAAB	
Saab 95 & 96 (66 - 76)	0198
Saab 99 (69 - 79)	0247

Title	Book No.
Saab 90, 99 & 900 (79 - Sept 93)	0765
Saab 9000 (4-cyl)(85 - 95)	1686
SEAT	
Seat Ibiza & Malaga (85 - 92)	1609
SIMCA	
Simca 1100 & 1204 (67 - 79)	0088
Simca 1301 & 1501 (63 - 76)	0199
SKODA	
Skoda 1000 & 1100 (64 - 78)	0303
Skoda Estelle 105, 120, 130 & 136 (77 - 89)	0604
Skoda Favorit (89 - 92)	1801
SUBARU	
Subaru 1600 (77 - Oct 79)	0237
Subaru 1600 & 1800 (Nov 79 - 90)	0995
SUZUKI	
Suzuki SJ Series, Samurai & Vitara (82 - 94)	1942
Suzuki Supercarry (86 - Oct 94)	3015
TALBOT	
Talbot Alpine, Solara, Minx & Rapier (75 - 86)	0337
Talbot Horizon (78 - 86)	0473
Talbot Samba (82 - 86)	0823
Talbot Sunbeam (77 - 82)	0435
TOYOTA	
Toyota 2000 (75 - 77)	0360
Toyota Celica (78 - Jan 82)	0437
Toyota Celica (Feb 82 - Sept 85)	1135
Toyota Corolla (rwd)(80 - 85)	0683
Toyota Corolla (fwd)(Sept 83 - Sept 87)	1024
Toyota Corolla (Sept 87 - 92)	1683
Toyota Hi-Ace & Hi-Lux (69 - Oct 83)	0304
Toyota Starlet (78 - Jan 85)	0462
TRIUMPH	
Triumph Acclaim (81 - 84)	0792
Triumph GT6 (62 - 74)	0112
Triumph Herald (59 - 71)	0010
Triumph Spitfire (62 - 81)	0113
Triumph Stag (70 - 78)	0441
Triumph TR2, 3, 3A, 4 & 4A (52 - 67)	0028
Triumph TR7 (75 - 82)	0322
Triumph Vitesse (62 - 74)	0112
VAUXHALL	
Vauxhall Astra (80 - Oct 84)	0635
Vauxhall Astra & Belmont (Oct 84 - Oct 91)	1136
Vauxhall Astra (Oct 91 - 96)	1832
Vauxhall Carlton (Oct 78 - Oct 86)	0480
Vauxhall Carlton (Nov 86 - 94).	1469
Vauxhall Cavalier 1300 (77 - July 81)	0461
Vauxhall Cavalier 1600, 1900 & 2000 (75 - July 81)	0315
Vauxhall Cavalier (fwd)(81 - Oct 88)	0812
Vauxhall Cavalier (Oct 88 - Oct 95)	1570
Vauxhall Chevette (75 - 84)	0285
Vauxhall Corsa (Mar 93 - 94)	1985
Vauxhall Magnum (73 - 77)	0294
Vauxhall Nova (83 - 93)	0909
Vauxhall Rascal (86 - Oct 94)	3015
Vauxhall Senator (Sept 87 - 94)	1469
Vauxhall Victor & VX4/90 FD Series (67 - 72)	0053
Vauxhall Viva HC (70 - 79)	0047

Title	Book No.
Vauxhall Diesel Engines 1.6 & 1.7 litres (82 - 94)	1222
VOLKSWAGEN	
VW Beetle 1200 (54 - 77)	0036
VW Beetle 1300 & 1500 (65 - 75)	0039
VW Beetle 1302 & 1302S (70 - 72)	0110
VW Beetle 1303, 1303S & GT (72 - 75)	0159
VW Golf 'Mk 1' 1.1 & 1.3 (74 - Feb 84)	0716
VW Golf 'Mk 1' 1.5, 1.6 & 1.8 (74 - 85)	0726
VW Golf 'Mk 1' (diesel)(78 - Feb 84)	0451
VW Golf 'Mk 2' (Mar 84 - 92)	1081
VW Golf 'Mk 3' (petrol & diesel)(Feb 92 - 96)	3097
VW Jetta 'Mk 1' 1.1 & 1.3 (80 - June 84)	0716
VW Jetta 'Mk 1' 1.5, 1.6 & 1.8 (80 - June 84)	0726
VW Jetta 'Mk 1' (diesel)(81 - June 84)	0451
VW Jetta 'Mk 2' (July 84 - 92)	1081
VW LT vans & light trucks (76 - 87)	0637
VW Passat (73 - Sept 81)	0238
VW Passat (Sept 81 - May 88)	0814
VW Passat (May 88 - 91)	1647
VW Polo & Derby (76 - Jan 82)	0335
VW Polo (82 - Oct 90)	0813
VW Polo (Oct 90 - Oct 94)	3245
VW Santana (Sept 82 - 85)	0814
VW Scirocco 'Mk 1' 1.5, 1.6 & 1.8 (74 - 82)	0726
VW Scirocco (82 - 90)	1224
VW Transporter 1600 (68 - 79)	0082
VW Transporter 1700, 1800 & 2000 (72 - 79)	0226
VW Transporter (air-cooled engine)(79 - 82)	0638
VW Type 3 (63 - 73)	0084
VW Vento (petrol & diesel)(Feb 92 - 96)	3097
VOLVO	
Volvo 66 & 343, Daf 55 & 66 (68 - 79)	0293
Volvo 142, 144 & 145 (66 - 74)	0129
Volvo 240 Series (74 - 93)	0270
Volvo 262, 264 & 260/265 (75 - 85)	0400
Volvo 340, 343, 345 & 360 (76 - 91)	0715
Volvo 440, 460 & 480 (87 - 92)	1691
Volvo 740 & 760 (petrol)(82 - 91)	1258
Volvo 940	3249
YUGO/ZASTAVA	
Yugo/Zastava (81 - 90)	1453

NEW TECH BOOKS	
Automotive Brake Manual	3050
Automotive Electrical & Electronic Systems	3049
Automotive Tools Manual	3052
Automotive Welding Manual	3053

CAR BOOKS	
Automotive Fuel Injection Systems	9755
Car Bodywork Repair Manual	9864
Caravan Manual	9894
Ford Vehicle Carburettors	1783
Haynes Technical Data Book ('87 to '96)	1996
In-Car Entertainment Manual (2nd Edition)	9862
Japanese Vehicle Carburettors	1786
Pass the MOT!	9861
Small Engine Repair Manual	1755
Solex & Pierburg Carburettors	1785
SU Carburettors	0299
Weber Carburettors ('79 to'91)	1784

003/05/96